**THEORIES OF
ENGINEERING
EXPERIMENTATION**

THEORIES OF ENGINEERING EXPERIMENTATION

Second Edition

Hilbert Schenck, Jr.

Professor of Ocean and
Mechanical Engineering
University of Rhode Island

McGraw-Hill Book Company
New York, St. Louis, San Francisco
Toronto, London, Sydney

THEORIES OF ENGINEERING EXPERIMENTATION

Library of Congress Catalog Card Number 67-26886

55262

4567890 MAMM 7543210

PREFACE

Experimentation has been described as "an art that must be learned but cannot be taught." Such a statement is probably true if we mean by experimentation the total act of discovery and the acquisition of new knowledge. Some experimenters, with the most meager and most questionable data, leap to great new concepts, while others, after an exhaustive investigation, miss the obvious. Yet, if we cannot learn the art of discovery, we can surely learn the art of preparing for discovery. We can be trained to exclude or account for the random effects of the environment, to plan and space our testing sequence, to evaluate our errors and their cumulative effects, to check and cross-check our developing data, and to lay out these data in an orderly and revealing manner. Then, if discovery, great or small, is possible, it is most likely to be made. It is this part of the art of experimentation that forms the subject of this book.

"Theories of Engineering Experimentation" is intended as a basic textbook and reference work for the young mechanical, civil, and electrical engineer to accompany his college laboratory work, to assist him in his study of an advanced thesis topic, or to serve him in experimental testing in an industrial context. The book is a complete break with the traditional laboratory textbook or manual and attendant detailed descriptions of instruments, machines, and specific experiments. In a burgeoning technology, too much stress on valve motion in a steam engine or on coal-ash analysis is hardly defensible. The student engineer may study such flow-measuring devices as a rotameter, an orifice, a weigh barrel, a weir, a current meter, and a pitot-static probe. In his first industrial job he meets an electromagnetic flowmeter. If his college study of flow measurement has centered around mere mechanical detail and use instruction, then he starts with very little indeed. But if he has learned, through a study of these "traditional instruments," such concepts as finding error in a measurement and the distribution of error around a "true" value, how single errors propagate in multiple measurement systems, how to plan a flow (or any other) measurement to minimize uncertainty, and how to check for precision or accuracy error, using a balance equation or extrapolation; then the engineer's new problem is really no more than a mechanical or electrical restatement of familiar difficulties met and understood. I believe that exactly what type of equipment is used in teaching engineers in laboratories is not important any longer. What matters today are the general principles of experimental work that are stressed.

About half this book is devoted to, or dependent on, simple statistical principles; yet this is *not* a statistics text. Derivations and proofs are held to a minimum, with statistics used like arithmetic, as a tool only. No previous statistical preparation will be needed for complete understanding, and only elementary differential and integral calculus are assumed of the reader. Numerical examples are used throughout to illustrate principles of experimentation. Where possible, these examples deal with basic engineering experiments that are common to the background of all engineers. Thus, some experience in undergraduate engineering laboratory, or its concurrent study, will be helpful, but not essential.

Many more analytic methods of use to the investigator than can possibly be handled in a single book are now available. I have chosen material with two restrictions in mind. First, a technique must be of major use to the average mechanical, civil, and electrical engineer. Second, it must be numerically simple enough so that machine computation will not be required, although the increasing availability of digital computers in even the smallest schools makes at least some discussion of digital data processing necessary. These selection criteria may have produced some choices that will puzzle the seasoned experimenter or professional statistician. Factorial experimental plans are stressed, for example, while the analysis of variance often applied to such plans is touched only lightly. This choice stems from my personal opinion that such plans offer the engineer certain unique advantages and control features now seldom utilized, but that few mechanical or electrical experiments require more than a simple graphical analysis of the results. Advanced material in the study of distributions and in correlation statistics has been omitted, not because such topics are not of use to engineers, but because they require, in general, more time than the average student or industrial test man can usually afford. If the reader wishes more detailed, powerful, and time-consuming tests and methods, he can and should consult the end-of-chapter references.

Any book that attempts to deal with as vast a subject as this takes on the aspect of a mathematical hardware store, offering the reader one analytic tool after another, many of them quite unrelated to one another. To restore some order and to provide a simple sequence for topic introduction, I have arranged the material in the same order that it would be met with or used in a typical test. Thus, the reader will find first, error in a single instrument (Chap. 2) and in a complete test (Chap. 3) with special reference to selecting instruments that are completely logical errorwise and to minimizing uncertainties when planning a test. Then, in Chap. 4, we take up the reduction of test variables through dimensional analysis, while Chap. 5 deals with some of the important theoretical considerations underlying the selection and combination of instruments. Chapter 6 studies the pretest spacing of the experimental variables, the sequence of data taking, and the problem of extraneous variables and control. In Chap. 7, we assume the test is under way, and we deal with apparatus malfunction and inconsistency in the developing data. The final four chapters deal with statistical, graphical, and numerical methods of reducing, studying, and interpreting engineering test data. Thus, the book sequence and the typical experiment sequence are as similar as possible.

There has been a steady disappearance of the engineering laboratory in the several years since "Theories of Engineering Experimentation" was first written. No firm trend in undergraduate laboratory work has emerged during this time, although emphasis on instrumentation and on experiment design is a welcome addition to curricular material that was old, in some areas, in 1900. In this edition, some general discussion of instrumentation system design has been added, although hardly enough to satisfy the requirements of a specialized course in this area. It seems important that "instrumentation lab" does not become one more power, materials-testing, or hydraulic lab, i.e., a "Cookbook" course with "canned" experiments based on rote learning of use-instruction from booklets and "poop sheets." Almost every instrument now being used in such a course will be more or less obsolete within the next decade.

An additional chapter has been added on digital data processing, intended for use by those schools fortunate enough to have digital equipment available to their students without special charges or permissions. FORTRAN programming has been selected because of its wide use and the frequent presence of the 1620 digital in so many undergraduate schools.

Additional problems have been added and various sections along the way clarified or modernized. The book is still based on a single concept: that the proper laboratory for student engineers is one stressing the total experiment and the *idea* of experimenting with minimum concern with the kind of tests run.

Many of my colleagues and students have aided in the preparation of this book. Notably helpful suggestions have been obtained from Professor Stephen Kline of Stanford University and Dr. Alfred Thimm of Union College. A number of senior engineering students have given additional time and effort to "piloting" some of the newer methods through some of the older laboratories. Typing and checking have been ably carried out by Mr. James McFarland and Mrs. Eileen Basham. To all of these persons I extend my grateful thanks and best wishes.

HILBERT SCHENCK, JR.

CONTENTS

THEORIES OF
ENGINEERING
EXPERIMENTATION

CHAPTER 1

Experimentation as a Subject for Study

The common link among engineers, physical researchers, and social scientists is the experiment and experimentation. The biologists testing new drug compounds on living animals, the physicists probing the tiny nucleus with huge items of equipment, the engineer comparing several production methods, all follow very diverse paths; yet, all run experiments. Furthermore, there are basic similarities in their experimental methods. They try to *control* their experiments or, as we will say, *eliminate the effect of extraneous variables.* They are all concerned with the *accuracy of their instruments and data taking.* Each experimenter wishes to *reduce the number of variables* in any given test, for this means both speed and economy in his work. No matter how simple the test, the *testing sequence should be planned* before the start. Once a test is under way, it is hard to imagine a situation in which the *detection of malfunctions* would not be important, providing we think of malfunction in its broadest sense. Related to this last point is *testing for reasonableness of the results.* Finally, every experiment requires *result analysis and interpretation*, for without this crucial step, the entire procedure is meaningless.

Now it is perfectly true that the relative emphasis on these particular topics will vary from one scientific field to another. The biologist, the agricultural researcher, and the social scientist are likely to think more in terms of pretest planning and statistical inference than the physicist or engineer. The experimental systems of the former are often living plants or animals, each with its unique

1

and uncomputable differences. Thus, many experimental variables are beyond the investigator's control, and he must somehow plan his tests to minimize or eliminate these extraneous influences. Furthermore, the biological experimenter will repeat his tests over and over again, whereas the physical experimenter is satisfied with a few readings only. But this does not mean that the sequence planning and statistical inference are of no use in engineering, for technological fields have their own special uses for such techniques. On the other hand, the engineering experimenter, with his relatively exact data, is more likely to utilize graphs and formulas to express his new-found data, whereas the biologist must often be content with simple tables or statistical figures. But we can make no hard and fast distinction. In industrial and production-line experiments where the worker and machine interact, the boundaries between the two types of experimental approaches dissolve, and the engineer must often resort to methods pioneered by persons in much removed fields of study.

1-1. The Engineering Experiment

We will consider the engineering experiment in this book and, specifically, tests involving mechanical, materials-testing, fluid-flow, and electrical phenomena. We will study such tests by using examples and methods from many areas of scientific thought, for through generality we can gain insight into the power of some of the analytic and statistical methods available. We will classify engineering experiments in a number of ways, depending on the number of variables, whether important extraneous variables are present, the ways in which these variables interact, and so on. We will not distinguish among industrial, production, research, development, pure, and applied experiments. Such classifications have, perhaps, meaning in sociological and political terminology, but they have little utility when subjected to scientific scrutiny and classification. The observation and measurement of northern auroras certainly qualify as a piece of pure research. Yet the data and their interpretation might look almost the same as the results of a study of truck traffic to and from Duluth over the past year, or an investigation of ceramic firing on days of differing humidity, temperature, and cooling rate.

Experiments and experimentalists differ, but virtually all follow a basic pattern, the same sequence of planning, operation, and analysis that is followed in the order of this book. Many experiments today, particularly those in the nuclear, electronic, and rocketry areas, are extremely expensive and, at first glance, very complicated. The reader who is acquainted with these fields may find it difficult to make the conceptual step from the immensely involved preparations, analysis, and precautions that precede a rocket flight or nuclear reactor start-up to the quite basic and sometimes very simple experiments described in the following chapters. Actually, this is a case of the forest obscuring the individual trees. No matter how involved a test may appear to an observer, he can gain comfort from the knowledge that the reportable result will differ little in form (although, let us hope, it will differ much in quality) from the average college laboratory exercise reporting on an internal-combustion engine run, test of a squirrel-cage motor, or calibration of a weir. A single rocket flight actually results in many reports—reports on motor performance, on down-range guidance, on flight programming mechanisms, on cosmic-ray counts in outer space, on cloud cover as sensed by photocell, on the biological performance of test animals, and so forth. Each of these separate reports is handled by separate experts whose only common meeting ground is at the test vehicle itself.

Any test, no matter how complex in appearance, terminates in the transmission of data, conclusions, and perhaps suggestions to other persons. This information may be passed on by graph or curve, by mathematical equation or nomogram, by table, by statistical terms, or by the written word. Using a curve, we are limited to a result R versus variable X relationship, or an R versus X and Y function if parametric curves are used. Going to R versus X, Y, and Z requires several sheets or isometric coordinates. Beyond this level of functional complexity we cannot graphically go since the mind is incapable of visualizing relationships more complex than this. Shifting to equation form, we can represent the relation of R to more variables, but few experiments go beyond the simultaneous investigation of more than three independent variables at once.

Statistical presentations can be elegant and sophisticated, but what they tell us is summed up in a few words. A statistic can give information on a population of data and the variation of individual members in the population. It may give us information about the significance of a cause-and-effect relationship and tell us the probability of a certain event happening in the future based on what we have observed in the past. We might note here that we will use statistical reasoning in two different parts of this book. First (in Chaps. 2 and 3), we will see the statistic as a means of indicating the errors in instrument and measurement systems. Then (in Chap. 8) statistics become a means of checking and/or revealing the significance of a test.

The transmission of data on a test by words, always a problem in the sciences, is the least efficient of all our reporting methods, yet one we can never ignore. There are undoubtedly certain tests being run today in physical laboratories having results that simply cannot be transmitted by the written word. In engineering, such tests are very uncommon, and much of the usual engineering report is taken up with word descriptions and explanations.

Thus, our apparently complicated rocket or reactor test is really no more than a large number of discrete experiments tied together by an expensive collection of test equipment. Furthermore, while we may be able to imagine an extremely intricate test with results that could only be comprehended intuitively by hours of intensive study, it is doubtful that such a test would have much purpose. We might sense a mass of subtle interrelationships deep within the data, but unless these relationships are reduceable to graph, equation, or words that can be assimilated by our professional colleagues, we have wasted our time. Most engineering tests should lead to action—a decision, more tests, or an admission of failure. Such results can only occur when we show others what we are doing.

In the author's opinion, many otherwise competent engineers perform expensive and poorly controlled experiments owing to a single conceptual failure. This is their total lack of self-questioning regarding the logic and reasoning behind each step they make. Too few engineers seriously ask themselves why a certain instrument is placed just where it is and why some other instrument is not used instead. This does not mean trivial questions like "Why is that thermocouple attached there?" to which the answer is, quickly, "Why, to read the temperature, of course." Rather we mean questions like "Why are you using an iron-constantan couple soldered to the pipe elbow and wrapped with asbestos tape and connected to a 0- to $-500°F$-range recorder with a print speed of four per minute and an accuracy (probable error? standard deviation?) of ± 3 per cent?" It is not likely that the average engineer will answer this series of questions in a hurry. We have raised queries, not just about a temperature measurement, but about the entire apparatus and the test itself. We have asked about the kind and attachment of the couple, anticipating a radiation error at the bond, perhaps progressive error increase due to corrosion or rust, perhaps even a problem of couple location that might make the time to reach steady state too long. We have asked about the range of the indicating recorder and about its error magnitude and thereby about the ranges and accuracies of all measurements, since they are all intimately related through the experimental functions under study. We have asked about the print speed and therefore about the rate of data assimilation and the possibility of extraneous variations that may fluctuate within, say, 15 sec. In short, we have called many aspects of this experiment into scrutiny. Other questions might call for thought on the sequence and size of variable changes, on variable spacing over the apparatus range, on reruns where accuracy is doubtful, perhaps even on the choice of the variables themselves.

The reader may feel that tests get run whether such questions are asked or not, that measurement accuracy is always in mind in any test, that variables are changed until a good curve takes shape, that reruns are made when scatter is broad, and so on. This is certainly true. But when the test engineer simply guesses at the desired accuracy of each of a group of instruments, when he thinks not at all about data-taking speed and extraneous variations, when he spaces his test runs by "feel" or intuition, when he ignores the possible biases introduced by a regular sequence of runs, and when he makes reruns as a sort of desperate afterthought to "fix" a badly scattered curve, then the chance that his experiment will be long, costly, and inaccurate is excellent. The chance that the test will reveal nothing useful at all is quite good. The chance that he will happen upon the most efficient and well-controlled plan or that he will pick out some new and subtle effect is about nil. Far too much is made in the popular press of such chance occurrences as the discovery of penicillin. Few important advances occur solely because of dirty culture bottles or sloppy test plans. It is the investigator who has methodically and completely thought through the possible extraneous effects and optimum methods of control who is most able to distinguish a truly unique and unusual effect from a host of side issues and extraneous error causatives. Accidental discoveries occur when all foreseeable accidents have been computed, predicted, or eliminated, and only the new and novel accidents remain to happen.

Sometimes the most difficult job is asking the proper questions about an experimental plan. In this book we will suggest what some of these basic questions should be, and then proceed to methods of getting the answers.

1-2. Definitions and Terminology

Certain words and phrases will occur throughout the book, relating to the description of tests and test systems. Some are well established in technical English, while others are used by different authors in different ways. It is not practical to be too rigid about word use in a field as broad as experimentation, but the following meanings will apply in most of the work that follows.

We can break our testing "hardware" into three components: instruments, the test apparatus or rig, and the test piece.

Instruments sense, count, read, measure, observe, and then record, store, correct, read out what they have been set to "see."

The *test apparatus* is usually taken to be everything required to perform a test including the instruments and the test piece.

The *test piece* is the specific hardware item that is undergoing test and may be replaced at will. Not every test apparatus has a test piece. For example, the test of a new production method using machines, workers, and material has no obvious test piece. If the test were designed to try out a new milling machine, however, then this machine would be the test piece.

The *experimental plan* is a general term relating to any specific set of test operating instructions that give sequence of test work, kinds and amounts of variable changes, and any replication decisions.

Sequence of testing refers to the order in which various operating changes are made in the test apparatus.

Replication means, in general, repetition, but more specifically a return to a previous condition. For example, if we are testing a fan at a specific speed, pressure boost, and flow, we might take a series of repetitive readings without making any operating changes. This would not be replication. If we operate the fan at some new speed, boost, or flow condition, and then go back to the previous condition and read again, we have replicated the first run. In agricultural and drug experiments, replication also implies a series of ground plots or animals that receive identical treatments.

Variable is used in a very general sense to imply any physical quantity that undergoes change. If we control this change independently of other quantities we have an *independent* variable. If a physical quantity changes in response to the variation of one or more independent variables, we have a *dependent* variable. If a physical quantity that affects our test is changing in a random and uncontrolled manner, we have an *extraneous* variable. We might have an electric motor in which input voltage and output load could be varied independently at the whim of the experimenter. The efficiency, winding temperature, and input current would be examples of the dependent variables, and the surrounding temperature and line-frequency variation (perhaps from a poorly stabilized generator) would be extraneous variables.

Independent variables can usually be set at selected levels or values according to our experimental plan.

A *controlled* experiment is one in which the effects of extraneous variables have been eliminated and in which the independent variables can be varied exactly as the investigator chooses. *Control* or the isolation of a test from its surroundings is one of the great, basic conceptions of Western scientific man.

Measurements are made of the independent, dependent, and, often, of the extraneous variables by the instruments. We will deal with a "best" value or "most probable" value for every measured quantity. This best value may always be made even better by installing more costly instruments, replicating the readings or test points, or hiring more skilled data takers. Thus, best is a relative term, having definite utilitarian and economic overtones.

Measurements may be accurate or inaccurate depending on our standards of accuracy in a given test. In Chap. 2, we will let the word *accuracy* refer to the fixed amount an instrument reading deviates from its known or *calibrated* input, regardless of how many times we make a measurement. Thus an accuracy error is a *fixed* error.

Measurements may be precise or imprecise depending on how well an instrument can reproduce subsequent readings of an unchanged input. Thus, a *precision* error is not a fixed quantity like an accuracy error, but is different for each replication of a reading. Using statistical methods, we can assign single, average values to such precision errors in test instrumentation.

Error is a number, 2 rpm, 0.6°F, 15 ohms, etc., and is defined as the calibrated or known input reading minus the instrument reading. Error is thus known or predicted only when we can calibrate or otherwise check the test apparatus.

Uncertainty, like error, is a number, but an estimated one. We define this uncertainty as "what we think the error would be if we could and did measure it by calibration."[1] Uncertainty will always

[1] Prof. S. J. Kline, personal communication.

be analyzed in this text like a precision error, that is, through statistical methods.

To summarize these three kinds of deviation from the correct reading: We replicate a reading several times, and it deviates a fixed amount from the known input. We have accuracy error. We replicate a reading several times, and it deviates a different amount each time from the known input. We have precision error. We cannot calibrate or replicate (we may not even have the test rig built yet) any readings, but we can make an estimate of the error, which we think may be a fixed or varying type or some combination of the two. We have uncertainty.

To make a run or *test run* means simply to put the test apparatus in a certain fixed condition or *configuration* and record all the instrument measurements. Usually each test run will result, finally, in a *data point* or *test point* where point implies an actual point on a real or imagined graph of the test results. In this book, point will be used in about the same sense as run, although usually in situations where an actual graphical point could result.

Data applies to all the "symbolic" products of an experiment. That is, data might be photographic images, magnetic impulses on tape, figures on sheets of paper, readings on mechanical counters, a simple yes-or-no answer in the mind of an observer, and so on. Data are not the pieces produced during a production test but are the written or remembered numbers of such pieces. *Raw data* are the symbolic materials obtained directly from the test instruments. *Processed data* are these symbolic materials after some additional mathematical operations have been performed on them, such as corrections by a calibration curve or plotting on a graph.

Processed data that are plotted form a curve or may lead to some functional relationship among the independent and dependent variables that usually takes the form of a formula.

These relationships may be more or less significant in that a cause-and-effect relationship may be very obvious or not at all evident. Sometimes a simple engineering curve will be sufficient to reveal such relationships, while at other times we may choose a statistical *test of significance*. Statistical analysis is intimately related to distributions of test readings or other data. When discussing the general theories of statistics, we will often deal with *populations* of errors, data, etc., which this book will take as the total set of an infinity of such errors, data, etc. Thus a *parent distribution* is simply a population of whatever we are discussing. From this

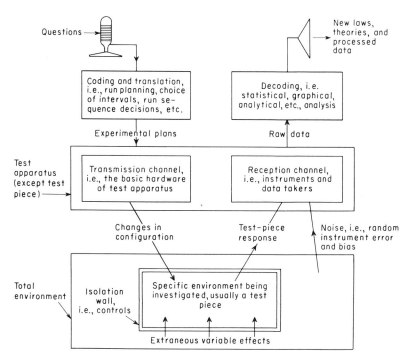

Fig. 1-1. A simplified block diagram of a typical experiment viewed as a communication network. In the sense of this diagram, the major aims of this book are to (1) ensure good "coding" and effective planning, (2) strengthen the "wall" blocking our specific environment from the outside, (3) reduce the "noise" due to instrument fluctuation, and (4) "decode" in such a way as to maximize the useful information coming from our fictive "loudspeaker."

infinity of readings, we obtain through our test a *sample* of readings, finite in number. The larger the sample, the more closely (we hope) its distribution will approximate the distribution of the population.

1-3. Nomenclature

A great many formulas from diverse technical fields will be used in both the body of this book and the problems at ends of chapters. In general, the exact technical meaning of the symbols is not important, for we are stressing here general experimental methods rather than specific application of engineering theory. In most cases, enough engineering explanation is given so that the reader can

orient himself in the specific technical area.   Some of the examples
are not based on specific, known experiments, but the author has
attempted to keep the numbers and the theory on a realistic basis.

The beginning of the alphabet in both upper and lower case
$(A, B, C, \ldots$ and $a, b, c \ldots)$ is used for a variety of purposes
but most commonly to represent constants in experimental equations.   The end letters in upper case (W, X, Y, Z) represent variables, usually controlled, or simple coordinates on graphs.   End
letters in lower case (w, x, y, z) represent deviations of actual or
measured values from the correct or calibrated value, which can be
identified by the subscript c.   Thus $X_c - X = x$, and so on.

In the statistical sections, we will often use *Greek* letters to refer
to quantities used in the evaluation of *population* parameters and
Latin letters for formulas involving *sample* parameters.   Table 1-1
gives some of the special symbols that are commonly used.

Table 1-1
Table of Nomenclature

Symbol	*Definition*
A, B, C, etc.	Equation constants or special symbols
a, b, c, etc.	Equation constants or special symbols
E_n	Expected number of occurrences (Chap. 8)
f	Function of
h	Index of precision for a sample (Chap. 2)
ln	log to the base e
N	Dimensionless number (usually with subscript)
n	Number of items (such as groups, readings, etc.)
P	Probability of an event (defined in Chap. 2)
p	Probable error (defined in Chap. 2)
R	Result, or dependent variable
$\% R$	Per cent error (defined in Chap. 7)
S	Length along a curve, arc length
s	Variance or standard deviation for a sample (defined in Chap. 2)
W, X, Y, Z	Independent and dependent variables
$\bar{W}, \bar{X}, \bar{Y}, \bar{Z}$	Mean or average value of independent variable for a sample
W_c, X_c, Y_c, Z_c	Best or correct value (which may be the mean value)
w, x, y, z	Deviation of independent variable from correct value
Δ	Small change or increment
η	Index of precision for a population
μ	Best value or calibrated input for a population
σ	Variance or deviation for a population
ϕ	Probable error of a population (used in Chap. 2)
ϕ	Function of

REFERENCES

Baird, D. C.: "Experimentation: An Introduction to Measurement Theory and Experimental Design," Prentice-Hall, Inc., Englewood Cliffs, N.J., 1962.

Beverage, W. I.: "The Art of Scientific Investigation," W. W. Norton & Company, Inc., New York, 1950.

Cohen, M., and E. Nagel: "An Introduction to Logic and Scientific Method," Harcourt, Brace & World, Inc., New York, 1934.

Cook, N. H., and E. Rabinowicz: "Physical Measurement and Analysis," Addison-Wesley Publishing Company, Inc., Reading, Mass., 1963.

Holman, J.: "Experimental Methods for Engineers," McGraw-Hill Book Company, New York, 1966.

Sci. Am., vol. 199, no. 3, September, 1958. Entire issue devoted to "Innovation in Science."

Wightman, W. P.: "The Growth of Scientific Ideas," Yale University Press, New Haven, Conn., 1953.

Wilson, E. B.: "An Introduction to Scientific Research," McGraw-Hill Book Company, New York, 1952.

CHAPTER 2

The Nature of Experimental Error
and Uncertainty

It is almost impossible to imagine an experiment in which some form of recorded data is not a basic end product. In the very simplest experiments, the final data may be very rudimentary and not liable to any error whatever. An example could be the counting of automobiles passing a given point (although the final *interpretation* of these data might be complex). Extremely difficult experiments, on the other hand, may be highly liable to poor precision and have large final errors. The estimation of star distances by angle measurements on opposite sides of the earth's orbit is a typically difficult test becoming increasingly dubious as more distant stars are selected. Between these two rather extreme cases lie the great majority of scientific and engineering tests and measurements.

In any basic examination of the theoretical aspects of general experimental work, a study of error and uncertainty is surely fundamental. All experiments contain error, be it large or vanishingly small. No experiment can be properly designed without a careful study of this crucial factor. Money, time, and personnel may be wasted when uncertainties are ignored or sloppily estimated. Worse, technical untruths may be forced upon the technological community, leading to all manner of dangerous failures and expensive embarrassments.

In this and in the next chapter we will study the basic nature of

12

experimental error.   First, we will analyze the classes and kinds of error that result from a single reading or a series of readings made by a single instrument or measuring tool.   Then, in Chap. 3, we will see how these separate errors can combine in a complete experiment to produce error or uncertainty in the final results, a combination that in some cases can totally negate the test.

These two chapters are placed in this leading position in the book for a definite reason.   The experimenter, whatever his field, will almost always follow a more or less regular pattern involving first planning, then purchase, then test operation, and finally analysis and reporting.   In the area of planning and purchase, error analysis must always be the initial step.   If technical limitations make the uncertainty too high or financial limitations prevent purchase of instruments of proper accuracy, the experiment is immediately judged an impossible one and its running set ahead to await improvements still to come.   It is impossible to estimate the amounts of government and private resources wasted on inaccurate tests, but the sums must be huge, and almost all is needless, careless waste.

2-1. Kinds of Error

We will postulate three basic error sources in physical measurements.   These are:

1. Failure of the primary sensing element to reflect the measured quantity.   *Example:* A thermocouple junction that is corroded or loose, or which has radiation and conduction losses that make the junction temperature different from the surrounding temperature.

2. Failure of the indicating or secondary portion of the instrument to reflect faithfully the sensing-element response.   *Example:* A potentiometer that gives an incorrect millivolt reading when fed by a thermocouple, due to improper standardization, calibration, or malfunction of its mechanical or electrical components.

3. Failure of the observer to record the instrument reading correctly.   *Example:* A person who reads the wrong scale on the potentiometer dial.

While all three sources of error may be present in a given determination, we expect that one or another may be the major trouble factor.   The skilled investigator will quickly see the weak link in this three-link chain of information transmission.   We have said nothing at this point of the fourth and perhaps most critical link, namely, the interpretive skill of the experimenter in gaining the maximum truths from his collected data.   This final link can only

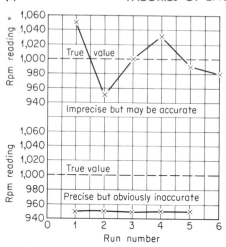

Fig. 2-1. Examples of data from two tachometers which illustrate the difference between precision and accuracy error.

be discussed after the data have been gathered, and we will consider it, as best we can, in later chapters.

These three trouble sources produce two basic classes of error in an experimental determination. The classes are errors of precision and errors of accuracy, and we expect all readings to possess an over-all error compounded of both classes but in different relative amounts. The relative weight of either depends on the instrument or test situation.

Precision error is always present when successive measurements of an unchanged quantity yield different numerical values. *Example:* A tachometer measures the speed of a constant-speed motor obtaining in successive measurements 1,050, 950, 1,000, 1,030, 990, and 980 rpm (see Fig. 2-1). Knowing the motor to be absolutely stabilized[1] on a given speed, we conclude that the tachometer gives data that are not perfectly precise.

Accuracy error is always present when the numerical average of successive readings deviates from the known correct reading and continues to deviate no matter how many successive readings are made. *Example:* In the above case of the tachometer, the average of the six readings is 1,000 rpm. If this checks a standard or calibration reading of 1,000 rpm, we may infer that little or no accuracy

[1] We will in this chapter assume that the measured quantity is not changing and that all variation is due to lack of precision of measurement. Should the variation be actually due to poor control over the variable, all the analysis we undertake will still hold, but the "fix" will be different. In many tests, the experimenter will sense which is the case.

error exists.   If the standard value is known to be 950 rpm, we infer that the tachometer is not accurate and at this speed reads about 50 rpm high.

An instrument may be very precise and very inaccurate.   *Example:* The tach gives 950, 952, 948, 951, and 950 rpm with a known input of 1,000 rpm.

An instrument may be very imprecise and yet quite accurate. *Example:* The tach gives 910, 1,050, 990, 1,030, 1,080, 890, 1,050, 1,060 rpm.   The motor is running at 1,000 rpm, which is the value of the average of this set of readings.   This suggests that the tachometer, though it shows a large spread, does not suffer from accuracy error.

The reader should carefully note that the word "accurate" is used here in a specialized and, perhaps, nontypical manner.   In the usual engineering case, the experimenter will take a single reading. In the case of the tachometer operating as shown in the upper half of Fig. 2-1, the chance that such a single reading will be accurate is very small indeed.   Thus accurate and accuracy error in this chapter refer to samples or groups of readings sufficient in number to establish whether the instrument is really scattering around the "true" value or whether it shows a continuous bias or "one-sided" deviation.   Practically, we would replace or repair the tachometer behaving as shown in the upper half of Fig. 2-1, whereas we might prefer to simply calibrate and use the one illustrated in the lower half of the figure.

The establishment of which of these two kinds of error we have requires that a calibration or similar test be made.   Perhaps the instrument manufacturer will give us such data, or perhaps we can obtain them ourselves.   But, in the plannings tages, we may not know anything about the kinds of error beyond anticipating that some deviations from the correct value must be expected.   In such cases we deal with uncertainty rather than error (as noted in Chap. 1), and we infer, compute, or (more likely) guess the magnitude of this uncertainty.   In this book, such uncertainty, after it has been estimated, will be treated exactly the same as precision error.   Thus everything we say about precision error will apply to uncertainty, even though our uncertainty may be (and probably is) made up of both precision and accuracy components.

One way that error is reduced is through *calibration,* which is the checking of an instrument over its range against a known standard.

Unless the investigator is prepared to make multiple readings at

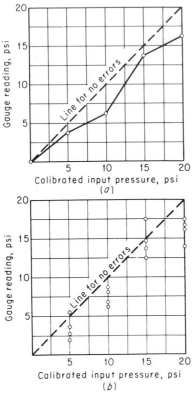

Fig. 2-2. Possible results of a dead-weight calibration of a faulty pressure gauge.

each configuration of his apparatus (called replication), calibration will only improve the performance of instruments having poor accuracy and good precision.

Suppose for example that we wish to calibrate a pressure gauge using a dead-weight tester, a device that applies a series of precisely known pressures to the instrument input. Applying known pressures of 5, 10, 15 psia, and so forth, we record the actual scale reading of the gauge and make up a *calibration curve* as shown in Fig. 2-2a, and this curve is then used with the instrument to change scale to correct reading. But suppose that the gauge mechanism is sticky or has backlash or has, perhaps, a pinhole leak in the thin-walled Bourdon tube. Such defects may cause erratic behavior such that the gauge has both poor accuracy and poor precision.

If such is the case, our calibration curve adds little, if any, accuracy to the basic readings. Using the dead-weight tester to recheck each pressure point over and over, we might obtain a plot as shown in Fig. 2-2b. Such a plot makes the worthlessness of the gauge apparent. Not only is the accuracy clearly poor (as Fig. 2-2a would lead us to suspect), but the precision is poor as well, and the gauge should be repaired or thrown out.

There are many areas of science and technology in which the precision of the instruments is unavoidably low. Agriculture, biological research, and psychological experimentation are examples. In these fields, the "test instrument" is often a living plant, animal, or human being, and the response of these instruments to a certain stimulus or "test configuration" may show extreme variability. In engineering, physics, and inorganic chemistry, such large precision error is usually not tolerated. Yet in many cases, particularly in very advanced technological areas and in factory production experiments (where an entire assembly line and the workers may be the instrument), poor precision is unavoidable and must be anticipated when the experiment is planned.

2-2. The Nature of Precision Error or Uncertainty

The mathematical nature of accuracy error is so elementary as to require no further discussion at this point. Known accuracy error is easily corrected in single instruments by calibration or repair. Accuracy error is easily detected by a very few checks against some standard input. In later chapters, we will see how accuracy errors may combine, how accuracy errors produced by malfunction during testing may be detected, and how final results may be corrected for accuracy error.

Precision error or uncertainty, on the other hand, is a far more complex matter. Once we measure a pure accuracy error, we can always thereafter predict its presence and effect. But though we know that precision error is present, we can never predict, absolutely, its magnitude in a single measurement. Thus a study of precision error in experimentation requires some understanding of the mathematical sciences of statistics and probability.

Suppose we have an unknown quantity to be measured, a simple quantity, perhaps, such as the length of a rigid rod. We provide a large number of investigators with rules, tapes, micrometers, and so on and ask them to determine the length. As we record each determination, we note that slight differences occur among the readings of observers A, B, C, and so on. As more and more observers record their results, we build up a sample of a distribution. Suppose we take small, equal intervals of length ΔX and count the number of readings that fall into each interval. If we now plot the center value X of each interval ΔX versus the number of readings that fall in each interval, we obtain a *bar graph* that might look like Fig. 2-3. As more and more readings are made, we can take a smaller and smaller interval, ΔX, and, in the limit, some sort of smooth *distribution curve* will result.

In advanced statistical work, a variety of distribution curves[1] are postulated and studied. We will consider at this point only one,

[1] See A. Hald, "Statistical Theory with Engineering Applications," John Wiley & Sons, Inc., New York, 1952.

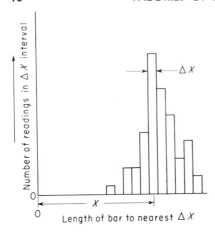

Fig. 2-3. A bar graph of length measurements made on a rigid rod.

the famous *normal curve of error*, often referred to as the *Gaussian distribution*. The equation of this distribution is often derived from the following two basic assumptions:

1. The final error in any observation is the result of a large number of very small errors, distributed in a random manner.

2. Positive and negative displacements from the correct reading are equally probable.

Starting with these assumptions an equation of frequency of occurrence of a deviation as a function of deviation magnitude may be derived in several ways,[1] yielding

$$y = y_0 e^{-\eta^2 x^2} \tag{2-1}$$

where y is the frequency of occurrence of any deviation x from the correct value μ_x, y_0 is the occurrence frequency at zero deviation, and η is a constant for any given normal distribution known as the *modulus* or *index of precision.* Holding y_0 and η constant and plotting y versus x gives the familiar bell-shaped curve as drawn in Fig. 2-4. Since Eq. (2-1) and its graphical form are continuous, they apply to a population having an infinite number of determinations. This is the *parent population* from which are obtained finite samples for study. The curve encloses the entire population of deviations from a given instrument, and we are interested first in the mathematical expression for the area A under the curve. Using

[1] For example, see A. G. Worthing and J. Geffner, "Treatment of Experimental Data," pp. 148–153, John Wiley & Sons, Inc., New York, 1943.

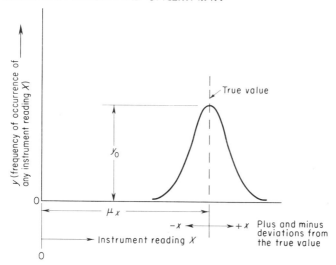

Fig. 2-4. A sketch of the density function of a normally deviating instrument, showing the nomenclature used in Eq. (2-1).

the calculus, this is found from

$$A = 2 \int_0^\infty y_0 e^{-\eta^2 x^2} \, dx \tag{2-2}$$

Equation (2-2) is a definite integral of some complexity. It may be evaluated[1] or may be found in most tables of integrals.[2] The area is

$$A = \frac{\sqrt{\pi}}{\eta} y_0 \tag{2-3}$$

It is convenient, for reasons that will soon be obvious, to let this area take the value of unity. Then $y_0 \sqrt{\pi}/\eta = 1$, and $y_0 = \eta/\sqrt{\pi}$. Equation 2-1 becomes, as a result of this *normalizing procedure.*

$$y = \frac{\eta}{\sqrt{\pi}} e^{-\eta^2 x^2} \tag{2-4}$$

y will then have the units of η, which in turn must have the reciprocal units of x. *Example:* The units of x for a tachometer might be rpm. Then y is in rpm^{-1}.

y is not a particularly useful quantity in its own right. In almost

[1] *Ibid.*, pp. 155–157.

[2] Such as R. S. Burington, "Handbook of Mathematical Tables and Formulas," McGraw-Hill Book Company, New York, 1949.

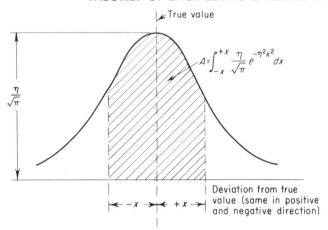

Fig. 2-5. A sketch of the normal density function showing the nomenclature of the normalized equation [Eq. (2-5)]. The area bounded by plus and minus x equals the probability.

all situations what we wish to know is the probability that any given deviation will occur. The total area under the y versus x curve includes every deviation of the instrument and has a numerical value of unity. Then the probability P of occurrence of a deviation between plus and minus x is equal to the area bounded by plus and minus x, lying under the normal curve, as shown in Fig. 2-5, or in mathematical symbols

$$P = \int_{-x}^{+x} \frac{\eta}{\sqrt{\pi}} e^{-\eta^2 x^2} \, dx \qquad (2\text{-}5)$$

2-3. Indicators of Precision Error

We have now established an equation (2-5) which can tell us the expectancy or chance that any given deviation will occur, providing that (1) the instrument in question deviates in a normal manner and (2) we can find its value of η. Unfortunately, this *probability integral* is difficult to evaluate, and recourse is usually made to tables. In order that the table may be compact, Eq. (2-5) may be rewritten in the form

$$P_{\eta x} = \frac{1}{\sqrt{\pi}} \int_{-\eta x}^{+\eta x} e^{-\eta^2 x^2} \, d(\eta x) \qquad (2\text{-}6)$$

where $P_{\eta x}$ is the probability that a given deviation will fall between

Table 2-1

ηx	$P_{\eta x}$	ηx	$P_{\eta x}$	ηx	$P_{\eta x}$
0.00	0.000	0.477	0.500 (ϕ)	0.90	0.797
0.05	0.056	0.50	0.521	0.95	0.821
0.10	0.113	0.55	0.563	1.00	0.843
0.15	0.168	0.60	0.604	1.1	0.880
0.20	0.223	0.65	0.642	1.2	0.910
0.25	0.276	0.70	0.678	1.3	0.934
0.30	0.329	0.707	0.682 (σ)	1.4	0.952
0.35	0.379	0.75	0.711	1.5	0.966
0.40	0.428	0.80	0.742	2.0	0.995
0.45	0.476	0.85	0.771	∞	1.000

the limits $+\eta x$ and $-\eta x$. Table 2-1 is a short table of solutions of this form [Eq. (2-6)] of the probability integral.

Example 2-1. A tachometer is assumed to give a normally distributed set of deviations having η of 0.04 rpm^{-1} at 1,000 rpm. If a sample of 20 readings is made at this speed, how many do we expect to fall between the limits of 990 and 1,010?

Solution. x here is ±10 rpm and ηx is then 10×0.04 or 0.4. From Table 2-1, the probability that a reading will fall within this deviation range is 0.428. Thus, we expect that out of 20 successive readings, 20×0.428 or 8.56 readings will be inside the limits 990 and 1,010 rpm or, practically, 8 or 9 readings. Since 20 is not a large sample we should not be surprised if 6 or 7 or 10 or 11 should actually fall within the range on any given test.

It is convenient to express precision (or the lack of it) of a given measuring system by a single number, or *precision index*. Let us consider two such indexes, either one of which will indicate the precision with which an instrument can measure the desired quantity. These are:

1. The *standard deviation* σ (or *variance*, which is the standard deviation squared, σ^2). This quantity is defined as that deviation value equal to the square root of the sum of the squares of all the deviations divided by the total number of such deviations n, or mathematically

$$\sigma = \left(\frac{\sum_{n=1}^{n=\infty} x^2}{n} \right)^{1/2} = \frac{y}{\sqrt{n}} \tag{2-7}$$

But

$$\sum_{n=1}^{n=\infty} x^2 = \int_{-\infty}^{+\infty} x^2 y \, dx \quad \text{and} \quad n = \int_{-\infty}^{+\infty} y \, dx = 1.0$$

for the normalized expression for the normal distribution. Then Eq. (2-4) inserted in Eq. (2-7) with the above gives

$$\sigma = \left(\frac{\eta}{\sqrt{\pi}}\right)^{1/2} \left(\int_{-\infty}^{+\infty} x^2 e^{-\eta^2 x^2} \, dx\right)^{1/2} \tag{2-8}$$

which is best handled by recourse again to a table of definite integrals. The result is

$$\sigma = \frac{1}{\sqrt{2}\,\eta} \tag{2-9}$$

and $\eta\sigma$ is 0.707. The probability of deviations falling within this plus-or-minus limit is, from Table 2-1, 68.2 per cent. Obviously, the definition of the standard deviation given by Eq. (2-7) can apply to any distribution and is not restricted to the normal case. The 68.2 per cent figure is thus meaningful only if we have an instrument with deviations following the normal law.

2. The *probable error* ϕ. This quantity is defined as that deviation which, in a plus-and-minus sense, encloses exactly one-half of the total population. For a normally distributed population we see from Table 2-1 that

$$\phi = \frac{0.477}{\eta} \tag{2-10}$$

and the probability of a deviation falling within $\pm\phi$ is obviously 50 per cent. The probable error is not now used at all in modern statistical literature for reasons that escape the writer. To the engineer and physicist, it is a convenient and meaningful index, easily estimated and understood and often used for expressing the uncertainty in fundamental constants and similar measurements.[1] The probable error identifies the deviation envelope for "one-to-one odds." That is, the chance that any reading will have a deviation greater than ϕ is the same as that it will have one less than ϕ.

The standard deviation and the probable error are related by simple proportion, providing we are dealing with a normal distribution. Knowing either one or η allows us to find the others.

[1] See, for example, J. Beardon and J. Thomsen, Résumé of Atomic Constants, *Am. J. Phys.*, **27**(8):569–576 (1959).

Example 2-2. In Example 2-1, we described a tachometer having η of 0.04 rpm^{-1}. What are the two precision indexes for this instrument, and what rpm ranges are enclosed by $\pm\sigma$ and $\pm\phi$?

Solution. From Eqs. (2-9) and (2-10) we see that

$$\sigma = \frac{0.707}{0.04} = 17.7 \text{ rpm} \quad\text{and}\quad \phi = \frac{0.477}{0.04} = 11.9 \text{ rpm}$$

Thus 68.2 per cent of all readings of a calibrated input of 1,000 rpm will fall between 982.3 and 1,017.7 rpm, while one-half of all readings will lie between 988.1 and 1,011.9 rpm.

2-4. Finding the Precision Error of an Instrument System

If we are told that an instrument deviates from a true value in a normal manner, and if we are given one of the precision indexes or η, we can easily estimate the general instrument performance in our experimental setup. In most practical situations, neither of these pieces of information is given. Instead, we may attempt to calibrate or check the instrument system against a known input or, quite typically in engineering tests, guess the amount of precision error from manufacturers' specifications or "specs," observation of the instrument in action, or past experience with similar measuring tools. It is unfortunately true that instrument manufacturers have not standardized their terminology. We often encounter an instrument whose scale bears a notation that the measured quantity is accurate to within plus or minus some percentage of the scale readings. A voltmeter might read "±5 per cent on all ranges" or some such inscription.[1] The question then arises, does this 5 per cent represent a standard deviation, a probable error, or just exactly what? If standard deviation is meant, for example, then a little over 68 per cent of the readings will fall within the noted percentage deviation.

Actually, the instrument may not give a normally distributed set of readings, so that, even if the standard deviation were known, we could not infer exactly what percentage of the deviations it might enclose. In such a case, it might be simpler to specify the percentage of readings enclosed by some given range of variations,

---

[1] The use of a *percentage uncertainty* is quite necessary on many instruments. A voltmeter having an error of ±1.0 volt would probably be very acceptable on its 0- to 1,000-volt range but certainly useless on the low range of 0 to 10 volts.

rather than to get involved in statistical terminology. Kline and McClintock suggest using the criterion of "twenty-to-one odds."[1] The deviation envelope that encloses 95 per cent of all the readings follows such a criterion.

Engineers responsible for instrument procurement can rapidly clear up the rather crude specification practices now prevalent in instrument work. You need only ask two questions of the manufacturer. First, what percentage of the readings will fall within the guaranteed range,[2] and, second, does the instrument deviate in a normal manner?

Often, a commercial instrument has no indication of accuracy at all. In such a case, and lacking the skill of the seasoned instrument expert, a crude rule of thumb is to assume that the *maximum possible error is equal to one-half the least count of the instrument.*

Fig. 2-6. The scale of a typical, inexpensive pressure gauge having a least count of 2½ psi in the range 10 to 60 psi.

For example, the pressure gauge shown in Fig. 2-6 has a one-half least count of 2½/2 or 1¼ psia. We expect only one in twenty or even one in a hundred of its readings to show greater deviation than this value. Notice that the range of 0 to 10 psia is probably less precise than this, a common situation with inexpensive Bourdon pressure gauges.

For an important experiment or a critical measurement for which a refined error estimation is essential, some form of check or calibration should be attempted. A major question to be answered is whether the deviations are roughly normal or at least symmetrical in their distribution. Although there are many complex and elegant mathematical approaches to this question, most engineers do not have the time, the computing facilities, or the patience to use

---

[1] S. J. Kline and F. McClintock, "Describing Uncertainties in Single Sample Experiments," *Mech. Eng.*, January, 1953.

[2] When an investigator wishes to describe a reading and its associated uncertainty in a paper or communication, the common notation of 110 volts ± 0.5 volt is generally used. This is usually taken to mean the probable error so that 110 ± 0.5 volts implies that one-half of the readings will fall between 109.5 and 110.5 and the remainder outside. See M. B. Stout, "Electrical Measurements," chap. 2, Minneapolis-Honeywell Regulator Company, Philadelphia, Pa., 1959.

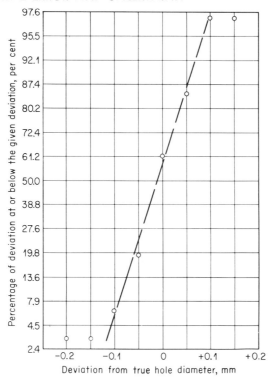

Fig. 2-7. A plot of the data from Example 2-3 on probability coordinates. The dashed straight line is drawn through the five inner points, ignoring the outer ones.

them.[1] A quick and simple way of testing for normality is the plotting of deviation data on *probability paper*. This is graph paper on which a normally distributed set of readings plots as a straight line. Probability paper may be purchased from the larger technical-supply houses, or it can be quickly made from standard graph paper (linear scales) in the following manner:

Along the x axis, plot the deviation scale, placing zero deviation in the center of the paper and selecting a scale that includes the complete range of the data available. In the center of the y axis mark the 50 per cent point. Then, beneath this and equally spaced, lay off eight intervals and label them in descending order: 38.8, 27.6,

[1] A. Hald, "Statistical Theory with Engineering Applications," chap. 6, John Wiley & Sons, Inc., New York, 1952.

19.8, 13.6, 7.9, 4.5, 2.4, and 1.2 per cent.   Above the 50 per cent
point, lay off eight more equal intervals and label these, in ascending order: 61.2, 72.4, 80.2, 87.4, 92.1, 95.5, 97.6, and 98.8 per cent.
The graph paper is now ready for plotting as shown in Fig. 2-7,
although the y scale is not a particularly convenient one.   As will
be shown by example, the y scale represents the percentage of measurements *below* a given deviation value x.

Example 2-3. Several student groups use a Brinell hardness-
testing machine on a specimen of known hardness.   The following
deviations from the correct indenter hole diameter (in millimeters)
occur: one reading of deviation -0.20 mm, one of deviation -0.10
mm, four of deviation -0.05 mm, thirteen of zero deviation, seven
of deviation $+0.05$ mm, four of deviation $+0.10$ mm, and one of
deviation $+0.20$.   All readings were first rounded to the nearest
0.05 mm.   Does this sample approximate a normal curve?

Solution.   There are a total of 31 readings.   Let us construct a
table from these data that will permit direct plotting on probability
paper:

Deviation	No. of dev. at or below this dev.	% of dev. at or below this dev.
-0.20	1	3.2
-0.15	1	3.2
-0.10	2	6.4
-0.05	6	19.4
0	19	61.2
$+0.05$	26	84
$+0.10$	30	97
$+0.15$	30	97
$+0.20$	31	100

The first and third columns of this table are plotted in Fig. 2-7.
While the resulting curve is irregular, it does pass close to the $x = 0$,
$y = 50$ per cent point which any symmetric distribution, including
the normal one, must intersect.   Notice that the outlying points at
either end are markedly affected by the presence or absence of one
or two values.   If we ignore the four outer points, the five inner
ones form a reasonably straight line suggesting that this experimental sample is part of an infinite parent population that is normal
or close to it.

Certainly skill and experience are needed to properly evaluate
this test for normality.   How straight, we might wonder, is straight,

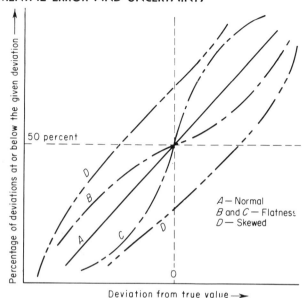

Fig. 2-8. A sketch on probability coordinates showing possible plots for (A) normal distribution, (B) a symmetric distribution with a top more flattened than the normal one, (C) a symmetric distribution with a top more pointed than the normal one, and (D) two possible skewed distributions.

and how close to the (0,50%) central point must we pass? Such decisions depend on the instrument, the test, and the number of data available for our plot,[1] and all we can do here is point out two of the obvious symptoms of departure from normality as revealed by a probability plot.

Skewness occurs when the xy distribution curve has a steeper slope on one side of its maximum point than on the other. A skewed curve might plot as an approximately straight line on probability coordinates, but could never pass through the (0,50%) point.

Flatness refers to a curve in which the top peaks either too sharply or too bluntly. For these conditions the probability plot will have the forms shown in Fig. 2-8. Many other departures from nor-

[1] Different or closer intervals on our homemade probability paper can be quickly obtained from any table of the probability integral (such as Table 2-1). Select evenly spaced values of ηx. Read the probability and divide this by 2. Descending values are these values subtracted from 0.5, and ascending values are found by adding each in turn to 0.5. Multiply the results by 100 to obtain percentages.

mality have been catalogued and may be found in advanced books
on statistics.[1]

There are a variety of complex and sophisticated tests for normality, skewness, flatness, and so on.   They are quite tedious to
carry out, require large numbers of data (as many as 250 items for
some tests), and are not too practical for the great majority of
engineering experiments.

It should not be inferred from this discussion (1) that we can
only apply meaningful statistics to a normally deviating instrument, (2) that the standard deviation or variance is not a useful
and meaningful quantity for nonnormal instruments, or (3) that
we can only find the best value for normally deviating instruments.
The advantage of proving (or disproving) that an instrument follows the normal law in its precision behavior is that we can often
gain new insight into our measurement problem.   A normally deviating instrument probably cannot be fixed to give more precise
readings, short of a complete redesign, while an instrument that
gives a heavily skewed or otherwise abnormal distribution of readings is possibly broken or being used incorrectly.

Suppose, for example, a series of students read water depth using
a hook gauge to 0.001 in. and the plot of occurrence frequency versus
reading (also called the density function) looks like the curve in
Fig. 2-9, having two humps or peaks.   We should immediately
suspect that some of the students were bringing the hook up from
beneath the surface and that others were dropping the hook down
until it just submerged.   The detection of such a nonnormal distribution may thus raise interesting and important questions about
techniques of water-level measurement that might never be considered otherwise.

Having decided how our instrument system deviates, we now
wish to obtain the numerical value of the precision indexes.   In
Sec. 2-3, two such indexes were defined.   One of these, the standard deviation s, is easily found from a sample.   From the definition
of this quantity, we can write its formula for a finite sample of
deviations rather than the infinite parent population as in the
previous section:

$$s = \sqrt{\frac{\Sigma x^2}{n}} \qquad (2\text{-}11)$$

where s now replaces σ since we are dealing with a sample rather

[1] Hald, *op. cit.*, chaps. 6 and 7.

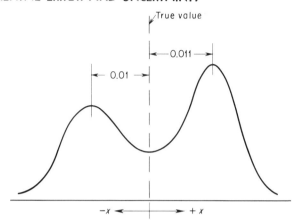

Fig. 2-9. A possible density function resulting from a large number of hook-gauge measurements of water depth, as described in the text.   In general, the shape of the two peaks would not be the same, nor would the same number of readings necessarily fall on either side of the true value.

than a population (see Sec. 1-3).   We see that, given a set of nx values normally distributed, s can be found by simple (though probably tedious) numerical computations.

Example 2-4.   Taking the deviation data on the hardness test of Example 2-3, what is s, and what is the index of precision of the data sample, assuming that the parent population from which the sample is drawn is, indeed, normal?

Solution.   Let us set up a simple table to solve Eq. (2-11):

x, mm.........	0.2	0.1	0.05	0
x^2.............	0.04	0.01	0.0025	0
No. of items...	2	5	11	13 (n is 31)
No. times x^2...	0.08	0.05	0.0275	0 ($\Sigma x^2 = 0.1575$)

Then
$$s = \sqrt{\frac{0.1575}{31}} = 0.0745 \text{ mm}$$

and from Eq. (2-9) now written for the case of a sample

$$sh = 0.707$$

so

$$h = \frac{0.707}{0.0745} = 9.45 \text{ mm}^{-1}$$

In Fig. 2-7 we showed that this sample of Brinell data deviations appeared to come from an approximately normal population. If this is the case, we can now say that roughly 68 per cent of all hardness determinations in this portion of the hardness scale will show deviations of plus or minus 0.075 mm or less. A limit of $2s$ is about the same as our noted twenty-to-one-odds criterion. Thus we expect that deviations of ±0.15 mm will enclose 19 out of 20 readings.

2-5. The "Best" Reading from Samples

So far, we have tacitly assumed that the correct or calibration reading, around which our instrument determinations randomly scatter, is known. When a new instrument is deliberately subjected to calibration against known inputs, this will be the case. In many experiments, however, it is impractical or impossible to establish the true value. We may wish to obtain the diameter of a pipe, the length of a lever arm, the resistance of a low-precision resistor, the flow of water through an orifice, or any of a hundred such measurements where we have no exact idea as to either the correct value or the precision of the instrument we use to obtain it. In many situations, we may be sufficiently suspicious of our instrumentation to take more than a single reading before we change the measured variable to a new setting. If the second reading deviates markedly from the first, and the third from either of the others, our suspicions are justified, and we are faced with a reading having serious precision error.[1]

In such a situation, we might ask two questions: How do we obtain the best estimate of the reading from a set of readings, and how many separate readings should we take? Consider a sample of n readings having values $X_1, X_2, X_3, \ldots, X_n$ that result from repeated measurements of an unchanged quantity. We will assume that these readings are part of an infinite normal distribution with a correct value that is unknown. The reading X_1 falls within a tiny interval Δx, as shown in Fig. 2-10. Thus, the probability of its

---

[1] Or, as already suggested, a variable that is poorly controlled. Mathematically, it does not matter in what follows in this section.

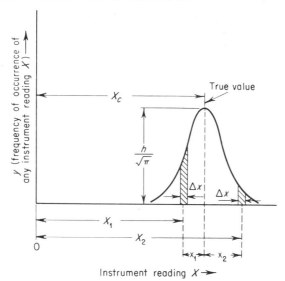

Fig. 2-10. A sketch showing the nomenclature of Eq. (2-12).

occurrence is the area of the little rectangle $y \, \Delta x$, or mathematically

$$\Delta P_1 = \frac{h}{\sqrt{\pi}} \, \Delta x \, e^{-h^2(X_c - X_1)^2} \qquad (2\text{-}12)$$

where h is used rather than η since we are dealing with a sample. Similar expressions will hold for the probability of occurrence of X_2, X_3, and so on. The probability that the entire sample of n readings will occur is equal to the product of the probabilities that each single reading will occur, or $\Delta P_1 \times \Delta P_2 \times \Delta P_3 \times \cdots \times \Delta P_n$. This basic assumption from probability theory can be demonstrated by coin tossing. The chance of a single head is 50 per cent or probability 0.5. The probability of two consecutive heads is 0.5×0.5 or 0.25 and of three consecutive heads, $0.5 \times 0.5 \times 0.5$ or 0.125, and so on. Then, if ΔP_{total} is the over-all probability that the set of n readings will occur

$$\Delta P_{\text{total}} = \left(\frac{h}{\sqrt{\pi}} \right)^n \Delta x^n \, e^{-h^2[(X_c - X_1)^2 + (X_c - X_2)^2 + \cdots + (X_c - X_n)^2]} \qquad (2\text{-}13)$$

We now make one of those basic assumptions on which many of

the theories of statistics and probability are founded.[1]   We assume
that *the readings X_1, X_2, . . . , X_n will collectively deviate from the
"true" reading X_c such that the over-all probability of these deviations
occurring is a maximum.*   A direct consequence of this statement
when applied to Eq. (2-13) is that

$$(X_c - X_1)^2 + (X_c - X_2)^2 + \cdots + (X_c - X_n)^2 \rightarrow \text{minimum}$$

or the sum of the squares of the deviations from the best or correct
reading must be a minimum.   This important result is the basis of
the widely used least-squares method of curve plotting which we
will consider in later chapters.

Following the above rule of combined probabilities, we see that
our unknown best value X_c must be such that ΔP_{total} is a maximum.
Differentiating Eq. (2-13) with respect to ΔP_{total} and X_c, we obtain

$$\frac{d(\Delta P_{\text{total}})}{dX_c} = -\left(\frac{h}{\sqrt{\pi}}\right)^n \Delta x^n\, 2h^2[(X_c - X_1) + (X_c - X_2) + \cdots$$
$$+ (X_c - X_n)]e^{-h^2[(X_c-X_1)^2+(X_c-X_2)^2+\cdots+(X_c-X_n)^2]} \quad (2\text{-}14)$$

There is only one way that this derivative can equal zero.   That is
when

$$X_c = \frac{X_1 + X_2 + \cdots + X_n}{n} \quad (2\text{-}15)$$

and a test of the second derivative will show that this is a maximum
and not a minimum point of the function.   Thus, we have proved
that the most probable value of X_c is equal to the numerical average of the n readings, a proposition used without conscious thought
by engineers and scientists the world over.   Again we do not restrict
the use of the numerical average to normally distributed density
functions but only say that for such a normal distribution the mean
is the best estimate we have of the correct or true value.   For a
pathological density function (such as Fig. 2-8) the mean might or
might not represent the best estimate.   If the true water level lies
exactly between the curve peaks, the mean will only be a valid
estimate if as many readings were made going down as coming up.

Notice that in this proof we used the symbols for the finite sample,
h and X_c, rather than those for the infinite population, η and μ_x.
It is not to be expected that X_c found from n readings of an instrument will exactly equal μ_x found from an infinity of readings.   We

[1] See H. Cramer, "The Elements of Probability Theory," John Wiley &
Sons, Inc., New York, 1955.

now wish to consider just how closely X_c will approximate μ_x, and how rapidly the difference $(X_c - \mu_x)$ will approach zero as n gets larger.   On an average, we expect a single instrument reading to be off by one probable error p.   An infinite number of readings will surely average exactly to μ_x if they are not pathologically distributed.   Unhappily, the improvement from about one probable error to no error at all is quite slow, since the *error of an average is inversely proportional to the square root of the number of readings making up the average.*   Sixteen readings are only twice as precise as four, and 64 only three times as good.   On the other hand, only four readings are twice as precise as one, so that some replication is often well worthwhile.   We can thus say that an instrument of satisfactory accuracy but poor precision can yield better data as its readings are replicated, but the improvement is slow.

The reader should now note that there are two possible ways of obtaining the correct value in any measurement problem.   The first way is simply to supply a known or calibration input and then read a succession of instrument outputs, comparing these with the known input to find a succession of deviations.   This sample of deviations is then used to find the standard deviation using Eq. (2-11).   The second way of obtaining the correct value has just been described and consists in numerically averaging all the readings.   When the correct or best value must be found in this latter manner, statistical theory shows that a more exact value of the standard deviation results from

$$s' = \sqrt{\frac{\Sigma x^2}{n - 1}} \tag{2-16}$$

The $(n - 1)$ term becomes necessary because a best estimate found by averaging X_c will certainly deviate from the correct value μ_x by some amount unless we have a complete population instead of a sample.   Then the sum of all the squared deviation terms $\Sigma(X_c - X_n)^2$ will be smaller than if the true mean μ_c had been used.   Using $(n - 1)$ instead of n partially corrects for this situation.   Some statistics books imply that $(n - 1)$ is always used for computing the standard deviation of a sample, whereas this is not the case in many instrumentation situations.   Only when the true value is not *independently known* do we use $(n - 1)$.

Example 2-5.   An optical pyrometer is sighted on a glowing filament, and several determinations of temperature are made by various persons. The results are

Temperature, °F	No. of readings
1850	1
1900	9
1950	6
2000	18
2050	10
2100	2

What are the best values for the filament temperature, the standard deviation of the instrument, and the probable error, assuming this sample derives from a normal population?

Solution. We should first average the complete sample. An easy method is to average $(2{,}000 - X)$ rather than X alone so that

$2{,}000 - X$	150	100	50	0	-50	-100
No. of readings	1	9	6	18	10	2
No. times $(2{,}000 - X)$	150	900	300	0	-500	-200

This set averages to $+650$, which, divided by 46 readings, gives $+14.1$; so X_c is 1985.9°F. Since the readings have been rounded to the nearest 50°F, it is appropriate for further calculations to take X_c as 2000°F. Such rounding is a matter of choice and experience, but is quite proper in many engineering situations when relatively rough statistical indications are all that are desired. Now to obtain s':

x	150	100	50	0
x^2	22,500	10,000	2,500	0
No. of x^2	1	11	16	18 ($n = 46$)
No. times x^2	22,500	110,000	40,000	0 ($x^2 = 172{,}500$)

and
$$s' = \sqrt{\frac{172{,}500}{46 - 1}} = 62°F$$

By simple proportion, the probable error (for a normal population) becomes about 42°F. A realistic reporting of the temperature is $1986 \pm 42°F$, and we expect that half the readings will fall within this range at this temperature level. This analysis applies only for a single level. We expect pyrometers to show improved accuracy and precision at higher temperatures (brighter sources). Thus, at, say, 3000°F the standard deviation should be smaller.

In Example 2-5 we used the $(n - 1)$ term because the correct or best value was not exactly known before the data were taken, but had to be obtained by averaging the readings. Had the source on which the pyrometer was sighted been calibrated exactly at 2000°F, the computation of standard deviation would have been identical except for the use of n in place of $(n - 1)$. With a sample of 46 items, such a change is of no importance.

When a set of scattered data is available from which one wishes to obtain the standard deviation directly, without first obtaining the numerical average, the following expression,

$$(s')^2 = \frac{\Sigma x^2 - \dfrac{(\Sigma x)^2}{n}}{n - 1} \qquad (2\text{-}17)$$

is algebraically equivalent to the process described in Example 2-5. Applying Eq. (2-17) to the pyrometer data, we obtain

$$\Sigma x^2 = 1(150)^2 + 9(100)^2 + 6(50)^2 + 18(0)^2 + 10(-50)^2 + 2(100)^2$$
$$= 172,500$$

Also

$$\frac{(\Sigma x)^2}{n} = \frac{(150 + 900 + 300 + 0 - 500 - 200)^2}{46}$$
$$= \frac{+650^2}{46} = 9,300$$

From Eq. (2-17)

$$(s')^2 = \frac{172,500 - 9,300}{45} = 3,630$$

so that s' is 60.1°F. This differs from the value found in Example 2-5 (62°F) since it is an exact calculation, whereas in the example we rounded the average reading to 2000°F. Equation (2-17) is handy in statistical analysis problems of the sort described in Chap. 8.

2-6. The Effect of Nonnormal Error Distributions

Figure 2-11a is a hypothetical error distribution of 50 length measurements so adjusted as to deviate following the normal law

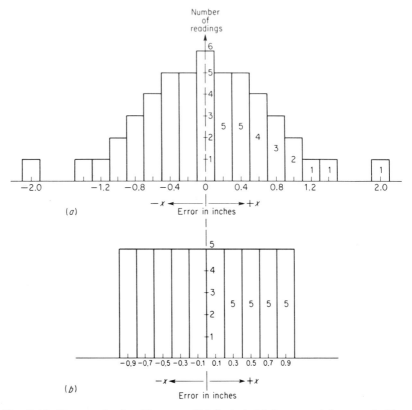

Fig. 2-11. Bar graphs for 50 errors distributed (a) in normal form and (b) following the "roulette wheel" distribution. The probable error of each distribution is approximately 0.5 in.

very closely. The sum of the squares of these 50 deviations is easily found:

$$\Sigma x^2 = 6(0)^2 + 10(0.2)^2 + 10(0.4)^2 + 8(0.6)^2 + 6(0.8)^2 + 4(1.0)^2 \\ + 2(1.2)^2 + 2(1.4)^2 + 2(2)^2$$

$$= 26.52$$

and from Eq. (2-16) the standard deviation is 0.737 in. Equations (2-9) and (2-10) combine to yield the probable error in terms of the standard deviation,

$$p = 0.675s' \qquad (2\text{-}18)$$

so that the sample probable error in this case is 0.495 in. Checking

Fig. 2-11a, we note that an x deviation of ± 0.5 in. encloses half the total sample or 25 items.

Now consider Fig. 2-11b, which is an example of the so-called "roulette wheel" distribution, so named because every deviation is equally probable just as every number on an honest roulette wheel is equally probable. This distribution is adjusted to contain 50 readings and to have a probable error of ± 0.5 in. as before. Computing the sum of the squared deviations again,

$$\Sigma x^2 = 10(0.1)^2 + 10(0.3)^2 + 10(0.5)^2 + 10(0.7)^2 + 10(0.9)^2 = 16.5$$

Eq. (2-16) now gives a standard deviation of 0.58 in. compared with the value of 0.737 in. found for the Fig. 2-11a case.

Suppose we were to assume that the Fig. 2-11b distribution were normal, perhaps because we had only a few readings instead of the 50 shown. Following this assumption, we might obtain the probable error from Eq. (2-18), which is based on the normal law equations. This equation would predict a probable error of 0.392 in. instead of the correct value of 0.5 in. that is easily obtained by inspection of Fig. 2-11b.

It should be obvious that few real error distributions will deviate from normality as drastically as does Fig. 2-11b. Yet even in this extreme case, the (incorrect) assumption of normality leads to a prediction of the plus or minus deviation enclosing half the readings that is only a little over 20 per cent lower than the correct value. A single example is not sufficient to prove a principle. Nevertheless, the implication of this brief analysis—that large departures from normality do not lead to important mistakes—is amply borne out in practical experimentation. The problem is not, as some statisticians and other specialists would have one believe, that a model or method may be used clumsily or in the wrong place. Far more serious in the present state of engineering experimentation is that the statistical model will not be used at all.

One precaution might be appended to these rather optimistic conclusions concerning the application of the normal model. When an engineer is interested in extreme value situations, crude or superficial model selections can lead to serious mistakes or real disasters. A civil engineer who estimates that a given stream reaches a particular extreme and unlikely flood level only once in 100 years may be embarrassed when the level turns out to occur on an average once every 5 years. Such questions deal with the "tails" of statistical distributions, and great care must be exercised when extreme values may produce dangerous or destructive occurrences.

2-7. Summary and Precautions

We have seen that all experimental errors can be imagined as resulting from a combination of two error classes, accuracy error and precision error. Pure accuracy error is easily detected by a simple calibration procedure and admits effective correction when the experimental results are processed. Precision error, on the other hand, implies a random fluctuation of the instrument about the true value of the measured quantity. In many experiments, we cannot separate the precision and accuracy components of error since we cannot calibrate or check the test apparatus. Such tests have uncertainty which we must estimate if meaningful planning is to be undertaken. Although this uncertainty will, in general, be made up of both accuracy and precision components, we treat uncertainty as though it were purely due to precision errors. Thus, we visualize the uncertainty as having a distribution of values around the true reading, and we deal with it using standard statistical principles. While the distributions of the deviations of an imprecise instrument could be of many kinds, we often assume the normal law or distribution on which a great deal of mathematical work has been done. If the distribution is approximately normal, and we can check this by a plot on probability paper, we then know the number of deviations enclosed by one or more of the precision indexes. These indexes are simply plus and minus limits on the deviation magnitude, between which limits lie various percentages of the total number of readings in an infinite population. When the correct measured quantity is not known, we can estimate it using a simple numerical average, providing the distribution of the deviations is not seriously pathological. We can improve the estimate from such averages by taking more and more readings, but the rate of improvement is slow and varies as the square root of the number of readings. Whether the correct value is known from calibration of the input or found from averaging, we can, by applying Eq. (2-11) or (2-16), find the standard deviation of the sample. Then, by simple proportion, any other indexes can be computed as desired, providing the deviations are normally distributed.

If the instrument is deviating badly but in a roughly normal manner, it is usable if we are prepared to replicate each reading many times. If the instrument has poor precision and the deviations are skewed, we should probably fix or discard the instrument. No hard rule can be given for the number of reading replications needed with a given imprecise measuring device although some suggestions can be made:

If the deviation permitted by the experimenter is greater than two or three times the standard deviation, a single reading should suffice.

If the deviation permitted by the experimenter is roughly equal to the probable error of the instrument system, one-half of all readings will lie outside the desired accuracy range. If a given reading is replicated four times, we would expect, on the average, twice the precision of a single reading, or two reading averages, to fall inside the limits for each one outside. Nine replications should put three reading averages in for each one out.

If the deviation permitted is one-half or less of the probable error, as many replications should be made as possible, or more likely the instrument should be replaced.

Much of this is concerned with the existence of normality, a condition that, rigorously, may never occur. Let us briefly consider some distributions that might at first glance seem normal but can be easily shown to be skewed.

1. In a purely mathematical sense, any instrument that has a zero or maximum point on its scale cannot deviate in a perfectly normal manner. Consider a pressure gauge with a probable error of 2 psi measuring a base pressure of 5 psi. There is a small but finite probability that this gauge will read 12 psi with the 5-psi input. But owing to the stop pin at zero pressure, no reading at -2 psi can ever occur. Thus the minus deviation "tail" has been trimmed off owing to the construction of the instrument. In most practical cases this is not important since any instrument with such an extremely wide deviation curve would not be suitable.

2. Many basic instruments show deviations that are sensitive to the previous reading. For example, a voltmeter might tend to stick, causing a high, or plus, deviation when shifting from a high to a low reading. Going from a low to a high reading would produce the opposite effect. The deviation population from such an instrument could only be symmetrical if the direction of approach was from high and from low an equal number of times. Furthermore, the amount of error might depend on the difference between the new and previous reading, so that all readings would have to be scattered about in a random manner (see Sec. 5-2 on such random

experiment plans). Such a random approach may be possible around center scale but is obviously impossible at maximum or minimum scale positions, where the approach direction can only be one way.

3. It is doubtful that any complex instrument that accepts a given input and then operates on it can possibly yield normally distributed deviations. Consider an instrument that senses the weight of a ball bearing but reports, at its output, the diameter. The weight-sensing element might deviate in a normal manner so that for a 1-oz bearing there would be as many 1.3-oz readings as 0.7-oz readings. The diameter is, however, a function of the volume or weight to the one-third power. Thus, the output reading would be some constant times 1.092 for the 1.3-oz reading, constant times 1.0 for the 1-oz reading, and constant times 0.89 for the 0.7-oz reading. If the weight readings are normal, the diameter readings will be skewed, while normal diameter readings mean skewed weight readings. Since there is no reason to think that the over-all instrument is less likely to give a normal distribution than a part of it, it is only reasonable to admit that probably neither weight nor diameter will represent a set of perfectly normal deviations.

In spite of these and other objections to the occurrence of normal deviations, the normal assumption is a good approximation to many naturally occurring distributions in instrument work.

PROBLEMS

2-1. A hook gauge measures water depth, and its readings are normally distributed with η of 10 ft^{-1}. If a large number of determinations are made, one-quarter of them will fall outside what range of depths when the correct depth is 1.5 ft?

2-2. The altitude detector on an automatic parachute has an η value of 0.00134 ft^{-1}. Parachutes opening less than 100 ft from the ground will smash the equipment. In a series of drops with the detector set to open parachutes at 1,000 ft, what percentage will smash their load?

2-3. An ohmmeter measures a standard 10,000-ohm resistor a large number of times. One-half of all the readings lie outside the range, 9,850 to 10,150 ohms. Estimate h for this instrument. What is the percentage error on this range, if this is defined as the probable error over the true reading?

2-4. Find the two precision indexes σ and ϕ in Probs. 2-1, 2-2, and/or 2-3.

2-5. Twelve readings are made with a sextant as follows: all 22° plus 30′, 40′, 40′, 10′, 30′, 20′, 0′, 30′, 60′, 20′, 40′, 30′. The correct reading is 22°30′. (*a*) Draw a bar graph of this distribution. (*b*) Test the normality of this distribution on probability paper. (*c*) If satisfied with the probability plot, find the standard deviation of the instrument.

2-6. Sketch the form of curve you would expect to obtain on probability coordinates for the following nonnormal distributions:

a. A normal distribution with the lower "tail" clipped off

b. A distribution that is symmetrical with two peaks and a hollow at the correct value

c. A distribution that is symmetrical and in the form of a rectangle

d. A distribution that is triangular with the leg of the negative deviation side longer than on the positive side, but with the apex at the correct value

The following data resulted from a series of student determinations of Rockwell hardness. For specimen *A*, 97.0, 98.7, 99.9, 99.5, 97.1, 99.5, 92.0, 100.6, 99.7, 98.0, 98.5, 99.5, 99.7, 99.5, 99.0, 98.5, 99.5, 98.8, 98.5, 99.1, 98.4, 96.6, 97.2, 101.7, 97.2, 98.2, 97.5, 97.7, 99.0, 99.0, 97.5. For specimen *B*, same machine and groups, 85.6, 87.1, 87.9, 86.9, 85.6, 85.2, 85.5, 85.7, 84.7, 86.4, 80.0, 85.0, 82.0, 86.0, 86.0, 87.3, 84.5, 87.0, 87.3, 85.4, 91.0, 90.0, 90.8, 89.2, 91.0, 90.4, 84.1, 81.7, 87.4, 84.0, 85.2.

2-7. Find the average of each distribution, and use this to plot the distribution of deviations from the average on probability paper. From this plot, *estimate* the probable error and the standard deviation for each distribution. (*Note:* The data may be rounded to the nearest 0.5 hardness number.)

2-8. Compute the standard deviation and the probable error of the machine for the two specimens—the higher the Rockwell number the harder the specimen. Would you say that this hardness tester was more or less accurate on harder surfaces?

2-9. Assuming that the average of the Rockwell data on specimen *B* is correct, select in a random manner 1, 4, 9, 16, and 25 readings from the list. Show whether the theorem relating to the precision of an average increasing as the square root of the number of readings is revealed in this case. (*Hint:* Plot the difference between the true reading and the average of sets of 1, 4, 9, 16, and 25 items on log paper versus *n*. Ideally, what shape should this curve have?)

2-10. An electronic pipe sizer is checked by running the same piece of pipe through it again and again. The results are:

Reading, in.	Number of readings	Reading, in.	Number of readings
1.31	2	1.37	19
1.32	6	1.38	10
1.33	22	1.39	0
1.34	38	1.40	0
1.35	57	1.41	2
1.36	44		

Careful hand measurements reveal that the correct reading is 1.35 in. Plot this distribution on probability coordinates, and then sketch how this deviates from a normal curve on a plot of number versus reading. Assuming that the population is actually normal, estimate the probable error of this sample directly from your probability plot and without further computation.

2-11. A large number of readings are made by an electromagnetic flowmeter of a fixed flow known to be 23 lb/sec. One-half of all the readings made fall between 21.8 and 24.2 lb/sec, and the sample gives a straight line through the proper point on probability coordinates. What is h for this instrument? If the flowmeter gives a reading of 20 lb/sec (with correct at 23) an alarm will ring. If the flow is automatically checked four times a day, how many alarms will occur in 30 days? What will the value of h have to be to reduce the number of false alarms by a factor of 2?

2-12. A precision sports-car odometer is checked over a measured mile a number of times and found to have a standard deviation of 1 per cent. Out of 20 trials, 10 fell within ±0.07 per cent of the correct distance. Comment on the normality of this error distribution as indicated from these two sets of data.

2-13. It is estimated that the probable error in splash-down point of a returning Mercury capsule is 35 miles. The Glenn capsule missed its impact point by 45 miles. Assuming a normal distribution, what is the probability that at least one of the next three orbital flights would miss the splash-down point by more than Glenn did?

2-14. The variation of a 1-in. shaft is found to be normally distributed with half the samples falling within ±0.005 in. The variation of bearing-hole diameter (around a nominal 1 in.) is also normal with half the values falling within ±0.0025 in. Assuming we hand-fit by trial as many shafts and bearing holes as we can, how many of the 50 shafts will not fit?

2-15. Given the situation in Prob. 2-14, what nominal bearing-hole diameter (instead of 1 in.) should we specify such that all 100 parts will mate by hand fitting?

2-16. The average number of hours of "useful" sun recorded in a particular location over selected days during several years is 3.4 hr/day. The distribution is approximately normal, allowing for the impossibility of having negative "useful" hours in a given day. If 40 days a year have 0.5 hr of "useful" sun or less, how many can be expected to have 7 hr or more?

2-17. The average annual birth date of an insect pest is noon on day X. Half the specimens studied fall within ±36 hr of this time, and the distribution is about normal. An insecticide has a lethal duration of two days and a kill probability of 98 per cent during this period. How few applications are necessary to be certain of killing 95 per cent of the pests? What time, in relation to noon of day X, should the first application occur?

2-18. A series of small, apparently identical, electrical fuses is tested to determine their blow-out current. The following data result:

Failure current, ma.......	92	93	94	95	96	97	98	99	100	101
No. of fuses.............	3	4	9	10	13	10	8	8	2	2

These are actual data, made up of $\frac{1}{16}$-amp fuses under a rapid loading condition. Using a probability plot, estimate the mean value, standard deviation, and the probable error. Comment on the normality of the data. Now compute the mean blow-out current and the standard deviation based on it. How well do the rough graphical results compare?

2-19. In the fuse experiment reported in Prob. 2-18, a single fuse blows out at 108 ma but is not included in the tabulation. How many fuses following the above general distribution should we have to test before finding one that blows out at 108 ma?

2-20. Suppose that the right side of Fig. 2-11a is reversed with the left side and the extreme values moved in to give the following double-peaked and symmetric error distribution:

x, in...	-1.4	-1.2	-1.0	-0.8	-0.6	-0.4	-0.2	0	$+0.2$	$+0.4$	$+0.6$	$+0.8$	$+1.0$	$+1.2$	$+1.4$
No....	3	5	5	4	3	2	2	2	2	2	3	4	5	5	3

Sketch a density function in bar-graph form of this distribution, and estimate by inspection the approximate $\pm x$ value that encloses half the reading errors. Now compute, using all 50 items, the standard deviation of the sample. Suppose one were to assume this a normal distribution and use this standard deviation to predict the $\pm x$ range that will enclose 50 per cent of all the errors. What would be the value of this predicted x range, and how would it compare with that found from the density function itself?

2-21. A Geiger-counter error distribution has 25 per cent of its readings exactly one count too low, that is, at an x value of -1.0 count. Fifty per cent of its readings are at x of zero (correct number of counts), and 25 per cent of its readings are at an x value of $+1.0$ (one count too high). Sketch the probability plot of this distribution. Find its standard deviation. What is the chance of getting three consecutive readings that are either exactly correct or smaller than the correct number of counts?

REFERENCES

Baird, D. C.: "Experimentation: An Introduction to Measurement Theory and Experimental Design," chaps. 2 and 3, Prentice-Hall, Inc., Englewood Cliffs, N.J., 1962.

Beers, Y.: "An Introduction to the Theory of Error," Addison-Wesley Publishing Company, Inc., Reading, Mass., 1957.

Boonshaft, J. C.: Measurement Errors: Classification and Interpretation, *Trans. ASME*, **77**(4):409–411 (May, 1955).

Cramer, H.: "The Elements of Probability Theory," part I, John Wiley & Sons, Inc., New York, 1955.

Davis, H. E., G. E. Troxell, and C. T. Wiskocil: "The Testing and Inspection of Engineering Materials," 3d ed., McGraw-Hill Book Company, New York, 1964.

Fisher, R. A.: "Statistical Methods for Research Workers," chap. 3, Hafner Publishing Company, Inc., New York, 1954.

Hald, A.: "Statistical Theory with Engineering Applications," chaps. 5, 6, and 7, John Wiley & Sons, Inc., New York, 1952.

Palmer, A. deF.: "The Theory of Measurements," McGraw-Hill Book Company, New York, 1930.

Parratt, L. G.: "Probability and Experimental Errors in Science," John Wiley & Sons, Inc., New York, 1962.

Stout, M. B.: "Electrical Measurements," chap. 2, Minneapolis-Honeywell Regulator Company, Philadelphia, Pa., 1959.

Tippett, L. H.: "Technological Applications of Statistics," chaps. 8 and 9, John Wiley & Sons, Inc., New York, 1950.

Wilson, E. B.: "An Introduction to Scientific Research," chap. 9, McGraw-Hill Book Company, New York, 1952.

Worthing, A. G., and J. Geffner: "Treatment of Experimental Data," chaps. 6 and 7, John Wiley & Sons, Inc., New York, 1943.

Youden, W. J.: Systematic Errors in Physical Constants, *Phys. Today,* **14**(9):32–43 (September, 1961).

Young, H. D.: "Statistical Treatment of Experimental Data," McGraw-Hill Book Company, New York, 1962.

CHAPTER 3

Error and Uncertainty in Complete Experiments

In the previous chapter we studied the kinds of error that can occur in the measurement of a single quantity by an instrument system comprised of a sensing element, a secondary or indicating portion, and an observer. The majority of engineers are concerned with experimental systems in which several instruments are reading several quantities, and these measurements must be combined through some mathematical process to yield a final result. That such a situation may be fraught with difficulty should be evident. Measurements, which in their raw form may appear quite accurate, may turn out at the end of a computational chain to possess errors that virtually destroy the purpose of the test. Or, if luck is with the investigator, seriously imprecise data may play so small a role in the final analysis that their questionable nature can be ignored. But there is no need to count on luck, for it is usually possible to thoroughly investigate the matter of result accuracy before a single piece of test apparatus is erected or even purchased.

As soon as we deal with the readings, errors, or uncertainties of more than a single instrument, we introduce the problem of considering the various instruments on a common basis, as far as their error or uncertainties are concerned. In this chapter, we will assume that all instruments involved suffer from either precision error or uncertainty, which we treat as precision error. In Chap. 2, we saw that we could express this error or uncertainty as having a distribution (probably normal in form) and as being described by a precision index (such as the standard deviation, probable error, or modulus of precision). When we are to combine the errors or uncertainties of two or more instruments, we must, of course, put them all on the same basis.

3-1. The Precision Index of a Product or Quotient

As we shall see in the following chapter, one of the commonest types of functions found in experimental work is combinations of products and quotients (the dimensionless numbers). Typical examples are the familiar Reynolds number (velocity times a length times a density divided by viscosity), the Mach number (vehicle velocity over speed of sound), the amplification factor of a vacuum tube (change in plate voltage over a change in grid voltage), and so on. Consider a general result R that is a function of the product of two measured quantities X and Y,

$$R = kX \cdot Y \qquad \qquad (3\text{-}1)$$

where k is some fitting constant that we assume to be exactly known. Now assume that a sample of X readings shows a standard deviation S_x and the Y reading sample shows an S_y deviation. If x_1 is a given deviation from X_c because of the precision error of the x measurement, and y_1 is the deviation of the Y measurement occurring at the same time, Eq. (3-1) for this specific pair of readings (out of a sample of n such pairs) becomes

$$R_c + r_1 = k(X_c + x_1)(Y_c + y_1) \qquad (3\text{-}2)$$

where r_1 is the deviation of the result and the subscript c refers, as in Chap. 2, to the correct or average reading. Equation (3-2) becomes

$$R_c + r_1 = k(X_c Y_c + x_1 Y_c + X_c y_1 + x_1 y_1) \qquad (3\text{-}3)$$

where the term $x_1 y_1$ is of second order and may be ignored. Then, Eqs. (3-1) and (3-3) yield

$$r_1 = k(x_1 Y_c + y_1 X_c) \qquad (3\text{-}4)$$

Similarly for other pairs of X and Y values

$$r_2 = k(x_2 Y_c + y_2 X_c) \qquad (3\text{-}5)$$

and so on. From the definition of s in Eq. (2-11) we see that

$$s_r{}^2 = \frac{\Sigma r^2}{n} \qquad (3\text{-}6)$$

and from the n equations, (3-4), (3-5), and so forth,

$$\Sigma r^2 = k^2[Y_c^2\Sigma x^2 + X_cY_c\Sigma(xy) + X_c^2\Sigma y^2] \qquad (3\text{-}7)$$

The term $\Sigma(xy)$ we assume equals zero since any particular product of x and y is as likely to be positive as negative and the summation of a large sample of such products will tend to zero. Then, Eq. (3-7) in Eq. (3-6) yields

$$s_r^2 = k^2\left(Y_c^2\frac{\Sigma x^2}{n} + X_c^2\frac{\Sigma y^2}{n}\right) \qquad (3\text{-}8)$$

Applying again the definition of s from the previous chapter, and inserting Eq. (3-1), we obtain finally

$$\frac{s_r^2}{R_c^2} = \frac{s_x^2}{X_c^2} + \frac{s_y^2}{Y_c^2} \qquad (3\text{-}9)$$

which is directly applicable, as will be shown in an example. Following the same method as outlined here, it is easily proved that Eq. (3-9) will hold for the case

$$R = \frac{X}{Y}k$$

so that when

$$R = \frac{XY}{Z}k$$

the expressions

$$\frac{s_r^2}{R_c^2} = \frac{s_x^2}{X_c^2} + \frac{s_y^2}{Y_c^2} + \frac{s_z^2}{Z_c^2} \qquad (3\text{-}10)$$

will apply. Notice that the term s_r/R_c represents the percentage of the correct reading represented by the standard deviation and is thus a type of per cent error. Thus Eq. (3-10) is a general mathematical form of the rule: "When the result is a function of quotients and/or products of a series of measurements, the square of the per cent error of the result is equal to the sum of the squares of the per cent errors of the individual measurements."

The foregoing analysis is not restricted to the use of the standard deviation or to instruments that deviate only in a normal manner. Kline and McClintock have extended the method to include a general deviation limit $\pm w$ where w might enclose 68, 50, 95 per cent, etc., of all the readings of a given instrument.[1] If $\pm w$ encloses

[1] S. J. Kline and F. McClintock, Describing Uncertainties in Single Sample Experiments, *Mech. Eng.*, January, 1953.

95 per cent of all the readings, Kline speaks of twenty-to-one odds that a reading will fall outside this limit. For this general deviation, Eq. (3-10) becomes

$$\frac{w_r^2}{R_c^2} = \frac{w_x^2}{X_c^2} + \frac{w_y^2}{Y_c^2} + \frac{w_z^2}{Z_c^2} \tag{3-11}$$

each w must enclose same

We must, of course, be sure that each w encloses the same percentage of the total population and, furthermore, that each of the several instruments deviates in a symmetrical manner. If a distribution is skewed, the terms Σxy in Eq. (3-7) will not, in the limit of n-equals-infinity, be zero. Another restriction on Eqs. (3-10), (3-11), and most of the equations yet to come in this chapter is that precision errors or uncertainties, w_x, w_y, and w_z, be independent.[1] For example, the index of refraction N of a prism as a function of two measured angles A and B may be given as

$$N = \frac{\sin (A + B)/2}{\sin (A/2)}$$

It is a temptation to treat the problem of finding the uncertainty or error in N as a function of the quotient of two quantities, $\sin [(A + B)/2]$ and $\sin (A/2)$, but this would be incorrect since these two quantities are not independent. Thus Eq. (3-10) or (3-11) cannot be used, and we must obtain a more general expression for error propagation capable of handling sines, logs, and so on.

Example 3-1. Water is flowing in a pipe at a certain measured rate. The temperature of the water is measured by a thermocouple, and the viscosity and density are then found from tables of water properties. At the minimum- and maximum-flow conditions, the following absolute values and probable errors p are estimated from a study of the instrumentation and the tabular material:

Quantity	Min flow value	Max flow value	p	% error (Min)	% error (Max)
Velocity V, ft/sec.......	1	20	0.1	10	0.5
Pipe diameter D, in......	0.4	0.4	0	0	0
Density ρ, lb/ft³........	62.42	62.42	0.05	0.08	0.08
Viscosity, lb/(hr)(ft).....	2.70	2.70	0.09	0.33	0.33

[1] A. G. Worthing and J. Geffner, "Treatment of Experimental Data," pp. 210–212, John Wiley & Sons, Inc., New York, 1943.

We wish to find the probable error in Reynolds number $VD\rho/\mu$ for the maximum-flow condition and the minimum-flow condition.

Solution. From Eq. (3-11) for the minimum-flow case

$$\frac{p(N_{re})}{N_{re}} = (0.10 + 0.0008^2 + 0.0033^2)^{\frac{1}{2}} = 0.10 \text{ or } 10 \text{ per cent}$$

For the maximum-flow case

$$\frac{p(N_{re})}{N_{re}} = (25 \times 10^{-6} + 0.64 \times 10^{-6} + 10.9 \times 10^{-6})^{\frac{1}{2}}$$

$$= 0.00605 \text{ or } 0.61 \text{ per cent}$$

This computation reveals the following facts: At the low-flow condition one-half of the computed Reynolds numbers will have an error greater than 10 per cent, but this deviation value improves to 0.6 per cent at the high-flow condition. Major improvements at either end will result in more precise velocity determinations. In fact, this is the only step worth taking at the low-flow end since the other errors are completely dwarfed by the 10 per cent probable error in velocity. If the experiment is run without changes, we can confidently expect the data at the low-flow end to show a broad scatter with the scatter becoming much smaller as the velocity is increased.

Statisticians refer to this scatter band as a *confidence interval*, which implies that we know the chances of a given reading falling inside or outside some given area on a plot such as Fig. 3-1. A more general term might be *uncertainty interval*, which implies that the interval has been obtained, all or in part, by estimation or guess, rather than from replicated tests of the instruments. We might have estimated, rather than the probable error, the uncertainty interval for twenty-to-one odds and followed exactly the same method to obtain this uncertainty interval in Reynolds number. Note that we still must be cautious about the noted rule regarding independence of individual errors or uncertainties. Suppose that velocity in this case is computed from a measured weight M over a measured time T divided by the density ρ times pipe area $\pi D^2/4$, or

$$V = \frac{4M}{T\rho\pi D^2}$$

M and T are independent of the other measurements, but now V includes D and ρ and our rule is violated if we apply the computational method already noted to find the error in Reynolds number.

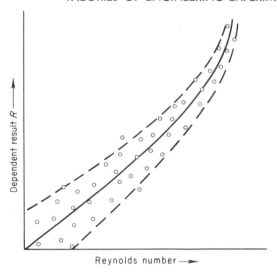

Fig. 3-1. A sketch of a possible data distribution showing a 95 per cent confidence or uncertainty interval which grows smaller at higher Reynolds numbers.

Instead, we rewrite N_{re} in its more basic form for this new experiment,

$$N_{re} = \frac{4M}{T\pi D\mu}$$

which reveals that ρ is unnecessary and its error of no importance in the computation of Reynolds number.

3-2. Finding Precision Indexes of a General Function

We could continue, as in Sec. 3-1, finding special rules for a variety of special cases, i.e., sums and differences, powers, logarithmic equations, trigonometric functions, and so on. But this would by no means complete our list, since we might find these classes of functions combined so that even more specialized and complex rules would be needed. Instead, let us develop a general method whereby any function can be analyzed to give the error in the result. Consider the general case of a result R, which is a function of the two measured variables X and Y:

$$R_c + r_1 = f(X_c + x_1, Y_c + y_1) \tag{3-12}$$

If this function is continuous and has derivatives (and it is difficult to imagine an experimentally determined one that fails such criteria), we can expand it in a *Taylor series*, using the first two terms only:

$$R_c + r_1 = f(X_c, Y_c) + \left[\left(\frac{\partial R}{\partial X_c}\right)_y \frac{X_c + x_1 - X_c}{1!}\right.$$
$$\left. + \left(\frac{\partial R}{\partial Y_c}\right)_x \frac{Y_c + y_1 - Y_c}{1!}\right]$$

Or, since $R_c = f(X_c, Y_c)$,

$$r_1 = \left(\frac{\partial R}{\partial X_c}\right)_y x_1 + \left(\frac{\partial R}{\partial Y_c}\right)_x y_1 \qquad (3\text{-}13)$$

where, as before, the lower case letters apply to deviations from the correct readings, and

$$\sum r^2 = \left(\frac{\partial R}{\partial X_c}\right)_y^2 \sum x^2 + 2\left(\frac{\partial R}{\partial X_c}\right)_y \left(\frac{\partial R}{\partial Y_c}\right)_x \sum xy + \left(\frac{\partial R}{\partial Y_c}\right)_x^2 \sum y^2$$

Again, Σxy tends to zero and $s_r^2 = \Sigma r^2/n$, so that

$$s_r^2 = \left(\frac{\partial R}{\partial X_c}\right)_y^2 s_x^2 + \left(\frac{\partial R}{\partial Y_c}\right)_x^2 s_y^2 \qquad (3\text{-}14)$$

and for the uncertainty interval w

$$w_r^2 = \left(\frac{\partial R}{\partial X_c}\right)_y^2 w_x^2 + \left(\frac{\partial R}{\partial Y_c}\right)_x^2 w_y^2 \qquad (3\text{-}15)$$

and so on for any other precision indexes.

3-3. Application of the General Equation

Equations (3-14) and (3-15) are important and their application is worth some study. Let us investigate two functions of engineering interest:

1. Given the experimental function

$$R = kX^b \qquad (3\text{-}16)$$

with k and b constant, what is the standard deviation in the result R for a given standard deviation s_x in the variable measurement X? Applying Eq. (3-15)

$$\frac{dR}{dX} = bkX^{b-1} \qquad (3\text{-}17)$$

and
$$s_r^2 = b^2 k^2 X^{2(b-1)} s_x^2 \qquad (3\text{-}18)$$

It is convenient, when possible, to write such equations in terms of per cent error. Dividing Eq. (3-18) by Eq. (3-16), squared, we obtain

$$\frac{s_r}{R} = b\,\frac{s_x}{X} \tag{3-19}$$

Example 3-2. The flow of water over a triangular weir is a function of the head of water to the 2.5 power. If the standard deviation in head reading is 3 per cent of the absolute value of head reading, what is the per cent error in flow, assuming any other quantities are precisely measured?

Solution. From Eq. (3-19),

$$\frac{s_r}{R} = 2.5 \times 0.03 = 0.075 \text{ or } 7.5 \text{ per cent}$$

Notice that, if an exponent is smaller than one, the error in the result can actually be smaller than the error in the measured quantity.

2. Given the function

$$R = \frac{XY}{X + Y} \tag{3-20}$$

we see that

$$\left(\frac{\partial R}{\partial X}\right)_y = \frac{Y(X + Y) - XY}{(X + Y)^2} \quad \text{and} \quad \left(\frac{\partial R}{\partial Y}\right)_x = \frac{X(X + Y) - XY}{(X + Y)^2}$$

Then Eq. (3-15) gives (assuming, for example, that $w = p$, the probable error)

$$p_r{}^2 = \frac{Y^4}{(X + Y)^4}\,p_x{}^2 + \frac{X^4}{(X + Y)^4}\,p_y{}^2$$

This is usable but it is usually better to obtain the per cent error, providing this does not give a more complex function. Introducing Eq. (3-20) with both sides squared

$$\frac{p_r{}^2}{R^2} = \frac{Y^4}{(X + Y)^4} \times \frac{(X + Y)^2}{X^2Y^2}\,p_x{}^2 + \frac{X^4}{(X + Y)^4} \times \frac{(X + Y)^2}{X^2Y^2}\,p_y{}^2$$

and, performing the indicated algebraic operations, we obtain

$$\frac{p_r{}^2}{R^2} = \left(\frac{Y}{X + Y}\right)^2 \frac{p_x{}^2}{X^2} + \left(\frac{X}{X + Y}\right)^2 \frac{p_y{}^2}{Y^2} \tag{3-21}$$

Example 3-3. The equation of the over-all heat-transfer coefficient U for a system of two fluids separated by a wall of negligible thermal resistance is $U = (1/h_1 + 1/h_2)^{-1} = h_1h_2/(h_1 + h_2)$, where

Table 3-1
A Few Equations of Error

Function R	Error in result p_r
a $k(X + Y)$	$(p_x{}^2 + p_y{}^2)^{\frac{1}{2}}$
b kXY	$R[(p_x/X)^2 + (p_y/Y)^2]^{\frac{1}{2}}$
and	
c kX/Y	
d kX^b	bRp_x/X
e ke^x	Rp_x
f $k \ln X$	$Rp_x/(X \log X)$
g $k \sin X$	$Rp_x/\tan X$

h_1 and h_2 are the individual coefficients of the two fluids. If h_1 is 15 Btu/(hr)(°F)(ft²) with a probable error of 5 per cent, and h_2 is 20 Btu/(hr)(°F)(ft²) with a probable error of 3 per cent, what will be the probable error in U?

Solution. From Eq. (3-21)

$$\left(\frac{p_u}{U}\right)^2 = \left(\frac{20}{20 + 15}\right)^2 0.05^2 + \left(\frac{15}{20 + 15}\right)^2 0.03^2$$

$$\frac{p_u}{U} = 3.1 \text{ per cent}$$

The propagated errors in certain basic functions are listed in Table 3-1. All can be found by the application of Eq. (3-14) or (3-15). Many other such relationships can be computed following the methods outlined, and the reader is warned against too careless a use of the few equations given in this text. For example, the equation given in Table 3-1 for the function

$$R = ke^x$$

is entirely incorrect for the function

$$R = ke^{-x}$$

3-4. Planning Experiments from an Error Analysis

Probably the most useful application of the ideas we have discussed in the previous sections occurs in the planning portion of the engineering experiment. Often the investigator will have a wide choice of instrument and test rig complexity, and he logically wishes to maintain a reasonable simplicity and expense level. One does not have to look very far in most industrial or government laboratories to see experiments in which instruments of all accuracy ranges are thrown indiscriminately into an apparatus. Tens of thousands of dollars may be spent on the best possible instrumentation to obtain final data that appear once in a half-page graph, of which the "standard deviation of interpretation" may easily be 10 per cent or more. The supervisor or responsible test engineer in charge who permits such slipshod planning is costing his facility huge sums that might otherwise be available for new and pressing research. The following two examples will show how error analysis can be useful in a planning situation.

Example 3-4. Given a sample of a mixture of gases in unknown proportion, we wish to determine the value of the mixture gas constant R/M from the familiar perfect-gas equation, $Pv = (R/M)T$, where P is the sample pressure, T the absolute temperature, and v the specific volume. The pressure gauge available has a scale of 0 to 100 psia with one-half the least-scale reading equal to 1 psia (which we will assume encloses 95 per cent of all readings). In the temperature region of 40°F (500°R), the estimated error is ± 10°R. The container has an exactly known internal volume of 1 ft³. If the sample specific volume is in the region of 1 ft³/lb, with what accuracy must the weight of the gas sample be determined if the error in 19 out of 20 R/M estimates shall not exceed 3 per cent?

Solution. R/M equals Pv/T. From Table 3-1, item c, we can write (with w the error or uncertainty in the various measurements)

$$\frac{w_r}{R} = \left[\left(\frac{w_p}{P} \right)^2 + \left(\frac{w_v}{v} \right)^2 + \left(\frac{w_t}{T} \right)^2 \right]^{\frac{1}{2}}$$

Since the pressure gauge is most accurate, percentagewise, at 100 psia, let us solve for w_v/v:

$$\frac{w_v}{v} = (0.03^2 - 0.01^2 - 0.02^2)^{\frac{1}{2}} = 0.02$$

If v is in the region of 1.0 ft³/lb, then the probable error in v and thus in the weight determination must be within 0.02 lb. Presumably a vessel containing 1 ft³ of gas at 100 psia will be quite heavy, weighing perhaps 50 lb or more, so that its weight will have to be very carefully determined.

Example 3-5. Figure 3-2 shows an apparatus consisting of a duct flowing air containing an unknown vapor concentration (expressed in milligrams per liter) with symbol C_{max} and an absorbent chemical

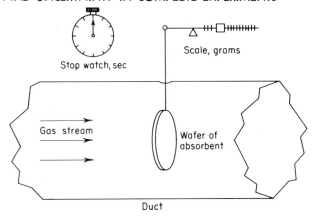

Fig. 3-2. A diagram of the apparatus described in Example 3-5.

which gradually extracts the vapor from the flowing air, following the equation

$$\Delta C = kC_{\max}e^{-b/\Delta\theta}$$

where ΔC = weight of vapor in chemical after time $\Delta\theta$ sec has passed

k = known constant (value unity in this case) with units liter^{-1}

b = known constant that expresses geometry and chemical nature of absorbent system, with a value of 3 sec

We wish to use this test system to determine $C_{\max}$ by measuring ΔC and $\Delta\theta$. The probable error (deviation enclosing half the data) in our time measurement is found to be 0.2 sec, and p for ΔC is 2 grams. We wish the determinations to be made as fast as possible, and we anticipate that $C_{\max}$ will be in the region of 20 grams/ liter. What is a good operating plan? What probable error will occur in $C_{\max}$? How can we best improve the accuracy and speed of these determinations?

Solution. The experimental function governing the finding of $C_{\max}$ is $kC_{\max} = \Delta C \, e^{b/\Delta\theta}$. It will be left as an exercise to show that the probable error in $C_{\max}$ is found from the equation

$$k^2\left(\frac{p_c}{C_{\max}}\right)^2 = \left(\frac{p_{\Delta c}}{\Delta C}\right)^2 + \left(\frac{b}{\Delta\theta}\right)^2\left(\frac{p_\theta}{\Delta\theta}\right)^2$$

For $C_{\max}$ of 20 grams/liter, let us construct a table for ΔC and

$\Delta\theta$ from the experimental equation and the noted values of the constants b and k:

$\Delta\theta$	$3/\Delta\theta$	$e^{3/\Delta\theta}$	$(1 \times 20)/e^{3/\Delta\theta}$
1	3	20	1
3	1	2.6	7.65
30	0.1	1.15	17.4
300	0.01	1.01	20

Now we can use these values of $\Delta\theta$ and ΔC in the equation for probable error of the result. For $\Delta\theta$ of 1 sec and ΔC of 1 gram

$$\frac{p_c}{C_{\max}} = \left[\left(\frac{2}{1}\right)^2 + \left(\frac{3}{1}\right)^2 \left(\frac{0.2}{1}\right)^2 \right]^{\frac{1}{2}}$$
$$= 2.09 \text{ or } 209 \text{ per cent}$$

When $\Delta\theta$ is 3 sec and ΔC is 7.65 grams

$$\frac{p_c}{C_{\max}} = (0.0675 + 0.00445)^{\frac{1}{2}}$$
$$= 26.8 \text{ per cent}$$

When $\Delta\theta$ is 30 sec and ΔC is 17.4 grams

$$\frac{p_c}{C_{\max}} = (0.115^2 + \sim 0)^{\frac{1}{2}}$$
$$= 11.5 \text{ per cent}$$

and, when $\Delta\theta$ is 300 sec and ΔC is maximum or 20 grams, $p_c/C_{\max}$ is 10 per cent, the minimum uncertainty possible.

Viewing this series of computations we can now answer the three questions posed in the problem statement. Given this set of probable errors and constant values, the best plan is to make a 20- or 30-sec determination. Any smaller time intervals give uncertainties that are clearly excessive. Longer times decrease the probable error very little. With this operating plan, the probable error in $C_{\max}$ will be between 10 and 15 per cent, which is quite high. To improve the speed and the accuracy of the experiment, it is obvious that a reduction in the uncertainty of the time measurement will have little effect. Thus we should concentrate our efforts on improving the accuracy with which we measure the weight increase of the absorbent.

To summarize the point of these two examples, we can say that a study of error propagation in experimental systems can bring out the following aspects: Such a study can predict errors in complete systems; it can help us to purchase a set of instruments having accuracies that are consistent with the whole test; it can reveal weak or "soft" areas of measurement; and it can help us to decide on a proper operating plan during test operation.

3-5. Uncertainty Propagation Using Charts and Curves

So far in this chapter we have assumed that the function relating the measurements X, Y, Z to the result R was known, and we then applied the special or general methods of Table 3-1 or Eq. (3-14) or (3-15) to this known function.   In many engineering situations, instrument readings are processed using functional relationships in the form of curves, function scales, charts, nomograms, or tables. To utilize such pictorial, graphic, or tabular functions we must generally apply a *finite-difference* approach. We might, for example, use an instrument yielding a reading X, which we estimate to have an uncertainty w_x and wish to use with a curve of R versus X to obtain the result R. The general equation for this situation from Eq. (3-15) is

$$w_r = \frac{dR}{dX_c}\, w_x \qquad (3\text{-}22)$$

If Fig. 3-3 represents the R-versus-X function, we can obtain the derivative dR/dX graphically by drawing the tangent at X and

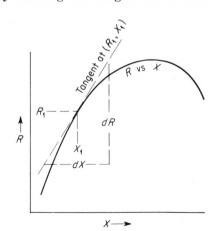

Fig. 3-3. A sketch showing one method of finding the derivative dR/dX at point (R_1, X_1) for use in error propagation formulas.

measuring its slope. Equation (3-22) is then easily applied if w_x can be estimated.

In some situations, the use of a smoothed curve introduces uncertainty or error even if the instrument readings are perfectly precise. The universally used Mollier chart for steam and its associated tables are considered to have about a 1 Btu/lb maximum uncertainty. Thus, if we enter these tables with temperatures or pressures having their own uncertainty, we must consider all these various anticipated deviations.

Example 3-6. A steam calorimeter gives readings for pressure and temperature of the throttled steam. We note a pressure of 15 psia and a temperature of 240°F. We also estimate the maximum uncertainty in pressure to be 0.2 psia and in temperature to be 5°F, this latter figure due to the impossibility of perfectly insulating the calorimeter. What will be the maximum uncertainty in enthalpy as read from tables?

Solution. The steam tables[1] give the following tabulation of enthalpy in the region of interest (in Btu per pound):

Absolute pressure, psia	Temperature, °F		
	220	240	260
14	1154.6	1164.4	1174.0
15	1154.3	1164.1	1173.7
16	1153.8	1163.7	1173.4

The general equation for uncertainty in h as a function of uncertainties in T and P is simply Eq. (3-15) in the form

$$w_h{}^2 = \left(\frac{\partial h}{\partial T}\right)_P^2 w_t{}^2 + \left(\frac{\partial h}{\partial P}\right)_T^2 w_p{}^2$$

We wish to first evaluate $(\partial h/\partial T)_P$ around the h value at 15 psia and 240°F. From the small table we see that

$$\left(\frac{\Delta h}{\Delta T}\right)_P = \frac{1,173.7 - 1,154.3}{40}$$

or $(\partial h/\partial T)_P \approx 0.48$. Making a similar finite-difference approximation, $(\partial h/\partial P)_T = 0.35$. Notice that we do not keep track of

[1] J. H. Keenan and F. G. Keyes, "Thermodynamic Properties of Steam," John Wiley & Sons, Inc., New York, 1936.

signs since we will square both quantities. The application of Eq. (3-15) can now be made as follows:

$$w_h{}^2 = (0.48)^2 5^2 + (0.35)^2 0.2^2 = 5.8 + 0.005 = 5.8^+$$

Notice that the pressure uncertainty is insignificant in contributing to the final uncertainty in enthalpy. Then w_h is 2.4 Btu/lb with the uncertainties as given, assuming the tables are exactly correct.

But we noted that there may be an uncertainty of as much as 1 Btu/lb in the table entries. We would certainly not expect the values in the small portion of the table considered to vary this much from one another, but it might be that this part of the table would be off by as much as 1 Btu/lb over all. Then the enthalpy has two possible uncertainty sources: one the basic "smoothing uncertainty" in the tables themselves having a magnitude of 1 Btu/lb or less, the other the propagated uncertainty calculated as 2.4 Btu/lb. It is not obvious how these should be best combined. Actually, we would probably be content with the two separate figures. We see that our calorimeter has not yet reached the potential limit of accuracy set by tabular uncertainties, and that we should attempt to reduce the temperature uncertainty. If this can be brought to $\pm 2°F$, the net error in h due to T and P uncertainties would drop to 0.76 Btu/lb, somewhat less than the maximum tabular uncertainty. It is doubtful if any further improvement in sampling precision would be justified.

3-6. Linear Propagation and Uncertain Constants

The propagation formulas used herein are well accepted by statisticians and others in measurement specialties. It is still possible, however, to find books and articles in engineering and physics[1] which do not utilize the basic square-propagation formula as shown in Eqs. (3-14) and (3-15). In some books it is suggested that the deviation percentages predicted be added directly rather than inserted in Eq. (3-14) or (3-15). Since it is little more work to square the percentages, such an approach is now considered old-fashioned and will not give so valid an estimate of the random error or uncertainty in a result as will the application of the methods herein described.

[1] To the interested reader is commended the following series of articles and notes which discuss these methods: R. T. Birge, *Am. Phys. Teacher,* **7**:351–357 (1939); H. Fleisher and L. Olsen, *Am. J. Phys.,* **18**:51–52 (1950); R. Hanau, *Am. J. Phys.,* **19**:382 (1951); and W. Rowles, *Am. J. Phys.,* **27**:62–63 (1959).

The reader may occasionally find himself faced with a fixed measurement or constant that will enter all computations in the same way. Examples of such a fixed quantity are lever-arm lengths, resistances in Wheatstone bridges, tare or zero readings, physical and mechanical constants, such as a specific heat or spring constant, and "natural" constants, such as the velocity of light, gravitational acceleration, and so forth. Such quantities are not actually random variables or susceptible to a changing precision uncertainty during a test. Once we select a lever-arm length, we are committed to that single value over a number of different runs. Nevertheless, we will consider such constants to be susceptible to a random fluctuation and thus to have an estimated uncertainty with a distribution of values about the correct one. This is a perfectly reasonable approach and simply means that during a test we will not replicate the reading of such constants. Obviously, if it should happen that the estimated uncertainty in such an unchecked quantity is too high, we replicate it if possible. The following example may make this point clearer.

Example 3-7. Figure 3-4 shows a simple Wheatstone bridge circuit to be constructed of standard resistances. The unknown resistance R_u is a variable sensing element in a test apparatus, and we wish the relay to open when null current occurs between the bridge arms. This will occur when

$$R_u = \frac{R_x R_y}{R_z}$$

Let us assume that the known resistances will be drawn from catalogue stocks. What must their tolerance be in per cent, if R_u is not to deviate from a design value by more than 5 per cent?

Solution. Here is a case in which we actually have no random variable at all. Once we select the three resistances, the apparatus will always have a null point at a fixed R_u. Yet, we can visualize that each resistor comes from a population having a symmetrical distribution falling within some, yet unknown, limits. Let us use Eq. (3-11) where the w's now represent some maximum deviation (enclosing perhaps 19 in 20 or possibly 99 in 100). Then $0.05^2 = 3(w_R/R)^2$, and $w_R/R = 0.029$, assuming that we wish all three fixed resistors to have the same tolerance. Commercial resistors can be obtained with a standard 2 per cent tolerance, and these would undoubtedly serve in this application. Thus, even in a situation in which there is no real random variable at all, it is possible

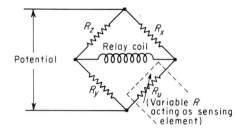

Fig. 3-4. A Wheatstone bridge null-sensing circuit discussed in Example 3-7.

to imagine the fixed values to have a deviation distribution and proceed accordingly.

3-7. Propagation of Nonnormally Distributed Errors

In the derivation of Eq. (3-14), there is no requirement that the error distributions being combined should be normal. Since Eq. (2-11) is simply a definition of s and since the summation of the squared-error terms comes directly from a simple algebraic manipulation, Eq. (3-14) will be entirely correct even if one or more of the combined distributions are flat, peaked, triangular, or of the "roulette wheel" type. The only requirement imposed on (3-14) by its derivation is that no error distribution should be excessively skewed such that the Σxy terms do not sum to zero as n becomes large.

Equation (3-15) [and Eqs. (3-11), (3-21), and those in Table 3-1] involves an additional assumption: that the relation between w (any given uncertainty interval) or p (the probable error) and the standard deviation s is the same for all error distributions. Mathematically, the requirement may be stated

$$w_x = k_1 s_x \qquad w_y = k_2 s_y; \text{ etc.} \qquad \text{but}$$

$$k_1 = k_2 = \cdots k_n \qquad (3\text{-}23)$$

These proportionality constants (the k's) will be equal only if the various error distributions are all of the same type, the normal distribution being usually assumed.

Suppose we wish to propagate the error distributions shown in Fig. 2-11, A and B, in a sum-type function as follows:

$$R = C(A + B)$$

where C is a fitting constant without error. This leads (see Table 3-1) to

$$s_r = (s_a{}^2 + s_b{}^2)^{1/2} \qquad (3\text{-}24)$$

The A distribution was found to have a standard deviation of 0.737 in. and a probable error of 0.459 in., so that

$$p_a = 0.657s_a \qquad (3\text{-}25)$$

The B distribution had an s_b of 0.58 in. and a p_b of 0.5 in., so that

$$p_b = 0.86s_b \qquad (3\text{-}26)$$

Clearly, the requirements just stated for writing Eq. (3-24) in the form found in Table 3-1,

$$p_r = (p_a{}^2 + p_b{}^2)^{1/2} \qquad (3\text{-}27)$$

are *not* met. The two constants noted in Eq. (3-23) are not the same. In addition, we have no easy way of knowing just what the relationship between s_r and p_r will be.

Now suppose that we were to start with known probable errors for the A and B distributions, change them to standard deviations using Eqs. (3-25) and (3-26), and combine these s values in Eq. (3-24) to obtain the standard deviation of the result. If we know that distribution B is of the "roulette wheel" type, we can obtain the correct s_b of 0.58 in. from Eq. (3-26). With an s_a of 0.737 in., Eq. (3-24) gives the *true* s_r of 0.938 in. Note, however, that although we know the standard deviation of the error distribution of the result, we do not know what percentage of the total this plus or minus error may enclose. Remember that $\pm s_r$ only encloses about 68 per cent of all the readings if *all the distributions involved are normal*.

Now imagine that we, incorrectly, assumed that the B distribution was of the normal type. We would now take the known p_b of 0.5 in. and use the normal curve relationship, Eq. (3-25), to obtain an erroneous s_b of 0.737 in. Now Eq. (3-24) gives the *wrong* s_r of 1.04 in. compared with the correct value of 0.938 in. This modest error of under 10 per cent in s_r would be considered negligible in most computations of this type.

It is true that the more usual analysis would be to go in the opposite direction, from s to p (or w). Still, it should be evident from this example that the use of Eq. (3-15) or Table 3-1 equations with non-normal error distributions is not apt to produce serious mistakes in over-all error estimates. *Vastly more bad testing will result from the simple failure to apply Eq. (3-15) than will ever occur from using it with doubtful error estimates.*

When the test is a complex or sophisticated one, involving error-prone instruments, doubtful tabular data, and possibly skewed or pathological error distributions, and when financial or humanitarian considerations require the most exhaustive sort of analysis of the test performance, the engineer should usually resort to a computer simulation of the complete instrument-plus-test-rig system. In this sort of analysis, the complete experiment is actually "run" on a computer over and over again with proper error distributions being sampled to provide realistic readings for each simulated run. A short discussion of the computer simulation of instrument systems will be found in Chap. 11.

3-8. Summary

We have studied a method whereby errors or uncertainties can be mathematically combined to yield the error or uncertainty of the result. This statistical method is best applied when a reasonably sound estimate of the statistical nature of the uncertainties can be established. We should try to convince ourselves that the individual deviation populations are normal or at least symmetrical in character and that we can estimate with some degree of accuracy the probable error or some similar precision index. When an instrument manufacturer gives a plus-or-minus accuracy range, we generally assume that this includes 95 to 99 per cent of all the readings of the instrument. When no data are given, we may take one-half the least count or scale reading to enclose this range. For important or questionable tests, an experimental determination of instrument error as discussed in Chap. 2 may be desired.

When the probable error or standard deviation is established for the relevant measurements, Eq. (3-14) or (3-15) is applied and a general error propagation equation obtained. Table 3-1 gives such equations for selected simple functions, but a wide variety of other equations may occur in engineering work and may be analyzed with more or less ease.

Propagation equations are useful from more standpoints than simply finding the uncertainty in a result. They can serve to indicate desired accuracy ranges for instruments and also suggest ways of operating the test apparatus or choosing test variable values so as to minimize uncertainties.

When an algebraic function is available, the entire computation of uncertainty propagation can be performed using calculus. In some situations, we may have to arrive at our result through the manipulation of charts, tables, nomograms, or similar graphic devices. To find the derivatives necessary in the solution of Eq. (3-14) or (3-15), we apply finite-difference or graphic (slope-measurement) methods. In many experiments, we will have an irreducible uncertainty, owing entirely to smoothing errors and previous experimental uncertainties inherent in our graphic devices. There is little point in reducing the propagated error or uncertainty far below this basic error, unless we can find better graphic material at the same time.

Uncertainty or error can be introduced by fixed quantities as well as by random variables, and we must estimate the uncertainty in such fixed quantities just as though it were a true random variable in our test. Such a fixed quantity is essentially a random variable with zero replication.

PROBLEMS

3-1. Prove that, when $R = X/Y$, the analytic method outlined in Sec. 3-1 (not the general method) gives the error equation (3-8).

3-2. We wish to construct a 50-ohm resistor by combining two 100-ohm resistors in parallel. If the 50-ohm unit is to have an error no greater than 1 per cent, what accuracy limits (in percentages) must we place on the two 100-ohm units?

3-3. Obtain one or more of the following items from Table 3-1 using the general equation for probable error (3-15): a, d, e, f, g.

3-4. The Carrier equation gives the actual vapor pressure P_v in terms of the saturated vapor pressure at the wet-bulb temperature P_{sat}, the barometric pressure P_b, the dry-bulb temperature T_{db}, and the wet-bulb temperature T_{wb} as follows:

$$P_v = P_{sat} - \frac{(P_b - P_{sat})(T_{db} - T_{wb})}{2,800 - 1.3T_{wb}}$$

With P_{sat} of 0.178 psia, T_{wb} of 50°F, T_{db} of 70°F, P_b of 14.68 psia, what will be the percentage uncertainty in P_v if all the quantities are error-free except P_{sat} and T_{wb}, which may have an uncertainty of ± 6 per cent?

3-5. The orifice coefficient C for a flat-plate orifice is given by

$$C = q \frac{[1 - (A_2/A_1)^2]^{1/2}}{A_2(2gh)^{1/2}}$$

q, the volume rate of flow, equals 20 ft³/min with no error; A_1 is the pipe area, 10 in.², A_2 is the orifice area, 5 in.², and each has a probable error of 0.1 in.²; g is 32.2 ft/sec²; and h is the pressure change across the orifice equaling 2 in. of the flowing fluid with p_h of 0.1 in. Find the error in C, and decide which of the measurements should be increased in accuracy for best improvement in the precision of C.

3-6. A hinged-end column with compression load P of 1,000 $\pm$ 50-lb load, eccentricity e of 0.01 $\pm$ 0.001 in., deflection δ to be found, moment of inertia I

of 1 in.[4], modulus of elasticity E of $10 \times 10^6 \pm 0.5 \times 10^6$ psi, and length L of 12 in. follows the equation

$$\delta = e \left\{ \sec \left[\left(\frac{P}{EI} \right)^{\frac{1}{2}} \frac{L}{2} \right] - 1 \right\}$$

What will be the error in deflection?

3-7. Prove that the experimental function in Example 3-5 gives the error equation shown there.

3-8. We wish to measure the refractive index N of a transparent substance by measuring the angle of the incident beam θ_i and of the refracted beam θ_r and solving the equation

$$N = \frac{\sin \theta_i}{\sin \theta_r} \qquad \mathcal{F}\,\dot{u}\,\acute{t}.= \mathcal{F}\,refr.$$

If the index is in the neighborhood of 1.5 and the incident beam can take any angle θ_i between 0 and 90° and either angle has an uncertainty at all angles of $\pm 0.2°$, at what angle of θ_i should we run the test?

3-9. The log-mean-temperature difference is defined by

$$\text{LMTD} = \frac{\Delta T_1 - \Delta T_2}{\ln (\Delta T_1 / \Delta T_2)}$$

If $\Delta T_1 = 2 \, \Delta T_2$ and each has the same per cent error, what must be this error for LMTD to have a per cent error of no more than 5?

3-10. The true pressure differential in a test system is to be found from a two-fluid manometer in the range of 0 to 1 in. of water. h is the indicated difference in liquid heights with an error of 4 per cent, SG_1 is the specific gravity of the lighter fluid and SG_2 of the heavier fluid, and R is the ratio of tube area to reservoir area with a value of 0.10. An instrument is available to measure liquid specific gravities to within ± 5 per cent, and the following liquids are available: SG-A 0.86, SG-B 1.0, SG-C 1.08, SG-D 1.56, SG-E 2.2, and SG-F 3.0. If the equation of the instrument is $\Delta P = h(SG_2 - SG_1 + R \times SG_1)$, select the two fluids that will give the most accurate determination of ΔP in the range desired.

3-11. The equation expressing the variation of resistance R with temperature T is $R = R_0(1 + \alpha T)$, where R_0 and α are constants to be determined by test. If R is 10.3 ohms at 50°F and 11.7 ohms at 150°F and p_r is ± 0.1 ohm and p_t is ± 1°F, what is the error in R_0 and in α?

3-12. Taking the same uncertainties given in Example 3-6 for a steam measurement, estimate the propagated uncertainty in h for the region P of 500 psia and T of 1000°F.

3-13. What will be the per cent error in viscosity, specific heat, thermal conductivity, and density of water at 100°F if the temperature is uncertain by 2°F? Repeat for air at 14.7 psia. Use either curves of properties or tabulations of properties from some standard handbook.

3-14. In a test of radiant heating panels, q, the energy input to the panel, is measured at 1000 Btu/(hr)(ft²) with no error assumed. The panel is at 570°R and radiates to a constant temperature sink at 490°R. Assuming that the absolute error in temperature (in degrees Rankine) is the same for either temperature measurement, how large can it become if the maximum error in emissivity e of the panel is to be less than ± 10 per cent? The equation is

$$q = (FA\sigma\alpha)(e)(T_{\text{panel}}^4 - T_{\text{sink}}^4)$$

where $(FA\sigma\alpha)$ are known constants without error and together equal 3.45×10^{-8} Btu/(hr)(ft²)(°R⁴). Note that e is a dimensionless ratio that lies between zero and 1.0.

3-15. The mean area of a seepage-flow system is given in terms of the entrance and exit areas A_1 and A_2 by

$$A_{\text{mean}} = \frac{A_1 - A_2}{\ln A_1 - \ln A_2}$$

A_1 is twice A_2, and the estimation error in each is 7 per cent. What is the propagated error in A_{mean} due to these errors?

3-16. An experimental apparatus measures the ratio of the surface tension at $T(S)$ to the surface tension at 0°C (S_0) and the ratio of the surface film temperature T to the critical temperature of the fluid T^*. Such data are related by the equation

$$\frac{S}{S_0} = \left(1 - \frac{T}{T^*}\right)^n$$

and the purpose of the test is to find the important dimensionless parameter n. The maximum error in S/S_0 is 0.05 and in T/T^* is 0.03. What will be the maximum error in n in the region where S/S_0 and T/T^* are both equal to 0.5? Decide whether the test is a practical one and how it can be improved.

3-17. The rate of growth of a crystal is assumed to obey the following law:

$$T = Ce^{m/m_0}$$

where T is the time of growth, C a kind of time constant based on the concentration of the solute with units in hours, and m/m_0 the per cent change in mass of the crystal. If the error in m/m_0 is 1 per cent with m/m_0 equal to 2.0 and C is 0.3 hr with an error of 0.05 hr, what is the expected error in T?

3-18. The flow over a contracted weir W as a function of the measured head on the weir H is given by

$$W = 3.33(B + 0.2H)H^{3/2}$$

where B is the width of the weir and assumed exactly known. Obtain an equation for the error in W as a function of the error in H, with no other errors present. Using this formula, decide which of these two weirs (which pass the same flow) would be the better design. Weir X has a B of 1.4 ft and an H of 2 ft. Weir Y has a B of 3 ft and an H value of 1 ft. Assume that the error in H is more or less constant and equally difficult whatever the head on the weir.

3-19. The potential in volts E of an experimental battery is to be found from

$$E = E_0 + 0.08 \ln \frac{C_{\text{ox}}}{C_{\text{red}}}$$

where E_0 is -0.2 and without error, C_{ox} is the molar concentration of the oxidizer with value 5 moles/liter and probable error of 0.6 mole/liter, and C_{red} is the concentration of the reductant with value 1 mole/liter and probable error of 0.2 mole/liter. What will be the percentage probable error in E?

3-20. The following three equations are to be used to process the results of a heat-transfer test on a condenser:

$$\text{NTU} = \ln \frac{1}{1 - \epsilon} \tag{A}$$

$$\text{NTU} = \frac{UA}{wC_p} \tag{B}$$

$$\epsilon = \frac{T_{c,\text{out}} - T_{c,\text{in}}}{T_h - T_{c,\text{in}}} \tag{C}$$

a. If T_h is equal to 212°F with no error, $T_{c,\text{in}}$ equal to 60°F with an error of ± 1°F, and $T_{c,\text{out}}$ equal to 180 ± 1°F, find the error in ϵ from Eq. (*C*).

b. Obtain the error formula for NTU with a known error in ϵ from Eq. (*A*) and use the results of the above computation to estimate the error in NTU (which is dimensionless).

c. The purpose of the test is to find U in Eq. (*B*). With w of 500 lb/hr $\pm$ 5 lb/hr, C_p of 0.25 Btu/(lb)(°F) with no error, A of 50 ft² with no error, what will be the error in U including the already found error in ϵ? Comment on improvements in the experiment.

3-21. Refer to Prob. 2-20 involving a double-peaked distribution. What would be the propagated error if this distribution's standard deviation were combined with that of the distribution pictured in Fig. 2-11a in a sum-type [Eq. (3-24)] function? Now suppose that the Prob. 2-20 standard deviation were obtained from its probable error, assuming the deviation was normal [using Eq. (3-25)]. What does s_r become, and what is its error? What is the equivalent of Eq. (3-26) for the Prob. 2-20 distribution?

REFERENCES

Deming, W. E.: "Statistical Adjustment of Data," chap. 3, John Wiley & Sons, Inc., New York, 1943.

Kline, S. J.: discussion of paper by Thrasher and Binder, *Trans. ASME*, vol. 79, no. 2, February, 1957.

——— and F. McClintock: Describing Uncertainties in Single Sample Experiments, *Mech. Eng.*, January, 1953.

Volk, William: "Applied Statistics for Engineers," chap. 7, McGraw-Hill Book Company, New York, 1958.

Wilson, W. A.: Design of Power-plant Tests to Insure Reliability of Results, *Trans. ASME*, **77**(4):405–408 (May, 1955).

Worthing, A. G., and J. Geffner: "Treatment of Experimental Data," chap. 9, John Wiley & Sons, Inc., New York, 1943.

CHAPTER 4

Reduction of Variables—
Dimensional Analysis

The study of individual uncertainty and uncertainty combinations, as discussed in the previous two chapters, is certainly the most crucial and imperative aspect of experimental planning. If potential errors are excessive, no amount of ingenious planning or advanced statistical "fixes" will accomplish very much. If, however, the uncertainty analysis shows that all is well, the investigator can then turn to more refined aspects of planning technique. The purpose of such planning can be simply stated; it is to obtain the maximum amount of useful data under the best possible control with a minimum expenditure of operating and calculating time.

As we shall see, there are several quite simple ways in which a given test can be made compact in operating plan without loss in generality or control. The best-known and most powerful (for the engineer) of these is *dimensional analysis*. Some fifty years ago, dimensional analysis was used primarily as an experimental tool and specifically as a means whereby several experimental variables could be combined to form one. The fields of fluid mechanics and heat transfer benefited greatly from the application of this tool, almost every major experiment in these areas being planned with its help. As the technique gradually became a part of engineering curriculums, the original purpose behind the methods slipped away. Instead of a principle whereby modern experimenters can substantially improve their working techniques, dimensional analysis is frequently presented as a pedagogical device or a historical curiosity. It is often applied to experimental problems dating back thirty or more years, or else serves as a neat and rapid way of deriving certain functional relationships without recourse to complex theory.[1]

As a result, young engineers often look on dimensional analysis as no more than an ingenious way of getting some already known results, or as a historic curiosity having little relevancy to modern technology. It is hoped that this chapter will in some measure counter such ideas by presenting this technique as it was originally conceived, namely, a method whereby many experiments are made shorter without loss of control. If the reader finds certain important historical developments in engineering made more convincing through dimensional analysis, well and good, but our main interest here should be for the future and not the past. There are just as many experimental programs in solar power, thermonuclear energy, and space flight that can benefit from this technique as ever occurred in river hydraulics, ship design, or steam condenser work.

4-1. The Buckingham Theorem

To properly apply this method, the investigator must know completely the kind and number of *fundamental variables* in his test. A fundamental variable we will define as any experimental variable that influences the test and can be changed or altered independently of the other test variables. Fundamental variables must be distinguished from *controlled variables*. We could, for example, change the acceleration of gravity independently of all other test variables by moving the apparatus to the moon (so that it is certainly fundamental), but we realize that, practically, this is impossible for the usual laboratory test.

Assuming that the experimenter does know all his variables, he can immediately reduce their number through the application of the first part of the *Buckingham theorem*, which states: "If any equation is dimensionally homogeneous, it can be reduced to a relationship among a complete set of dimensionless products."

A *dimensionally homogeneous* equation is one whose form does not depend on the fundamental units of measurement. An example is the familiar Fanning friction-factor equation, $\Delta P = f(L/D)V^2/2g$, where the variables might be in units of feet and seconds, meters

---

[1] For some excellent examples of this side of dimensional analysis see G. T. Conn and E. Crane, Some Applications of the Methods of Dimensions to Atomic Physics, *Am. J. Phys.*, **24**:543–549 (1956).

and hours, rods and minutes, or any consistent system.   Conversely the equation relating the heat flow per unit area q/A from a radiating body at temperature T as proposed by Dulong and Petit, $q/A = C(1.0077)^T$, is not homogeneous since using T in degrees Kelvin will require a very different function from using Rankine temperatures.   The correct formula for this situation was found later to be $q/A = \sigma T^4$, with σ as a dimensional constant.   Indeed, we should doubt that any natural occurrence can possibly be explained by a nonhomogeneous equation, except as a temporary or approximate expedient.

The *dimensionless products* noted in Buckingham's rule are simply products and quotients made up of the variables such that the dimensions cancel in each group.   In the case of the Fanning equation, we can write it in terms of three dimensionless products or groups: $\Delta P/(V^2/2g)$, f, and L/D.   The Buckingham theorem is by no means so trivial as might appear from this simple example, nor is its proof obvious.[1]

We have already suggested that nonhomogeneous equations cannot represent the complete mathematical statement of a natural occurrence.   We may not be able to recognize all the variables that influence a test, but we should realize that they and their dimensionless equation have reality whether or not it is apparent.   Failure to obtain a set of dimensionless products is thus a sure sign that something is missing.

In the most general form of the Fanning friction equation, we note that ΔP is usually the quantity of interest.   We see that it is a function of the pipe length L, the diameter D, and the flow velocity V, all of which are individually variable.   The gravitational acceleration g is not easily changed, but must be included.   More thought should convince us that the fluid properties of density and viscosity are independently variable (by changing the type of fluid or its temperature), and an examination of various pipe interiors will show that roughness height e is also variable.   This makes eight fundamental variables and we can write the general equation

$$\Delta P = \phi(L,D,V,\rho,\mu,e,g) \tag{4-1}$$

where ϕ means "a function of."

[1] For an interesting geometric proof see S. Corrsin, *Am. J. Phys.*, **19**:180–182 (1951).   Most proofs involve determinants.   See P. W. Bridgman, "Dimensional Analysis," Yale University Press, New Haven, Conn., 1931.

Buckingham's theorem states that this functional relationship (if it be homogeneous) can be written in terms of dimensionless products. We know from long experience that these can be

$$\frac{\Delta P}{V^2/2g} = \phi'\left(\frac{L}{D}, \frac{VD\rho}{\mu}, \frac{e}{D}\right) \tag{4-2}$$

which can be seen to be dimensionless if consistent units are used throughout. For the experimentalist, finding the function ϕ' in Eq. (4-2) is far easier than finding the function ϕ in Eq. (4-1). Instead of varying each of seven variables in turn, some of which may be hard to manipulate, the investigator need only vary each of three groups. This is experimentally a great simplification and makes plotting and data analysis far quicker and more accurate.

Let us see how the above groups in Eq. (4-2) can be obtained in a simple and systematic way. We will follow the so-called Rayleigh method of solving dimensional systems, and we begin by writing the variables in the friction loss system in terms of three *fundamental dimensions,* mass M, time θ, and length L. A list of the basic dimensional formulas will be found in Appendix B.

Name of variable	Symbol	Dimensional formula
Heat loss in pipe...............	ΔP	L
Length of pipe................	L	L
Pipe diameter................	D	L
Fluid velocity................	V	L/θ
Fluid viscosity...............	μ	$M\theta^{-1}L^{-1}$
Fluid density................	ρ	ML^{-3}
Roughness height.............	e	L
Acceleration of gravity........	g	$L\theta^{-2}$

We now assume that there exists a relationship between these quantities such that

$$\phi(L^a, D^b, V^c, \mu^d, \rho^e, e^f, g^g) = \Delta P \tag{4-3}$$

Now Eq. (4-3) can be rewritten with the dimensional formulas of the above table inserted,

$$\phi[L^a, L^b, (L\theta^{-1})^c, (M\theta^{-1}L^{-1})^d, (ML^{-3})^e, L^f, (L\theta^{-2})^g] = L \tag{4-4}$$

If this equation is to be dimensionally homogeneous, the following relationships among the exponents must apply:

For M: $0 = d + e$
For L: $1 = a + b + c - d - 3e + f + g$
For θ: $0 = -c - d - 2g$

We have three equations and seven unknowns. Let us simplify as far as possible eliminating e, c, and b. Then, $e = -d$, $c = -d - 2g$, and $b = 1 - a - d + g - f$. These equations can now be substituted for the exponents in Eq. (4-3),

$$\phi(L^a, D^{1-a-d+g-f}, V^{-d-2g}, \mu^d, \rho^{-d}, e^f, g^g) = \Delta P$$

Now, collecting terms with like exponents, the dimensionless groups are easily formed,

$$\phi\left[\left(\frac{L}{D}\right)^a, \left(\frac{VD\rho}{\mu}\right)^{-d}, \left(\frac{e}{D}\right)^f, \left(\frac{Dg}{V^2}\right)^g\right] = \frac{\Delta P}{D} \qquad (4\text{-}5)$$

The original eight variables of the problem are reduced to five groups, and the investigator has gone as far as possible in this problem with dimensional analysis. Now, he would begin to test for the actual function that includes these groups and expresses the behavior of the pipe friction system. Experiments in the laminar region should soon reveal the following function:

$$\frac{\Delta P}{D}\left(\frac{Dg}{V^2}\right)^1 = 32\left(\frac{L}{D}\right)^1\left(\frac{VD\rho}{\mu}\right)^{-1}\left(\frac{e}{D}\right)^0$$

(Later chapters will consider some of the means by which this could be discovered from test data.) Thus, the final result is the familiar equation for laminar friction loss in a round pipe:

$$\frac{\Delta P}{V^2/2g} = \frac{64}{N_{re}}\frac{L}{D} \qquad (4\text{-}6)$$

Only three groups are thus needed here (four in turbulent flow), but we could not infer this from dimensional reasoning. Still, the experimental simplification is obvious.

4-2. The Pi Theorem

Let us consider another fluid system involving a submarine of characteristic dimension d moving at various speeds in a viscous fluid and impeded by a drag force D, as shown in Fig. 4-1. Again,

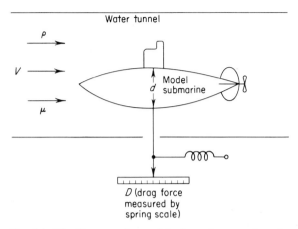

Fig. 4-1. The diagram of a model submarine experiment, showing the variables expected to influence the problem.

we will use the same fundamental dimensions of mass, time, and length, so that the table of variables becomes:

Name of variable	Symbol	Dimensional formula
Fluid velocity..............	V	$L\theta^{-1}$
Characteristic dimension.......	d	L
Fluid density..............	ρ	ML^{-3}
Fluid viscosity..............	μ	$M\theta^{-1}L^{-1}$
Drag force..................	D	$ML\theta^{-2}$

Since we have chosen a system of fundamental dimensions made up of mass, time, and length, we have derived the dimensions of force from these basic dimensions and the equation of Newton's second law. As will be noted later, force can be taken as a fundamental dimension if the analyst so chooses. As before

$$\phi(V^a, d^b, \rho^c, \mu^d) = D \tag{4-7}$$

and $\quad \phi[(L\theta^{-1})^a, L^b, (ML^{-3})^c, (M\theta^{-1}L^{-1})^d] = ML\theta^{-2}$

So, the exponent equations become

For M: $\qquad c + d = 1$

For L: $\qquad 1 = a + b - 3c - d$

For θ: $\qquad -2 = -a - d$

Solving in terms of d only,

$$c = -d + 1 \qquad b = 2 - d \qquad \text{and} \qquad a = 2 - d$$

and Eq. (4-7) becomes

$$\phi(V^{2-d}, d^{2-d}, \rho^{1-d}, \mu^d) = D$$

and

$$\frac{D}{\rho V^2 d} = \phi'\left(\frac{\mu}{V d \rho}\right)$$

or in its more usual form,

$$C_d = \phi' N_{re} \tag{4-8}$$

where C_d is the familiar drag coefficient which is a function of the Reynolds number only. Thus, to represent the behavior of this submarine, we need not plot drag versus V, d, ρ, and μ separately, but only find a single curve of C_d versus N_{re}. It should be obvious that many fewer test points are needed for this latter job, as Fig. 4-2 reveals.

Notice, however, that the resulting curve will only hold for submarines that are *geometrically similar*. Our single characteristic dimension d can only specify the over-all size of the boat, but can tell us nothing about its shape, taper, streamlining, and so on. To obtain a general expression for submarines of any shape would require a huge number of dimension ratios and a test effort too vast to consider. Thus the investigator must beware of drawing too extensive conclusions from dimensional analysis or trying to apply his results too liberally.

Both the pipe friction and the drag problem illustrate the second part of Buckingham's famous theorem which is useful in checking the results of a dimensional analysis. This is the so-called *pi theorem* that states: "If there exists a unique relation $\phi(A_1, A_2, \ldots, A_n) = 0$ among n physical quantities that involve k primary dimensions, then there also exists a relation (M, θ, L)

$$\phi'(\pi_1, \pi_2, \ldots, \pi_{n-k}) = 0$$

among the $(n - k)$ dimensionless products made up of the A's." Both the previous examples follow this rule. The friction case had eight physical quantities n, and we chose three primary dimensions k so that the pi theorem would predict $(8 - 3)$ or five dimensionless products of pi's. This is mathematically what was obtained, although experimental work then showed that only three or four were actually required. In the drag problem there are five variables

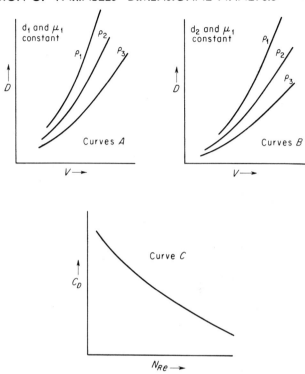

Fig. 4-2. Without dimensional analysis, many curves like A and B would be required to express the submarine data. With dimensionless groups, only a single curve C is necessary.

and three primaries yielding two pi's as found, both of which, it happens, are necessary.

4-3. Selection of Groups and Variables

At first glance, dimensional analysis and the Rayleigh analytic method of finding groups seem relatively automatic in application, but such, unhappily, is often not the case, particularly when one is dealing with new and strange experiments. Consider our submarine problem again. Suppose we had solved these three exponent equations in terms of c instead of d. We then obtain

$$d = -c + 1 \qquad a = c + 1 \qquad \text{and} \qquad b = c + 1$$

Putting these values in Eq. (4-7) as before, we obtain

$$\frac{D}{Vd\mu} = \phi'' \frac{Vd\rho}{\mu} \tag{4-9}$$

Equation (4-9) is surely as correct as Eq. (4-8). The groups are dimensionless and either equation checks the pi theorem. To the experienced investigator, Eq. (4-9) is not as useful as Eq. (4-8). The group $D/\rho V^2 d^2$ includes the drag force, the kinetic energy of the flowing fluid, and a dimension squared that suggests an area, perhaps a frontal area on which the fluid impinges. Thus, this group could be taken as the ratio of the actual drag to the force due to impact of the fluid on the submarine frontal area. The group $D/Vd\mu$, on the other hand, is not an obviously meaningful collection of variables. The combination of viscosity with a length and a velocity is unusual and not especially significant. Another not very useful group can be obtained by solving the exponent equations for a, getting $\rho D/\mu^2$. If this group only contained fluid properties, it might be of interest, but it also includes the drag force and is of questionable utility.

The point, then, is that there are several solutions to many dimensional systems, and that, while all solutions may be correct, they are not equally useful. Also, as we will see in a later section of this chapter, the presence of error or uncertainty may suggest the choice of one series of groups rather than another.

The reader may have begun to wonder about the inclusion or exclusion of certain variables in an experimental system. Why, for example, did we include the acceleration of gravity in the friction problem and not in the drag-system analysis? Suppose we miss some important variable? Suppose irrelevant variables are mistakenly included?

Consider a system of two bodies in open space, revolving around each other owing to mutual gravitational attraction. We suspect that the following variables might specify the behavior of this system:

Name of quantity	Symbol	Dimensional formula
Mass of body 1...............	M_1	M
Mass of body 2...............	M_2	M
Distance of separation.........	R	L
Period of revolution...........	P	θ

Then we write

$$\phi(M^a, M^b, L^c) = \theta$$

but it is obvious that an error has occurred. Time appears on one

When your extracted groups don't cancel, there has been a term left out.

side of the equation but not on the other, and a dimensionless number is not possible. This could mean that the revolution period is not an important variable, but, since this is the variable we wish to find, such an explanation must be rejected. Either this is a case of a nonhomogeneous equation or (more likely) we have left out something important. Any astronomer can quickly supply the missing item. It is the gravitational constant G with units $M^{-1}L^3\theta^{-2}$. Including this in our analysis we could easily obtain

$$\frac{PG^{\frac{1}{2}}M_2^{\frac{1}{2}}}{R^{\frac{3}{2}}} = \phi'\left(\frac{M_2}{M_1}\right) \tag{4-10}$$

and, with almost no knowledge of celestial mechanics, we have found that the revolution period of a double-star system is directly proportional to the separation distance to the $\frac{3}{2}$ power, a fact that is certainly not intuitively obvious. But, the reader may wonder: Why do we put a universal constant like G in the problem when it is by no stretch of the imagination a variable? No really satisfying answer is possible, but we might say that a universe having a G value less than this one would show a longer period of revolution with nothing else changed. That no such universe probably exists is ✳ philosophically interesting but of no concern in dimensional analysis. *We require G because the system is not completely described without it.*

In the double-star system, the failure to include an important variable was immediately obvious. Let us now consider a circular disk of diameter d and negligible thickness, rotating in the center of a fluid-filled cylindrical casing completely enclosed and filled with a viscous liquid. Figure 4-3 shows the various important variables.

Name of quantity	Symbol	Dimensional formula
Disk diameter..............	d	L
Internal diameter............	D	L
Fluid viscosity..............	μ	$ML^{-1}\theta^{-1}$
Clearance...................	c	L
Angular velocity............	w	θ^{-1}
Torque.....................	T	$ML^2\theta^{-2}$

We have six variables and three primaries; so we require three groups. The system is quite easily handled by *inspection*, without recourse to the formal Rayleigh method. For example, one group will logically be D/d, a second group might be D/c, and the third

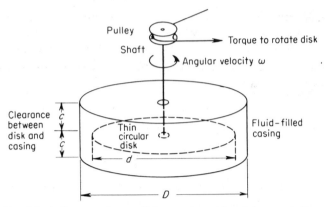

Fig. 4-3. A diagram of a possible experiment involving a rotating thin disk in an enclosed viscous fluid, showing some of the nomenclature.

group could be $d^3 w\mu/T$. When groups are found by inspection, it should be obvious that *all variables must appear at least once.* Then

$$\frac{T}{d^3 w\mu} = \phi\left(\frac{D}{d}, \frac{D}{c}\right)$$

This might, at first glance, seem all right, but we should be suspicious. Motion in or of a fluid almost always yields a Reynolds number, for which we need density. Looking at our system, we should be able to see that fluids with different densities will surely give different results even if all else is the same. Let us then add this new variable and rewrite the groups in a more logical fashion.

$$\frac{T}{\rho(wd)^2 D^2 c} = \phi\left(\frac{wD^2\rho}{\mu}, \frac{D}{c}, \frac{D}{d}\right) \tag{4-11}$$

The equation now seems to make more sense. A Reynolds number based on rotary velocity appears. The term $\rho(wd)^2$ is related to the fluid kinetic energy at the disk edge while $D^2 c$ is easily transformed into the total volume of the container. Thus the denominator of the torque group can be "built" into some sort of kinetic energy term based on a reference lip velocity. We might wonder about the two groups, D/c and D/d (which could just as well be c/d and c/D and so on). Are both these groups needed to completely specify the system behavior? Although we might suspect that they are not, we cannot so assume on the basis of dimensional

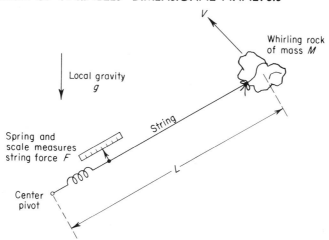

Fig. 4-4. The whirling-rock system and some of the possible variables.

analysis.   The pi theorem demands four groups, and experimentation must take over at this point.

The reader may now wonder: What about gravitational acceleration g?   Surely, if the fluid did not fill the container so that a free surface remained, the position of the apparatus in the gravity field would be crucial.   But if, as we assumed, the fluid fills the container, we suspect that gravity has little effect on the motion of the disk or fluid.   Whether to insert g or not is a major puzzle, and real insight is needed if the proper decision is to be made.   In the frictional system, we included g because the head loss ΔP was given in feet of the flowing fluid: feet, that is, in a gravity field of value g.   In the drag problem, we sensed that the drag is independent of the value of local gravity.

Consider now a string of length R connected to a fixed point with a rock of mass M at the other end.   The rock whirls with a constant velocity, and we are interested in the force F in the string:

Name of quantity	Symbol	Dimensional formula
Mass of rock.................	M	M
Linear velocity of rock........	V	$L\theta^{-1}$
String length	R	L
Acceleration of gravity........	g	$L\theta^{-2}$
Force in string..............	F	$ML\theta^{-2}$

Then $\qquad$ $F = \phi(M^a, g^b, V^c, R^d)$

and $\qquad$ $ML\theta^{-2} = \phi[M^a, (L\theta^{-2})^b, (L\theta^{-1})^c, L^d]$

For M: $\qquad$ $a = 1$

For L: $\qquad$ $1 = b + c + d$

For θ: $\qquad$ $-2 = -2b - c$

and $\qquad$ $a = 1$ $\qquad$ $c = 2 - 2b$ $\qquad$ and $\qquad$ $d = -1 + b$

This gives a grouping of

$$\frac{FR}{MV^2} = \phi'\left(\frac{gR}{V^2}\right) \tag{4-12}$$

Let us imagine now that we run an experiment with rocks of different masses whirling at different speeds and then plot our results. We would soon find (as any elementary physics student should suspect) that the plot in Fig. 4-5 results. The straight, horizontal line shows simply that we have one too many variables. Our error here was the inclusion of g in our table of variables. A little more thought might convince us that the acceleration of gravity has little effect on this sytem, that the force in the string will be the same on the moon as on the earth. Leaving out g, we obtain a single group so that

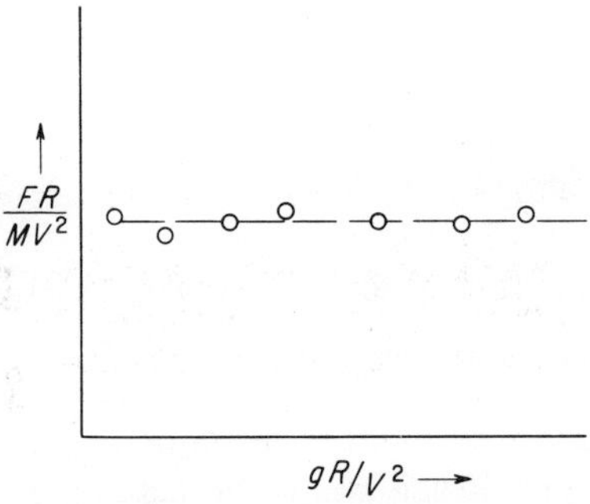

(handwritten margin notes: Important; plot of, straight line means too many variables)

Fig. 4-5. The probable result of an experiment on whirling rocks using all the variables noted in Fig. 4-4.

$$\frac{FR}{MV^2} = \text{const} = k \tag{4-13}$$

is the complete relationship, and only k remains to be determined. (It would be a rather poor engineer who would need tests to find k in this case.)

4-4. A Stepwise Method

The Rayleigh method of finding dimensionless groups is often extended by the application of determinants, particularly where the exponent equations are complex. Through determinants a fuller understanding of the intricacies and pitfalls of dimensional analysis may also be gained. A newer and equally powerful method is described by Ipsen[1] and called by him the "step-by-step" approach. In this method the primary dimensions are "eliminated" through variable combinations in a sequential fashion.   The method is quite simple and can best be followed through example.

Suppose we are running tests on a series of identical pumps having characteristic impeller diameters D, impeller rotational speed N, fluid density ρ, and fluid volumetric flow rate Q.   The dependent or measured test variable is to be ΔP, the pressure rise in the pumped fluid.   Now we write

$$\Delta P = f(Q,N,\rho,D) \qquad (4\text{-}14)$$

which is dimensionally, in the $ML\theta$ system,

$$\frac{M}{L\theta^2} = f\left(\frac{L^3}{\theta}, \frac{1}{\theta}, \frac{M}{L^3}, L\right)$$

Now, if Eq. (4-14) expresses the true experimental situation,

$$\frac{\Delta P}{\rho} = f(Q,N,\rho,D) \qquad (4\text{-}15)$$

is equally correct and general.   But we have eliminated the primary dimensions M from all the variables but ρ itself.   Thus ρ cannot have a proper place in Eq. (4-15) since it is the only term now having the dimension M.   Equation (4-15) should therefore be written

$$\frac{\Delta P}{\rho} = f(Q,N,D) \qquad (4\text{-}16)$$

or dimensionally

$$\frac{L^2}{\theta^2} = f\left(\frac{L^3}{\theta}, \frac{1}{\theta}, L\right)$$

We can now eliminate the time dimension θ in a similar fashion using the variable N:

$$\frac{\Delta P}{N^2\rho} = f\left(\frac{Q}{N}, N,D\right) = f\left(\frac{Q}{N}, D\right) \qquad (4\text{-}17)$$

which, in dimensional form, is

$$L^2 = f(L^3,L)$$

[1] D. C. Ipsen, "Units, Dimensions, and Dimensionless Numbers," chap. 11, McGraw-Hill Book Company, New York, 1960.

Finally, using D will eliminate the L dimension,

$$\frac{\Delta P}{N^2 \rho D^2} = f\left(\frac{Q}{ND^3}\right) \tag{4-18}$$

showing that a dimensionless "pressure-boost term" will be some experimental function of the important dimensionless pump parameter Q/ND^3.

In this case, we were able to eliminate the primary dimensions by using the original variables. This is not always possible and is, in any case, not necessary, as the first example in the next section will show.

The Ipsen stepwise method is not quite so easy as may appear here, especially when many variables and four or five primary dimensions are involved. It has the great advantage, however, of giving the analyst very good control over the form of his groups, through both his selection of the sequence with which the primaries are eliminated and the choice of just which variable will be used to eliminate a particular dimension.

4-5. The Choice of Primary Dimensions

So far we have assumed that the dimensions mass, length, and time are sufficient to construct all the needed system variables. Suppose we were to take the previous example of the pump test and construct its experimental variables in an $ML\theta V$ system, V now being the *primary dimension*, volume, and appearing wherever we had L^3 before. The dimensions of Eq. (4-14) now become

$$\frac{M}{L\theta^2} = f\left(\frac{V}{\theta}, \frac{1}{\theta}, \frac{M}{V}, L\right)$$

Using the stepwise method as before, we first eliminate M to obtain Eq. (4-16) having the dimensional form

$$\frac{V}{L\theta} = f\left(\frac{V}{\theta}, \frac{1}{\theta}, L\right)$$

Next, we eliminate θ, as before, obtaining Eq. (4-17) with dimensions

$$\frac{V}{L} = f(V, L)$$

Now let us eliminate the V dimension using Q/N and obtaining

$$\frac{\Delta P}{\rho N^2} \frac{N}{Q} = \frac{\Delta P}{\rho N Q} = f\left(\frac{Q}{N}, D\right) = f(D) \tag{4-19}$$

and the dimensions are

$$\frac{1}{L} = f(L)$$

Notice that we have here used the combined variable Q/N to clear the equation of the V primary dimension, rather than using a single variable.

Finally, we must eliminate the L dimension with the D variable obtaining

$$\frac{\Delta PD}{\rho NQ} = \text{const} \tag{4-20}$$

Comparing Eq. (4-20) with Eq. (4-18) we seem to have made a dazzling improvement in our test program. We now need only a single test point to completely specify the form of Eq. (4-20). A little thought, however, should convince the reader that no pump follows a law as simplistic in form as Eq. (4-20). Clearly, we have made an error in our choice of the primary dimensions.

Some writers suggest the rule, "The dimensions chosen should be independent of each other," as a preventive of the kind of over-simplification that just occurred in the pump analysis.[1] Such a rule tends to also oversimplify the problem of selecting the appropriate set of dimensions. Ipsen, for example, shows how including the primary dimension, angle, leads to an important simplification in the dimensionless number set governing an electrical circuit system.[2] Angles are usually regarded as the dimensionless function of two lengths.

In free-convection heat transfer, the $ML\theta T$ system of primaries (with T now as temperature) will yield the following groups:

$$\frac{hL}{k} = \phi \left[\frac{L^2 \, \Delta T \, \rho k}{\mu^3}, \frac{L\mu(\beta g)}{k}, \frac{\mu C_p}{k} \right] \tag{4-21}$$

which checks the pi theorem $(8 - 4 = 4)$. Now if we use a system of five primaries, $LM\theta TH$, where H is the quantity of heat instead of $ML^2\theta^{-2}$, we get

$$\frac{hL}{k} = \phi' \left[\frac{L^3 \, \Delta T \, \rho(\beta g)}{\mu^2}, \frac{\mu C_p}{k} \right] \tag{4-22}$$

which is the experimentally proved grouping for this type of test.

[1] R. A. Deutsch, Dimensional Analysis, *Electro-Technol.*, **70**(2):107–114 (August, 1962).

[2] Ipsen, *op. cit.*, pp. 176–177.

Note that Eq. (4-22) is actually a special case of the more general
Eq. (4-21). Equation (4-21) becomes Eq. (4-22) only if the two
middle groups of (4-21) multiply directly.

The fact that using five primaries instead of four appears to give
a "good" result in a heat-transfer system, whereas the use of four
rather than three primaries in the pump analysis gave a "bad"
result, indicates how cautious the analyst must be when selecting
primary dimensions to describe a new or unfamiliar system.

Let us consider another heat-transfer system, this time a turbu-
lently flowing fluid in a pipe gaining heat from the pipe walls. We
assume this system is specified by the variables:

Name of quantity	Symbol	Dimensional formula
Film coefficient...............	h	$H\theta^{-1}L^{-2}T^{-1}$
Diameter....................	D	L
Fluid velocity...............	V	$L\theta^{-1}$
Fluid density................	ρ	ML^{-3}
Fluid viscosity..............	μ	$ML^{-1}\theta^{-1}$
Fluid specific heat...........	C_p	$HM^{-1}T^{-1}$
Fluid thermal conductivity....	k	$HT^{-1}L^{-1}\theta^{-1}$

where we have chosen the $ML\theta HT$ system of primary dimensions.
It will be left as an exercise to show that one possible set of groups is

$$\frac{hD}{k} = \phi\left(\frac{\rho VD}{\mu}, \frac{\mu C_p}{k}\right) \tag{4-23}$$

A check with the pi theorem shows five primaries, seven variables,
but three groups! This demonstrates an important limitation of
the pi theorem, namely, the theorem only specifies the minimum
number of groups that make up a set. This is the number found in
the majority of solutions. But the theorem does not prohibit more
than this number of groups, as this example shows.

The presence of more than the pi-theorem-predicted number of
groups results, in the stepwise method, when two primary dimensions
are eliminated in a single step. Ipsen explains that the pi theorem
is still operative but that the analyst is not using the true minimum
number of Buckingham primaries.[1] In the case of Eq. (4-23), the
$ML\theta T$ system will yield the identical groups, indicating that H was
an extraneous primary in this case.

[1] *Ibid.*, pp. 173–174.

Van Driest[1] suggests a modification of the pi theorem to take care of such situations. His rule is, "The number of dimensionless products in a complete set is equal to the total number of variables minus the maximum number of these variables that will not form a dimensionless product." This "maximum number" is not particularly easy to determine in many cases. Taking the heat-transfer problem described by Eq. (4-23), we note that D, V, ρ, and h cannot be combined in any way to form a dimensionless group. The reader may convince himself by trials that the addition of C_p or k to these four will, with appropriate exponential values, make a dimensionless group. We could add μ to D, V, ρ, and h and still have the dimension H left over, but μ with V, D, and ρ only can form a group so that the Van Driest rule would be broken. Thus we find seven variables minus a maximum of four that cannot form a group, leaving three groups, as the rule predicts.

This rule is particularly handy in problems involving mechanics, where a choice of an $ML\theta$ or an $FL\theta$ system must be made with mass equal to $F\theta^2L^{-1}$. $FL\theta$ systems, being often without the θ dimension, are liable to a pi-theorem prediction of one number of groups, whereas the same system when analyzed by an $ML\theta$ system would be expected to produce a different number. The Van Driest rule will tell the analyst which is correct. The use of an $MLF\theta$ system might offer advantages in some cases, but care must be taken that the resulting groups are not "oversimplified."

A special type of fundamental dimension may be included in systems involving electrical, magnetic, and atomic phenomena. Many variables found in these fields, such as charge, capacity, potential, etc., are formed of the fundamental dimensions mass, length, and time plus either the dielectric constant K or the permeability μ. Speaking generally, these two fundamental primaries express the electrical or magnetic properties of the space in which we are working.[2] The situation is somewhat analogous to dynamics, where we noted that force or mass could be used. The dielectric constant K in terms of an $ML\theta\mu$ system of primaries is $\mu^{-1}\theta^2L^{-2}$ while the permeability in an $ML\theta K$ system is $K^{-1}L^{-2}\theta^2$.

---

[1] E. R. Van Driest, On Dimensional Analysis and the Presentation of Data in Fluid Flow Problems, *J. Appl. Mech.*, **13**(1):A-34–A-40 (March, 1946).

[2] The engineer not familiar with these important ideas should reread those portions of a basic physics book dealing with the properties and theory of magnetic and dielectric materials, e.g., F. W. Sears and M. W. Zemansky, "University Physics," complete ed., chaps. 27 and 35, Addison-Wesley Publishing Company, Inc., Reading, Mass., 1955.

Let us think of the energy per unit volume T in an electromagnetic field of electric strength E and magnetic strength H. We must also include the permeability and either the dielectric constant or the velocity of electromagnetic waves in the media c. K, μ, and c do not all have to appear since they are related by $K = (\mu c^2)^{-1}$ so that only two of the three have to be included in most electrical problems. (We have chosen electrostatic primaries.)

Name of variable	Symbol	Dimensional formula
Energy density...............	T	$ML^{-1}\theta^{-2}$
Electric field strength.........	E	$K^{-\frac{1}{2}}M^{\frac{1}{2}}L^{-\frac{1}{2}}\theta^{-1}$
Magnetic field strength........	H	$K^{-\frac{1}{2}}M^{\frac{1}{2}}L^{\frac{1}{2}}\theta^{-2}$
Permeability................	μ	$K^{-1}\theta^2L^{-2}$
Wave velocity...............	c	$L\theta^{-1}$

Then
$$T = \phi(E^a, H^b, \mu^c, c^d)$$

and either method leads to one possible grouping,

$$\frac{T\mu c^2}{E^2} = \phi'\left(\frac{H\mu c}{E}\right) \tag{4-24}$$

and although the pi theorem predicts only one group, two occur.

There is much more to the application of dimensional analysis in electrical and atomic phenomena than we can consider here. In dealing with microscopic systems, temperature is often not a primary but appears in terms of mass, length, and time (molecular kinetic energy). Certain quite basic numbers such as the "fine structure constant" can be studied through dimensional reasoning, but such matters are clearly beyond the interest and training of the engineering experimenter. The advanced and interested reader is referred to the reference list at the end of this chapter.

We have not yet mentioned the problem of variables that have no dimensions to start with, such as angles, "unit strain," area ratios, and so on. No confusion will exist if such variables are treated as separate dimensionless groups, since this is exactly what they are. For example, an angle is no more than a function of the ratio of two lengths. Unit strain is the ratio of the stretch of a specimen to its starting length. Usually, the introduction of such dimensionless variables will not upset the application of the pi theorem, providing the nature of the ratio "inside" the variable is taken into account.

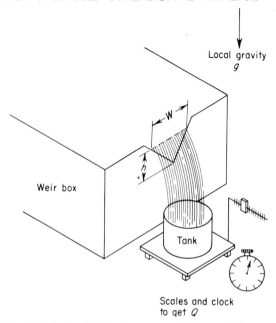

Fig. 4-6. A sketch showing some of the variables of a system to test a triangular weir.

Suppose we have a triangular weir as shown in Fig. 4-6, where the volume rate of flow Q is a function of density, viscosity, water height, width of the weir at water surface, and the value of local gravity. Then a possible group is

$$\frac{Q}{h^{2.5}\sqrt{g}} = \phi\left(\frac{h}{W}, \frac{\rho Q}{\mu W}\right) \tag{4-25}$$

It is not particularly convenient to measure the value of W for each run, nor is this necessary. Knowing the fixed weir angle θ there is no need to include W explicitly. Then if

$$Q = \phi(\rho, \mu, h, g, \theta) \tag{4-26}$$

the groups could be

$$\frac{Q}{h^{2.5}\sqrt{g}} = \phi'\left(\theta, \frac{\rho Q}{\mu h}\right) \tag{4-27}$$

which still checks the pi theorem.[1]

[1] For a discussion on the advanced aspects of "dimensionless variables," see L. L. Whyte, Dimensional Theory, Dimensionless Secondary Quantities, *Am. J. Phys.*, **21**:323–325 (1953).

4-6. Using Dimensional Analysis in Experimentation

We have seen that the method of dimensional analysis can greatly reduce the number of problem variables, form very generalized groups that are independent of the system of dimensions in use, and give at least some idea of the way in which variables may interact. From the viewpoint of this book, the variable reduction aspect is of major interest. As noted by the pi theorem, the amount of reduction depends on the number of primary dimensions chosen, but, since at least three of these are usually assumed, a reduction by three is to be anticipated. In many tests, such a favorable result does not occur since we often must include such variables as g, even though we do not need to vary or even measure them in practice.

So far, we have represented our dimensionless equations as general functions without suggesting the type. *Dimensional analysis cannot give the type of function that relates one group to another.* In many engineering experiments, however, it is proper to assume a power series (the first term only) unless data indicate a more complex function. Thus Eq. (4-2) would be assumed to have the form

$$P = k \left[\left(\frac{L}{D} \right)^a \left(\frac{VD\rho}{\mu} \right)^b \left(\frac{e}{D} \right)^c \right] \frac{V^2}{2g} \qquad (4\text{-}28)$$

where k is some dimensionless "fitting" constant to be found and the exponents a, b, and c are to be determined by test. As noted in Eq. (4-6), both experiment and theory predict for k a value of 64 and for the exponents a, b, and c the values of 1, -1, and 0 in the laminar region. The function for the turbulent regime is somewhat more complex and is usually represented by curves rather than equations. Equation (4-28) will approximate this region with a, b, c, and k found by test. Similarly Eq. (4-22) gives very good correlation of test data in the form

$$\frac{hL}{k} = \text{const} \left[\frac{L^3 \, \Delta T \, \rho(\beta g)}{\mu^2} \right]^a \left(\frac{\mu C_p}{k} \right)^b \qquad (4\text{-}29)$$

where c, a, and b take values (for example) of 0.56, 0.25, and 0.25 for convection flow over vertical plates with the boundary-layer laminar. Such simple forms as these are not, however, always possible. In forced-convection heat transfer, flow-laminar theory and experiment give the quite complex function

$$\frac{hL}{k} = k_1 + \frac{k_2(D/L)N_{Re}N_{pr}}{k_3 + k_4(D/L)N_{Re}N_{pr}{}^a}$$

where k_1 through k_4 are constants, a is an exponent, and the terms N_{re}, N_{pr}, D/L, and hL/k are dimensionless groups. Such a function can only be established through extensive experimental work coupled with a full theoretical treatment. A dimensional analysis only barely starts the problem.

In Sec. 4-3 we suggested that certain dimensionless groups had more physical meaning or utility than certain others and that the clever analyst sought the "best" configuration of the variables. This is entirely true when dimensional analysis is used as a historical approach or a purely analytic tool. In experimental work we have another criterion, one that lies at the root of almost all our actions and choices, the consideration of accuracy and precision. How does this matter affect our group configuration?

In the case of the drag problem as in Eq. (4-8), we found that there was a choice of at least three dimensionless groups, $D/\rho V^2 d^2$, $D/V d\mu$, and $\rho D/\mu^2$. From a dimensional standpoint any of the three is correct and usable. From a standpoint of common usage and good engineering practice, the first group is much preferred. But what is the best group if measuring accuracy is taken into account? Assuming that the general relation between drag group and Reynolds number is a simple exponential function of the kind just discussed, we can write

$$\frac{D}{\rho V^2 d^2} = k_1 \left(\frac{V d\rho}{\mu}\right)^a \tag{4-30a}$$

$$\frac{D}{V d\mu} = k_2 \left(\frac{V d\rho}{\mu}\right)^b \tag{4-30b}$$

$$\frac{\rho D}{\mu^2} = k_3 \left(\frac{V d\rho}{\mu}\right)^c \tag{4-30c}$$

where a, b, and c are constant exponents and k_1 through k_3, fitting constants. We can transform any of these equations to any other by simple algebraic manipulation. For example, Eq. (4-30a) can be altered to

$$\frac{V d\rho}{\mu} \frac{D}{\rho V^2 d^2} = k_1 \left(\frac{V d\rho}{\mu}\right)^a \frac{V d\rho}{\mu}$$

$$\frac{D}{V d\mu} = k_1 \left(\frac{V d\rho}{\mu}\right)^{a+1}$$

which is identical with Eq. (4-30b) when $k_1 = k_2$ and $b = a + 1$. Thus, it is easily shown that the three forms are completely equivalent if the k's are the same and $c = b + 1 = a + 2$. If this is done, we see that k is always $\mu^a D / \rho^{a+1} V^{a+2} d^{a+2}$ and the choice of dimensionless group will have no effect on the computation of k, whatever the accuracy of the various measurements, providing the k computation is by purely numerical means.

In most engineering tests, a single set of numerical values is not used to find fitting constants. Rather, a set of test points is plotted to establish the function, and these points are then averaged by drawing the best line through the entire set. Finally, this line is used to determine the necessary exponents and fitting constants. Now if this line is drawn in by eye (or as engineering slang would have it, "faked in"), we need not worry about the relative precision of the different groups. But in some cases the least-squares method of fitting a straight line to points is attempted. This method, which we will take up in a later chapter, is quite tedious and time-consuming. It is least complicated, however, *when the investigator can assume that all the uncertainty is in either x or y, but not both.* We would thus like to select our groups such that all the uncertainty is concentrated in only one of them. This is not always possible but is well worth keeping in mind. For example, if D, the drag, is the most uncertain quantity, then there is no reason to choose one of the groups over the other two. But if V is the most uncertain, then plotting the groups of Eq. (4-30a) or (4-30b) would not be sensible if least-squares methods are to be used. The group in Eq. (4-30c), $\rho D / \mu^2$, does not contain V. Similarly, if the viscosity were very uncertain, we would choose the groups in Eq. (4-30a).

This suggestion does not mean that strange groups should appear in a final or formal report in place of the conventional ones. Once a least-squares line has been drawn on the most logical coordinates, it is an easy matter to transfer the plotted line to the coordinate system desired for publication or use.

4-7. Summary

While the methods of dimensional analysis depend on sound physical insight into the particular problem, they are relatively automatic after the variables and primaries are chosen. It can thus be easily summarized in a "cookbook" fashion, remembering always that this "recipe" requires the cook to choose the ingredients. All we can do here is give some mixing instructions.

Step 1. Select those variables that are independent of each other and are believed to influence the system. Dimensional and natural constants must be included when they are judged to be significant. *This is the crucial step of the whole process.*

Step 2. Select a system of fundamental or primary dimensions in which all chosen variables can be expressed. Common systems are, for mechanics and fluid flow, $ML\theta$ or occasionally $FL\theta$; for thermal systems, $ML\theta T$ or $ML\theta TH$; for electrical and atomic systems, $ML\theta K$ or $ML\theta \mu$ with temperature as an additional primary or expressed in terms of molecular kinetic energy.

Step 3. Write the dimensional formulas of the chosen independent variables, and find the groups either by the formal methods or by inspection. The solution is correct if (a) every group is dimensionless, (b) at least as many groups appear as predicted by the pi theorem, and (c) each variable appears at least once.

Step 4. Examine the resulting groups from the standpoints of common usage, physical significance, and (if least-squares analysis is to be used) restriction of test uncertainty to one group if possible. If the groups are not satisfactory from these criteria, we can (a) again solve the exponent equations until a better set of groups turns up, (b) choose another set of primary dimensions and start over, or (c) reexamine our choice of independent variables.

Step 5. When a satisfactory collection of groups is achieved, the investigator can plan the actual variation of the groups by varying selected variables in his apparatus. Actual test-run planning is discussed in Chap. 6.

PROBLEMS

4-1. The buckling load on a column is related to its length, diameter, and modulus of elasticity. How many primary dimensions are needed? What group(s) is (are) best for this system?

4-2. A box of volume V containing a liquid of density ρ is suspended on a spring of elastic constant k. We are interested in the period of oscillation of the box in the gravity field. Is g needed? Find the best groups using an $ML\theta$ system. Now repeat using an $MVL\theta$ system where V is used in place of L^3. Which system gives the best groups?

4-3. The Weber number is composed of length, velocity, density, and surface tension. What form does it take?

4-4. Gas bubbles rising in different fluids have their velocities measured and their diameters taken by photograph as they pass a given point, D ft below the liquid free surface. Decide what variables affect this system, and construct the proper groups.

4-5. In electricity, the Langmuir-Child formula relates the saturation current density i and the voltage in an evacuated diode V to the e/m value for the electron and the linear spacing between the electrodes x. Find the best group(s). How many test points would be required (minimum) to check this formula, and how are i and V in the tube related?

4-6. In the test of a centrifugal oil pump, a common practice is to plot efficiency and horsepower in or out versus flow rate at constant rpm. Using dimensional analysis and including the pump-impeller diameter, obtain dimensionless groups involving (in turn, not all at once) power in, power out, and efficiency as a function of flow, rpm, fluid density, pressure boost, impeller size, etc.

4-7. Missile nose cones of characteristic shape D travel at various speeds in air of various pressures and temperatures. The tip temperature is measured. Construct groups. (*Note:* Do not omit the velocity of sound, which almost always appears in high-speed problems.)

4-8. A journal bearing is loaded with a force F. Important variables are diameter, bearing clearance, oil density and viscosity, oil pressure, and shaft rotation speed. Construct logical groups.

4-9. Ship propellers of given shape but different sizes are to be tested. Decide on logical groups after selecting the variables.

4-10. Satellite antennas of length L, diameter D, thermal conductivity k, surface emissivity ϵ, and root temperature T lose heat to open space at absolute zero. The Stefan-Boltzmann radiation constant must be included too. Find logical groups to fit a test program. (*Note:* The emissivity is a ratio of actual radiated energy to energy radiated by a black body at the same temperature.)

4-11. A pendulum swings in a viscous, incompressible fluid. The variables are the swing period, the gravitational acceleration, the pendulum length, the swing angle, the bob diameter, the mass of the bob, and the fluid density and viscosity. The string is assumed very fine and weightless. Decide how many groups are needed, and find a reasonable set by inspection of the variables.

4-12. In a structural test system, the following quantities are assumed to describe completely the experiment: beam stiffness (force per unit length), beam length, Young's modulus, a cross-sectional moment of inertia, and the unit density of the beam (in units of pounds mass per foot).

    a. Without performing any dimensional analysis or constructing any groups, decide whether this list is correct or whether there are too many or too few variables. (*Hint:* Write the variables in the $ML\theta$ and then the $FL\theta$ system. Which gives the most information?)

    b. Find a logical set of groups for these variables.

4-13. In the general case of a sphere moving in a compressible fluid, the following variables are assumed to govern the sphere's behavior: cross-sectional area of sphere A, fluid velocity V, fluid density ρ, fluid viscosity μ, fluid modulus of elasticity E, and drag of fluid on sphere D. Construct appropriate experimental groups, and compare with the drag analysis in Sec. 4-2. What group drops out when the fluid is incompressible?

4-14. The *Cauchy number* is a possible group involved in the system described in Prob. 4-13. This group includes the modulus of elasticity E, the velocity V, and the fluid density ρ. What form does it take?

4-15. An LCR series circuit is described by the following variables: resistance R, capacitance C, inductance L, charge q, frequency f, and voltage V. Construct appropriate groups.

4-16. Surface waves on a liquid are influenced by the following variables: wave velocity V, gravitational acceleration g, wavelength λ, liquid depth D, liquid density ρ, and liquid surface tension σ. What would appropriate experimental groups be? An oceanographic engineer deals often with two special cases: (a) where surface tension is unimportant and the wave velocity is almost independent of wavelength ("shallow" wave) and (b) where surface tension is unimportant and the wave velocity is independent of depth ("deep" wave). What do the groups become in these two cases?

4-17. A long transmission line with a voltage suddenly applied to one end is governed by current I, voltage E, resistance per unit length r, inductance per unit length l, capacitance per unit length c, and time t. What test groups might apply to this system?

4-18. In an oceanographic study of beach movement, waves with deep-water periods T_0 (seconds), lengths L_0, and heights H_0 were found to move Q cubic feet of sand per second per foot of wave crest. The waves were also measured to find their energy in foot-pounds per foot of wave crest, this energy being taken as relatively independent of the wave dimensions. What other variables are needed to construct groups to correlate the data?

4-19. A viscosimeter measures the amount of time t for a given amount of fluid of density ρ, viscosity μ, and tube length L to drain out. What other variable is needed? Show that for a given instrument, the time to drain is a function of the kinematic viscosity only.

4-20. The *Peclet number* is made up of fluid density, fluid specific heat, fluid thermal conductivity, the fluid velocity, and some characteristic dimension. What form does it take? The *Graetz number* replaces the density and velocity by a mass flow rate (pounds per second). What form does it take? How are the Peclet and Graetz numbers related for flow in a round tube of diameter D?

REFERENCES

Bridgman, P. W.: "Dimensional Analysis," Yale University Press, New Haven, Conn., 1931.

Conn, G. T., and E. Crane: Some Applications of the Methods of Dimensions to Atomic Physics, *Am. J. Phys.*, **24**:543–549 (1956).

Corrsin, S.: Simple Geometrical Proof of Buckingham's Pi Theorem, *Am. J. Phys.*, **19**:180–181 (1951).

Deutsch, R. A.: Dimensional Analysis, *Electro-Technol.*, **70**(2):107–114 (August, 1962).

Huntley, H.: "Dimensional Analysis," Rinehart & Company, Inc., New York, 1951.

Ipsen, D. C.: "Units, Dimensions, and Dimensionless Numbers," McGraw-Hill Book Company, New York, 1960.

Langhaar, H. L.: "Dimensional Analysis and Theory of Models," John Wiley & Sons, Inc., New York, 1951.

Murphey, G.: "Similitude in Engineering," The Ronald Press Company, New York, 1950.

Van Driest, E. R.: On Dimensional Analysis and the Presentation of Data in Fluid Flow Problems, *J. Appl. Mech.*, **13**(1):A-34–A-40 (March, 1946).

Whyte, L. L.: Dimensional Theory, Dimensionless Secondary Quantities, *Am. J. Phys.*, **21**:323–325 (1953).

CHAPTER 5

Aspects of Instrument-system Design

In the previous chapters, we have studied measuring systems in a highly generalized manner. The systems were assumed to err either randomly or with bias or in some combination of the two. The readings obtained could be combined in certain ways to make the test shorter, more accurate, or more usefully described. Every instrument or instrument system, whatever its nature, is likely to benefit from a study of such ideas.

In this chapter, certain simple, theoretical aspects of instrument systems, not so completely applicable but still general and important, will be discussed. As before, we will forego, as far as is possible, any detailed physical study or tabulation of specific measuring devices and concentrate rather on the basic problems and behavioral similarities that link many kinds of measuring problems together in broad categories. For example, the questions of interfacing and impedance, or loading across the interface, must be considered in electronic, pneumatic, and mechanical instruments and transducers. *Dynamic response*, the advantages gained by *redundancy*, and the interesting design aspects of *readout* from a test are considerations common to many scientific and technological fields. These are also all design factors that should be thought out before the experimental design reaches the "hardware" stage.

5-1. Instrumentation Interfaces

The term *interface*, traditionally the physical line of demarcation between two transmitting mediums (such as air and water), has taken on a new and broader meaning in the fields of data processing

94

and instrumentation. For example, the *man-machine interface* in computer technology refers to the parts of the computation system by which the engineer codes his requests to a computer and inserts these coded messages physically into the machine. This very modern interface will be studied in more detail in Chap. 11. In addition, the computer interface is usually thought to include the output methods whereby the machine "talks back" to its master. In instrumentation design, the "interface problem" occurs wherever a particular piece of information flowing from the test must change its essential energetic character or form. In measuring the pressure of a fluid, for example, we might physically draw some fluid up into a U tube, which is open to the atmosphere. The fluid will rise in the tube and against the gravitational field to a height proportional to its bulk pressure. Since the column fluid is continuous with the bulk fluid, there is no real instrumentation interface at all. In fact, the only important interfacing problems are similar to those in computer systems since they involve the informational contact between the experimentalist and the U-tube scales, verniers, and so on.

When pressure is read by a Bourdon-type gauge the fluid exerts a force on a hollow, curved spring (Fig. 5-1). The fluid pressure tends to reduce the curvature, and the gauge pointer is deflected through a mechanical gearing arrangement. An important interface now exists between the force-producing fluid and the force-indicating mechanical linkage.

A third level of complexity might involve the use of some electromechanical pressure-sensing device such as a diaphragm (see Fig. 5-1c) having a sensitive *strain gauge* attached. This gauge produces a detectable change in an electrical signal which is proportional to the deflection and, thus, the pressure. Now an interface exists between the bulk fluid and the diaphragm, force information transferring from the fluid to a deflecting mechanical membrane. A second interface occurs between the mechanical membrane and the electrical readout circuits consisting of the strain gauge and a *bridge circuit* that produces a current signal as the strain-gauge resistance is changed. Actually one might argue that the electrical apparatus itself involves several interfaces: strain gauge to bridge circuit, bridge circuit to current amplifier (if the signal is small), and current amplifier to readout meter or recorder.

If there is a basic rule of thumb of instrumentation design that is all-pervasive, it is the following: *the fewer the interfaces, the better the measurement.* And, like any such general rule, there is a variety

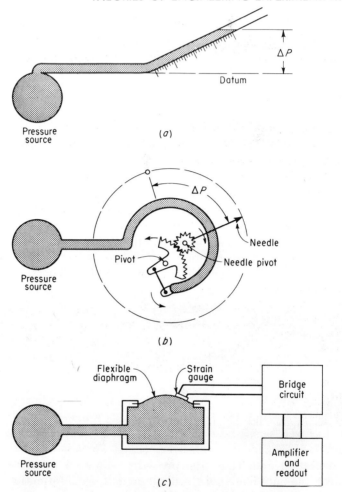

Fig. 5-1. Three methods of measuring pressure in which (a) the fluid itself provides the indication, (b) the fluid force is mechanically translated into gauge-needle movement, and (c) the fluid force mechanically moves a diaphragm whose movement produces an electrical signal.

of real or apparent exceptions.   If, for example, we are reading a sharply changing pressure signal, a simple U-tube manometer will not follow the transient variation at all, and the Bourdon gauge will represent the pressure pulsation as needle chatter.   If, on the other hand, we use a small and flexible diaphragm and appropriate circuits terminating in an electrical signal to an oscilloscope, we can measure rapid pressure changes with good accuracy. This, however, is not really a fair test of our rule. Neither the U tube nor the Bourdon gauge is designed or intended for reading pressure transients.

Suppose instead that we select a job which all three instrument systems are capable of handling: the reading of static fluid pressure. We might want to measure the fluid pressure in a swollen lymph gland using a hypodermic probe, the pressure being on the order of 2 lb/ft². If the fluid is mainly water, a fine U tube will show a rise of a little over ⅓ in. By inclining the U tube we can amplify this indication by a factor of five or ten producing a deflection of well over 1 in. on our instrument. Connecting this system, instead, to a miniaturized (and probably expensive) Bourdon gauge adds problems. The gauge may need so much fluid to operate its gearing that the pressure in the gland may be greatly reduced. The slightest catch or stickiness in the mechanical train of the gauge will destroy its accuracy. In a diaphragm system, the situation is even more problematical. Too much fluid will surely have to be taken off since the strain gauge sets a rather large minimum size on the diaphragm itself. The detection of the resulting tiny resistance variation might require a sensitive current-measuring circuit of high cost. In any case, the calibration of the electrical system would have to be done by an inclined manometer.

As a second example, suppose we wished to measure liquid or gas pressure in the 200-psi range but to detect a ¼-psi variation. If we can provide room for a vertical mercury manometer 33 ft high, we can incline the upper end and obtain a reading of 1 in. or more with each change of ¼ psi. It is true that there may be a gas- or liquid-to-mercury interface in such an instrument, but since both are fluids, this presents few interfacing problems because the basic character of the signal remains unaltered.

No standard Bourdon gauge would give this accuracy. We would need to build one with a limited range of, say, 298 to 302 psi. The gauge would then have to be calibrated, and the easiest way to do this would be to use our two-story mercury manometer.

Measuring such tiny changes in such a large total pressure with a diaphragm system would probably be impossible unless extraordinary amounts of time and money were available. The completed system would, of course, require calibration before it could be trusted in use.

The point of these examples, then, is simply this: The invention and production of new instruments and systems do not auto-matically eliminate the old. No electronic marvel has replaced the U-tube manometer, although many inventions have enhanced and extended it. If there is a choice of several instrument systems, all of which can do the job at hand, the experimenter is usually governed by both readout and accuracy requirements. As we briefly note in Sec. 5-5, electrical outputs from instruments permit the experimenter to display his test results in a variety of graphic and powerful ways. When, however, the signal from a test is small, confused, or required to very high accuracy, the experiment designer should seek the elimination of interfaces and the simplification of his instrument system.

5-2. Impedance and Loading

One of the major difficulties associated with instrumentation interfaces results from impedance and loading effects. *Impedance* is primarily an electrical term referring to the apparent electrical resistance of an instrument when "viewed" by an experimenter "looking" at its open output terminals. The idea of impedance has been extended to a variety of nonelectrical systems. For example, if we wish to measure sound-wave strength and frequency in an attenuated gas, we would certainly not use a fluid column of the Fig. 5-1a type. Sound waves are characterized by small and rapid displacements of small amounts of matter, whereas vibrations of a liquid column are characterized by large and slow displacements of larger amounts of matter. This is the reason that an underwater swimmer has such difficulty in hearing any sound that begins in air. We say that there is a serious impedance mismatch between the two mediums. The thin, small disk of a microphone, however, vibrates much more like sound in air, and thus the interface here has a much higher transmission capability.

If a measurement is to be made, there must be some form of energy transfer across the interface between the signal and the instrument sensing it. Maximum energy transfer occurs in electrical measuring systems when the output impedance of the measured system equals the input impedance of the measuring instrument. Such a maximum transfer may or may not be desirable.

In many electrical experiments, such a maximum transfer of energy would have disastrous effects on the test. Imagine, for example, the results of connecting an equal-impedance voltmeter across a load pulling 50 kva from a large generator. Instead, we construct our voltmeters to have a very high impedance and thereby minimize loading error. With a good voltmeter, only a tiny amount of energy transfers between the test system and the meter. Such voltmeters are characterized by their *input impedance* or by their *ohms-per-volt* rating. An electronic voltmeter with an 11-megohm impedance will have negligible loading effects on circuits having output impedances of less than, say, 100,000 ohms.

Moving-coil voltmeters may have a specification such as 10,000 ohms/volt. This means that the input impedance of the meter is equal to the maximum scale voltage times 10,000. A 0-to-10-volt meter would thus have an input impedance of $10 \times 10,000$ or 100,000 ohms. Using such a meter to obtain potentials in a 9-volt transistor circuit having an output impedance of 100,000 ohms could produce only the most disastrous loading errors and, possibly, ruin the circuit itself.

Maximum energy transfer is often desired in nonelectrical tests. In a sound-measuring test, for example, the size of a sensitive microphone is so small compared with the size of a typical sound-wave front that even maximum energy transfer from the wave front will produce almost no loading effects.

Excessive loading error is one of the most typical instrument problems to confront the neophyte experimenter. Two typical examples may help alert the reader to this important class of instrument difficulties.

a. Thermocouple or other small voltage measurement. Many sensing devices generate electrical signals on the order of micro- or millivolts. It is essential in such cases that there be no current loading whatever on the sensing device, since voltage drop in the connecting wires would introduce serious errors in the reading. For such measurements, a *potentiometer circuit* (Fig. 5-2) is often used. The small and unknown potential E is "bucked out" by an adjustable potential obtained from the voltage-divider potentiometer R_{vd} and a fixed external voltage E_0. The meter resistance R_m plays no part in the balanced circuit, providing R_{vd} has been adjusted to produce no meter deflection and thus an I_m of zero. For this circuit

$$\frac{E}{E_0} = \frac{R}{R_{vd}} \tag{5-1}$$

Such a scheme is clearly essential where the variable-length leads would otherwise have large effects on the potential read at some distance from the E signal.

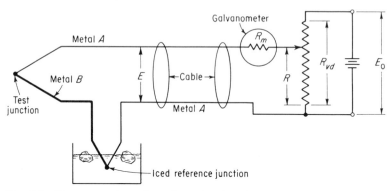

Fig. 5-2. Thermocouple and readout circuit using a potentiometer. At balance, zero current flows in the circuit.

b. Resistance-sensitive devices. Strain gauges, slide-wire displacement transducers, and a variety of temperature-measuring devices depend on the change in an electrical resistance to give the measurement indication. Figure 5-3*a* shows a circuit involving a current-sensing meter in series with the resistance device. This circuit not only produces an undesirable current loading on the often delicate sensing resistance but is nonlinear in its response. That is, the current read in the meter I is related to the measured resistance R by the relationship

$$I = \frac{R_m V_0}{R/R_m + 1} \tag{5-2}$$

Figure 5-3*b* shows a better circuit. If the voltmeter resistance is high, the voltage reading V_r is approximately related to the measured resistance by the linear relationship

$$V_r = V_0 \frac{R}{R_0} \tag{5-3}$$

The preferred bridge circuit is shown in Fig. 5-3*c*. With R_2 and R_3 fixed and R_u unknown, we adjust R_1 until the galvanometer shows zero current flow. At this condition

$$R_u = \frac{R_1 R_3}{R_2} \tag{5-4}$$

so that R_1 can be directly calibrated to read the R_u value. Alternatively, the bridge can be allowed to go out of balance and the relationship between the imbalance current and the R_u variation used to

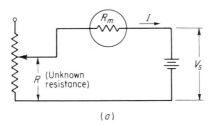

(a)

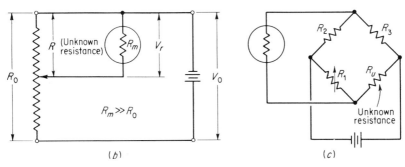

(b)   (c)

Fig. 5-3. Three methods of reading out the value of an unknown resistance: (a) on an ammeter, (b) on a voltmeter, and (c) on a dial affixed to a calibrated resistance.

indicate R_u variations. A variety of bridge circuits for different measuring duties plus their equations can be found in the several end-of-chapter references. One possible error inherent in a simple bridge is discussed in Example 3-7.

These circuits are mainly intended to minimize or eliminate *electrical energy loading* on the tested circuit. All manner of other loading conditions occur in practice. *Mass-flow loading* would result when we must withdraw too much fluid or gas from a system to operate the test instrument. *Thermal loading* would occur when the temperature-sensing instrument is large enough to leak heat energy away from the device under test.

Ideally, we wish our sensing instrument to be tiny, have zero mass and zero energy absorption, and have sufficiently large and accurate output signals to drive any readout device we wish.

5-3. Dynamic Response

When a measuring instrument cannot follow rapid changes in a measured signal, we recognize that an impedance problem exists across the test-rig instrument interface.   In the sense of the previous section, a serious impedance mismatch exists at the signal frequency, even though the impedance match at lower frequencies may be adequate for signal transmission.   Causes of poor instrument dynamic response include (1) inertia of sensing instrument or readout device, (2) thermal capacity and/or thermal conductivity of sensing thermocouple, (3) friction, and (4) recovery or "dead" time as in a suddenly discharged capacitor or ionized Geiger tube.

In an occasional experiment, the instrument will not only follow the test signal, but actually be driven by it to a resonant condition. The output reading in this case will be larger than is correct.

A few "fixes" for dynamic-response problems can sometimes be applied:

1. When the readout device is suspected to be lagging the signal, particularly when this device is some sort of pen recorder, the experimenter should parallel an oscilloscope across the signal output.   The virtually zero inertia of the electron beam in the scope permits it to track rapid signals very closely, and the scope and recorder outputs will show up any tracking failure.

2. Damping, of electrical or mechanical form, may be introduced into the measurement system either to shift the resonant point of the instrument or to eliminate resonant peaks.   This, however, requires a sound understanding of dynamic principles.

3. Compensating networks can sometimes be used to assist a "slow" instrument in "ignoring" low-frequency components of a signal and reporting the higher frequency (or sharper transients). The design of such networks is a matter of control engineering, and some discussion and design data will be found in end-of-chapter references.

Whatever the difficulty, three types of measuring error will usually be combined in a dynamic instrument system, as indicated in Fig. 5-4: errors in amplitude, errors in phase, and (less often) errors in frequency.   In many tests, amplitude is of major interest, and the application of damping or compensation may permit an instrument to yield a good estimate of maximum amplitude even though the over-all shape of the output signal may not match the true test output.   In some cases, it is useful to *simulate* the complete test and measuring system on an electronic analog computer and insert the output signal (such as b, c, or d in Fig. 5-4) from the test instrument as input to the computer.   The computer will then process this signal and offer the analyst a prediction of what the correct test

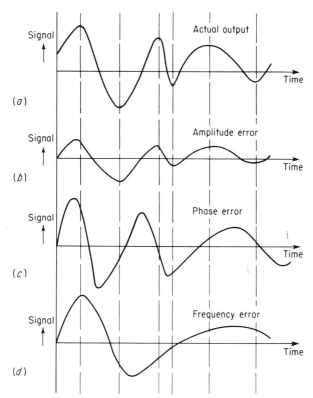

Fig. 5-4. Types of errors in dynamic measurements. In practical cases, two or more types are usually found combined.

signal must have been to yield the observed output (such as curve *a* in Fig. 5-4). Such techniques are very powerful using modern analog equipment but far beyond the scope of this brief chapter. Certainly of major importance is the realization that a dynamic measurement problem exists. Then, at least, expert help can be requested.

5-4. Redundant Instrumentation

Difficult measurements having considerable lack of precision often require multiple instruments or measuring efforts. The measurement of physical, electrical, thermal, or mechanical properties is often repeated by a variety of laboratories or by different workers within the same laboratory, inevitably resulting in differences among the various determinations. The possibility of large random effects on an instrument because of its location, time of operation, or other noise-producing causes may suggest duplication of measurements or *instrument redundancy.* Redundant components in space vehicles are quite standard for obvious reasons, although here the purpose is more of a "back-up" or emergency substitute measure than the simultaneous use of the duplicated parts.

There has been a tendency among test engineers to avoid redundant instrumentation on the basis that with one instrument they have a single usable reading while with two instruments they have two different readings, both in doubt. Probability theory (and common sense) denies such a view. The more readings one obtains, the more certainly one is able to fix the measured value. Furthermore, three "identical" measurements of a fixed and unknown experimental variable are strikingly more informative than two.

Consider a fixed value that is measured simultaneously by two apparently identical instruments or two apparently identical laboratories, A and B, giving values X_a and X_b with $X_a > X_b$. Notice that this is a somewhat different case from the ones described in Chap. 2. There we considered that both the single instrument and its input might be varying randomly so that the average of the replicated readings became a measure of the "best estimate" of the test variable, and the standard deviation became a measure of the dispersion of any given reading around this best estimate. Here we are saying that the input is truly fixed and that two separate and apparently identical determinations are made.

Now defining Δ from

$$\Delta = X_a - X_b \qquad (5\text{-}5)$$

we ask ourselves what is the probability P that the true value lies between $X_a + k\Delta$ and $X_b - k\Delta$. The following tabulation gives the answer for various k values:

k	0	1	2	3	4	5	6	7
P	0.5	0.795	0.874	0.910	0.930	0.942	0.951	0.958

This table indicates that the "location" of the true value based on our usual twenty-to-one odds criterion lies with a range 13Δ in extent and centering around the midpoint value between X_a and X_b.*

---

* W. J. Youden, Systematic Errors in Physical Constants, *Phys. Today,* **14**(9):32–43 (September, 1961).

Now suppose a third, and also "identical," instrument or laboratory gives value X_c such that $X_a > X_b > X_c$ and

$$\Delta' = X_a - X_c \qquad (5\text{-}6)$$

Now the probability that the true value lies between X_a and X_c is 0.75. Furthermore, there is a 19-in-20 chance (P of 0.95) that the true value lies with a span $3\Delta'$ wide, that is, between $X_a + \Delta'$ and $X_c - \Delta'$. Certainly if one feels the necessity of an additional instrument, test, or determination in the establishment of a fixed and unknown quantity, he should proceed at once to three measurements and gain the much greater predictive confidence inherent in three such determinations.

It should be clearly understood here that we are not suggesting the senseless multiplication of inadequate instruments. If, for example, a thermocouple cannot follow a thermal transient, the addition of another identical unit will add nothing to the test. It is in experiments having large and inescapable instrument biases, impossible to reduce by calibration, that the "rule of three" is most useful.

Where variations in system properties are anticipated, such as the velocity variations across an air duct or temperature variation across a thermal-conductivity sample, multiple instrumentation is, of course, essential. The trick here is to place the instruments in such a way that their readings are easily combined and, more important, such that the possible error of one of the instruments does not overshadow the others. In the case of a circular duct, the usual approach is to divide the duct into equal concentric flow areas and place a measuring instrument in the center of each area. If, instead of this logical approach, we located the instruments at equal radius increments, the measurements near the outer wall would refer to large areas and flows and those near the center to very tiny areas and insignificant flows.

Such multiple instrumentation is not really redundant since each probe is giving us a different and equally important piece of information. Redundant methods would occur in duct measurements if we had two complete instrument stations, each of which was giving an average velocity or average temperature. If the stations are close together and the readings are made simultaneously, we expect that we are measuring a parameter with no random variation at each instant of measurement. Following the previous discussion, if we feel the need of adding a second station because of inescapable bias in the averages, we should certainly add a third one at the same time.

5-5. Readout Designs

The considerable and ingenious developments in instrument engineering over the past decade or two have been heavily concentrated in the area of electronic readout devices. In these hurried times, it is often necessary to forego the undoubted accuracy and simplicity of a U-tube manometer or basic mercury thermometer for instruments that give output signals suitable for electronic processing. Few colleges or industrial labs have readout equipment comparable to that which received, interpreted, augmented, and presented the pictures resulting from the Mars flypast or the various "soft" landings by robot moon surveyors. Yet the ready availability of good XY pen recorders and multiple-trace "storage-screen" oscilloscopes puts into the hands of most engineers readout tools of sophistication and flexibility, tools that are seldom used to capacity in the colleges or smaller industrial laboratories.

The decision to use an XY recorder or scope immediately introduces an interface problem into most engineering tests, especially those not in the electrical or electronic fields. Fortunately, a huge array of transducers are now available which will convert most test signals, whatever their energetic nature, to electrical signals suitable for display on one or another of the variety of electronic readout devices. Although we noted some tests in Sec. 5-1 for which such transducers might not be suitable, the fact is that most common engineering experiments can now be handled by some form of electrical transducer plus electronic readout apparatus. Clearly, the readout desired must be anticipated when the test is planned and error and loading effects are examined. Some typical instrument readout designs will indicate the kind of data taking now readily possible at all levels of engineering sophistication. In addition, these examples will suggest how *hypothesis testing* can be carried out at the test site through careful attention to readout design aspects.

a. Comparison of two signals. The familiar *Lissajous figures* produced on a scope face by X- and Y-axis sine-wave signals of differing frequencies are examples of graphic output designed to give a direct measurement of frequency ratios. This method is described briefly in Appendix A, Example A-3, where it is used as a frequency standard. Figure 5-5 suggests an experiment designed

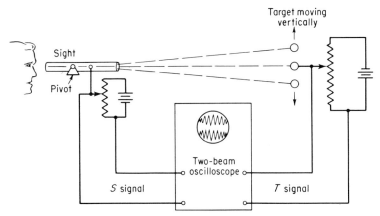

Fig. 5-5. Experiment to check the response of a moving sight attempting to follow an irregularly moving target.

to compare a tracking signal generated by a human observer with the actual motion of the tracked object.   In a practical application, the circuit was used to calibrate an optical tracking instrument used to obtain inshore wave profiles by following the rise and fall of an anchored buoy.   The target is moved by some form of random-motion generator and is tracked at some distance away by an optical sight moving in a small arc.   If this arc is less than 2°, a linear-motion potentiometer will yield a voltage signal S, directly proportional to the vertical motion of the sighted object which, in turn, is directly connected to a second and longer linear potentiometer which gives the "true" output voltage signal T.   A variety of interesting output displays is readily available to the engineer.

Figure 5-6a shows the possible output when S and T signals are shown against a horizontal time base on the scope face.   This presentation is the one most likely to occur to the beginner and is also the least interesting or useful.   Figure 5-6b suggests the traces when S and T are plotted against each other.   If the amplification of the X and Y amplifiers on the scope is adjusted to make maximum target excursion and maximum sight angle produce identical movements in the X and Y directions on the scope face, "perfect tracking" will result in a 45° line.   Multiple wavy lines and loops suggest tracking errors of various sorts.   Even more informative is the Fig. 5-6c scheme.   Here we use an external circuit (easily set up on even the smallest analog computer) to obtain a difference signal

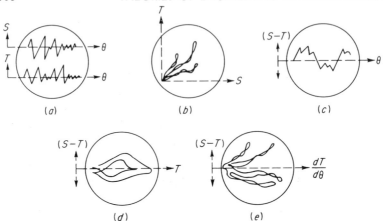

Fig. 5-6. Possible presentations of the data taken with the Fig. 5-5 apparatus as discussed in the text.

$(S - T)$ which is displayed against a horizontal time base. Such a presentation is useful to suggest whether we are primarily "undershooting" or "overshooting" the target. Imaginative readout design will often allow us to study various hypotheses by direct measurement. Suppose, for example, we suspected that the maximum error occurs at either the ends or the center of the target travel. Then we should display the difference $(S - T)$ versus the correct or "true" motion T, obtaining perhaps Fig. 5-6d. This display suggests that maximum error signals $(S - T)$ occur at the center of the motion rather than at its extremes. But if this is true, it suggests that maximum error $(S - T)$ is associated not with position so much as with velocity of the target. Thus we might wish to watch the behavior of tracking error $(S - T)$ against the derivative of the true signal T with respect to time $(dS/d\theta)$, again an output requiring the assistance of an analog computer. Figure 5-6e suggests a possible result: where $dT/d\theta$ is a maximum, tracking error $(S - T)$ is a maximum. Certainly a variety of other and more elaborate presentations involving higher derivatives, squares, square roots, and absolute values of $(S - T)$, and integrated or summed error outputs can be imagined here as well.

A considerable number of experiments involves the comparison of two signals; indeed, most instrument calibration is an experiment of this sort. Modern electronic aids permit both rapid and powerful analysis plus the testing of a variety of hypotheses about the test.

b. Current versus voltage diagrams. In electrical and electronic experiments, one of the most common requirements is a plot of current versus voltage when some third parameter of the circuit or circuit element is varied. Vacuum tubes, transistors, nonlinear resistors, and photocells are typical devices for which an EI plot may be required. Figure 5-7 suggests a generalized circuit for obtaining current and voltage signals for a silicon solar cell having variable light input. Terminals A-B yield a potential that is proportional to the current I in the circuit, whereas terminals A-C yield the cell voltage output. With light input held at some fixed value, varying the load resistance from zero to its maximum value will give a complete EI curve as suggested in Fig. 5-8a. The illumination level can then be changed, and a new curve obtained. If the circuit outputs are traced by an XY pen recorder, a complete family of EI curves can be traced out in a matter of minutes.

When a solar cell is to be used as a light-measuring device, Fig. 5-8a may be of primary interest, but when it is to be used for power generation, we are usually more interested in its power-voltage characteristics. Power output is the product of E and I, so that if we use an external analog circuit to produce a signal proportional to the EI product, we might produce Fig. 5-8b, which shows, for each illumination level, the voltage at which maximum power is produced. This type of characteristic curve is important when a number of solar cell modules are to be placed in parallel for battery charging or other similar duty.

These two examples only begin to suggest the variety of experi-

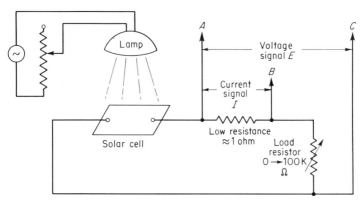

Fig. 5-7. Schematic of test circuit used to obtain EI curves of a solar cell at various light intensities.

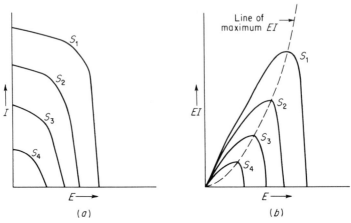

Fig. 5-8. Two possible output presentations of the Fig. 5-7 experiment.

ments that permit an integrated graphic output in X-versus-Y form. Additional tests of this sort might be stress-strain, materials-testing experiments of all types; pressure-displacement graphs obtained from steam, gasoline, and Diesel engine tests; flow rate versus head, rpm versus horsepower, and similar XY presentations related to pumps, turbines, and other hydraulic machinery; and fluid velocity versus drag of a towed or wind-tunnel model. In all these cases and a variety of others, the use of external circuitry to produce a signal proportional to the sum, difference, product, differential, or integral of the basic outputs may add power and insight to the test.

The readout designs suggested here are now possible in almost all test situations. In the near future, far more elaborate manipulations will become common, through the use of on-line data acquisition and processing with a digital computer as the end device of the instrument-readout chain. In this type of experimentation, the continuous signals coming from the various transducers are digitized and accepted by a modest computer operating "on line." Depending on the machine programming, the test data can be analyzed and cross-checked in a dozen different ways and the computer output displayed on scopes or XY plotters. By interconnecting the computer with the test controls, it may become possible for the machine to set new points and investigate areas and ranges of the experimental function chosen on a strictly rational basis. At present this is an expensive process, particularly the digitizing continuous instrument signals. On the other hand, the high cost of technical and engineering labor makes such methods attractive. They will probably become common in certain testing situations. For the present, inexpensive analog circuits plus XY pen recorders and multibeam storage scopes offer an array of possibilities barely exploited.

5-6. Summary

Instrument-system design, like all engineering design, involves a "trade-off" involving costs, accuracy, and convenience. Accuracy requires a minimum of interfaces, a simplicity of techniques, redundant instrumentation, and zero loading. Cost considerations suggest "off-the-shelf" measuring tools which may exact heavy loading penalties on the test apparatus, minimum redundancy, and the simplest of readout systems. Convenience (related to personnel costs) demands signal alteration through one or more interfaces to electrical form, advanced electronic signal manipulation that might hurt accuracy, and elaborate and expensive readout devices with a maximum of automatic features. Each test situation sets a basic limit on the experimenter, but the difference between stupid and clever experimental work with money and signal level fixed can be great indeed. No act involves more artistry and ingenuity, even though other phases of science and technology have enjoyed more prestige in the modern world.

The problem with experimentation is that no engineer is smart enough to identify the best possible test design. Whereas a mathematical or theoretical development or "discovery" is usually either right or wrong, an experiment may be described only as better or worse and then only when compared with some other example. Still, the personal satisfaction of watching an experimental system producing both accurate and easily interpreted data that sharply illuminate both the test and the hypothesis on which it is based has few parallels in the professions of technology.

PROBLEMS

5-1. Describe the interfaces in the following instrumentation systems where the basic character of the signal undergoes a fundamental change:

a. A tensile specimen in a testing machine has an extensometer that communicates extension through levers to a strain gauge that is read using a bridge circuit.

b. A *Prony brake* applies a torque to a rotating flywheel. The brake compresses a hydraulic cylinder of oil whose pressure is read by a Bourdon gauge.

c. A mercury-in-glass thermometer is designed such that the mercury in rising in the tube produces a change in capacitance of a capacitor formed around the thermometer barrel. This capacitance change is read on a capacitance bridge.

d. A vibrating-reed tachometer identifies the vibratory frequency of a motor by the rapid vibration of a given reed that oscillates only when its resonant frequency is approached. This vibration interrupts a light beam that is picked up by a series of photocells which operate associated relays.

5-2. A two-terminal device generating a voltage at its terminals X and Y and having an internal impedance R_i is connected to an external impedance R_{ext}. The voltage across the terminals X and Y becomes

$$E_{xy} = \frac{ER_{ext}}{R_{ext} + R_i}$$

where E is the internal voltage that is generated on open circuit. If the power delivered to the external resistance is E_{xy}^2/R_{ext}, prove that maximum power transmission occurs when $R_{ext} = R_i$.

5-3. In most measuring situations, we wish E_{xy} (see Prob. 5-2) to equal E. If R_i for a cathode-follower circuit is 5,000 ohms, what should our voltmeter input impedance be to have an error in E_{xy} of no more than 1 per cent?

5-4. A linear-motion potentiometer with resistance range 0 to 1,000 ohms is to indicate position, and its output will be changed to a current signal using the Fig. 5-3 circuit. If the ammeter resistance R_m is 4 ohms, what will be the current indication at an R value of 20 ohms? If we increase R by multiples of 20 ohms (40, 60, 80, etc.), by what multiples does the current increase in each step? Discuss with regard to the linear range of this instrument and output circuit.

5-5. Suppose the impedance of the voltmeter in Fig. 5-3*b* was not so large as to be disregarded. What does Eq. (5-3) become in this case? Let us define the voltmeter loading error from $[(V_r/V_0)_{true} - (V_r/V_0)_{apparent}]/(V_r/V_0)_{true}$, where $(V_r/V_0)_{apparent}$ is found from Eq. (5-3). Obtain an expression for this error in terms of the R/R_0 and R_m/R_0. Investigate the error magnitudes for several R/R_0 values when the meter resistance is one hundred times the total value of R_0.

5-6. Prove that the equation for the balanced bridge, Eq. (5-4), is correct by making a current balance on the arms of the bridge. At the balance point, there can be no current through the galvanometer.

5-7. Two laboratories report the thermal diffusivity of Pyrex glass to be 0.0230 and 0.0252 ft^2/hr, and we have no reason to believe either lab is giving the better value. We wish to select a value in a computation that will be safe on the low side. That is, our apparatus will be all right if the value in our equipment turns out to be higher than we expect, but damage will occur if the real value turns out lower. What value of diffusivity should we adopt if we want a 19-in-20 chance of being safe? A third lab makes independent determinations and sends us a value of 0.0237 ft^2/hr. What should our "safe" value be now?

5-8. A pressure transducer with strain gauge attached is to sense cylinder-head pressure. A small magnet on the connecting rod will interrupt an electrical field and produce a signal proportional to piston position or, if we wish, cylinder volume. How would we read out this data to give engine power at each stroke as a function of time?

5-9. A tensile testing machine can transmit stress directly as an electrical signal, and strain is obtained from a strain gauge mounted on the specimen under tension. We are testing steel specimens and wish a sensitive means of noting exactly at what stress the linear or Hooke's law portion of the stress-strain curve ends. What would be a possible readout method of doing this?

5-10. A thermistor is a semiconductor device with a negative coefficient of resistance. When the thermistor is connected in a circuit with a voltage source and a current-measuring instrument, all in series, the thermistor passes relatively little current, at first. As it warms because of I^2R heating, its resistance drops, and it passes more current until it reaches a maximum current value where the heat generated by the current flow is completely lost to the surroundings. A typical set of response curves is obtained by setting a series of voltages and reading current against a time base. How would we vary this output so as to obtain a set of curves of instantaneous resistance against time? How would we obtain a readout of instantaneous power generated within the thermistor as a function of time? How would we present the rate of change of current with respect to time as a function of current?

REFERENCES

Ambrosius, E., R. Fellows, and A. Brickman: "Mechanical Measurements and Instrumentation," The Ronald Press Company, New York, 1966.

Bair, E.: "Introduction to Chemical Instrumentation," McGraw-Hill Book Company, New York, 1962.

Beckwith, T., and W. Buck: "Mechanical Measurements," Addison-Wesley Publishing Company, Inc., Reading, Mass., 1960.

Cook, N., and E. Rabinowicz: "Physical Measurement and Analysis," Addison-Wesley Publishing Company, Inc., Reading, Mass., 1963.

Doebelin, E.: "Measurement Systems: Application and Design," McGraw-Hill Book Company, New York, 1966.

Dove, R., and P. Adams: "Experimental Stress Analysis and Motion Measurement," Charles E. Merrill Books, Inc., Columbus, Ohio, 1964.

Holman, J.: "Experimental Methods for Engineers," McGraw-Hill Book Company, New York, 1966.

Moore, M. B.: "Mechanical Engineering Measurements," D. Van Nostrand Company, Inc., Princeton, N.J., 1959.

Tuve, G. L.: "Mechanical Engineering Experimentation," McGraw-Hill Book Company, New York, 1961.

CHAPTER 6

Test Sequence and Experimental Plans

Having completed the instrumentation of a test and checked the apparatus for accuracy, we also examined the possibility of variable reduction using the powerful tool of dimensional analysis. At this point the experimenter may be ready, even eager, to "turn on the juice" or otherwise set his test in motion. Impatience and hasty starts will seldom bring quick completion. Rather, haste may result in overloading or straining some test component, and, if it does not produce physical trouble, it is sure to result in an inefficient test. Overlapping and duplication may occur over some ranges of the apparatus and incomplete coverage in others. The control over known and computed variations of the surroundings may be sloppy, and any accounting of natural or extraneous variations is likely to be nonexistent. Months later the engineer may realize that the apparent, even obvious, effect of high velocity was in truth due to the chance running of high-velocity points on second shift, and that his experiment has inextricably mingled a test of the apparatus with a test of the operating personnel—or weather variations—or some regular defect in the instruments and so on.

In this chapter, we will see how the engineering experiment can be rationally planned, point by point, to give speed of testing, minimization of error, maximization of useful data, and maximum control of extraneous and outside influences. In short, we will inquire into the ways in which an experiment can be made efficient without loss in meaning or accuracy.

6-1. The Spacing of Test Points

In very few tests is it possible to estimate the exactly correct amount of testing. Too little testing and the law or function may not be found, the accuracy of constants may be poor, or some small effect of large theoretical importance may be missed. Too many data, on the other hand, and the test becomes overlong, the data processing endless and expensive, and even the presentation of the material difficult. There are some tests in which excessive numbers of data may actually obscure rather than reveal certain important effects. For example, a stress-versus-strain test of a single tensile-strength specimen might easily show the little dip region at the end of the elastic range found with some low-carbon steels. But suppose we tested half a dozen specimens, in each of which the dip region might be displaced slightly along the stress or strain axis when compared with the others. If all the points are plotted in an undifferentiated manner, the dip region could disappear completely, as shown in Fig. 6-1. The multispecimen plot is the best if we wish to determine the average tensile-strength properties of the steel, but it is not so good as the single-specimen plot if we are studying the general behavior of metals in tension.

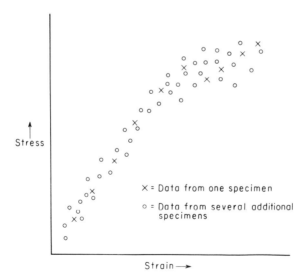

Fig. 6-1. Sketch shows how the "dip region" in a stress-strain curve for steel might be obscured if too many data from several different tests are plotted together.

The most obvious way in which an experimental plan can be made compact and efficient is to space the variables in a predetermined manner. If we are searching for a functional relationship between an independent variable X and a dependent variable Y, we hope that the function can be represented by a curve or line on (X,Y) coordinates. Such a line is made up of an infinite number of separate points, and we must choose from this infinite family some finite and practical number to represent the function. If the function has two independent variables, a complete data population will fill an entire plane area, and so on.

Thus, the choice of the finite population of test data is a legitimate and important area of pretest planning, although it can be done, and unhappily often is, while the test is under way. The most obvious way to start test-point selection is to decide on the end points or limits of the test apparatus since this will give the *test envelope* that encloses the complete family of data. Some typical limitations on engineer test equipment are compressor surge line, metallurgical temperature limits, structural-rotational speed limits, power-handling limits imposed by dynamometer size, thermal input limitations due to furnace size, flow limitations imposed by pipe areas, and so on. Such limit points can often be found or computed before operation, although often must be checked by test, particularly when untried items are up for initial performance checks.

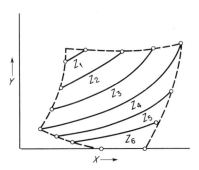

Fig. 6-2. A possible XYZ envelope with Z as parameter. The dashed lines enclose the total family of points that can be attained.

For the simple XY function, two points enclose all others. An XYZ function envelope is a plane area or *map*, and a large number of points may be needed simply to outline its extent. Functions involving more variables than this are usually broken down to a series of maps.

Let us consider the criteria for spacing points in our envelope, taking the basic XY function. (Note that the XYZ function is reducible to a set of XY functions as illustrated in Fig. 6-2.) There are two major criteria governing test-point selection:

a. The relative accuracy of data in different regions of the test envelope. This important criterion, so often overlooked by engineers, stems directly from our discussion of error and uncertainty in Chaps. 2 and 3. Many tests will show data that have unequal precision over the entire test envelope (see Example 3-1). In many mechanical engineering tests, we suspect that low-power, low-head runs will be the most imprecise. Civil engineers always doubt their low-head, low-flow points the most, while in certain electrical measurements very high resistance readings are questionable because of "sneak circuits." When our error analysis shows us that a part of the test envelope is in greatest question, we should naturally fill that portion in with more than its normal share of points. We can make no fixed rule on how many additional points to take in the doubtful regions, but the general rule relating precision improvement to additional readings can be expected to hold, so that four points are twice as effective as one; and nine, three times as effective. In Example 3-1, where the precision at one end of the envelope was found to be over ten times better than at the other, we should theoretically take 100 times as many points at the bad end to make the curve equally precise over its length. This is practical nonsense, and the experimenter must use his judgment.

b. The nature of the experimental function. In the majority of engineering experiments, the investigator usually has a good idea of his experimental function. If an uncertainty criterion does not suggest the point spacing and the function is partially or completely known, it is often well worth the time to set up a solution to find an even-spacing plan. For example, the loss of pressure through a new fitting as a function of flow and density may be an unknown matter until tests are carried out, but the experimenter familiar with hydraulic work should certainly suspect a function of the type

$$\Delta P = k \frac{\rho V^2}{2g}$$

where k may be constant with changing flow velocity V or might be a weak function of V. When the general function is known or suspected, a simple linear change in one of the variables can hardly be justified. In this case, the thoughtless experimenter might vary the controlled variable V over equally spaced intervals ΔV, obtaining a plot of ΔP versus V, as in Fig. 6-3. Such a spacing is obviously deficient. The high-velocity end is insufficiently filled with points, and the low end is needlessly overloaded. We could instead

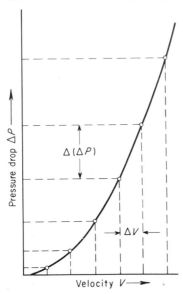

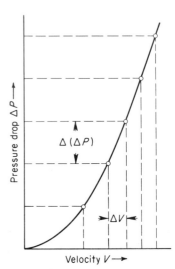

Fig. 6-3. Plot shows the point spacing for the equation $\Delta P = kV^2$ when equal intervals of velocity are chosen.

Fig. 6-4. A plot, identical with Fig. 6-3, except that equal pressure-drop intervals are now chosen.

operate the apparatus so that equal pressure-loss intervals are covered, as shown in Fig. 6-4. Here the points are concentrated at the high-velocity end. In many cases, low-pressure drops have high uncertainty, so that the equal-V-interval plan might be a good one. But suppose the precision is equal over the entire range of V and ΔP. Then we want our points spaced along equal distances or arc lengths of the experimental curve. If ΔS is a single interval along the curve, the general expression for arc length for any function that is continuous and has derivatives is

$$\Delta S = \left[1 + \left(\frac{dY}{dX}\right)^2\right]^{\frac{1}{2}} \Delta X \qquad (6\text{-}1)$$

For our fitting function involving V^2

$$\left(\frac{d\Delta P}{dV}\right)^2 = \frac{k^2\rho^2V^2}{g^2} \qquad \text{and} \qquad \Delta S = \left(1 + \frac{k^2\rho^2V^2}{g^2}\right)^{\frac{1}{2}} \Delta V$$

Then if we select a spacing ΔV_1 between two selected points at V_1, the next spacing ΔV_2 will be found (for $\Delta S_1 = \Delta S_2$) from

$$\Delta V_2 = \Delta V_1 \sqrt{\frac{1 + k^2\rho^2V_1^2/g^2}{1 + k^2\rho^2V_2^2/g^2}}$$

where V_2 is the velocity at the beginning of the next interval, ΔV_2. Following this procedure increment by increment we obtain a plot similar to Fig. 6-5, which is compact and logical.

Unfortunately, this mathematical approach is not too practical for many test situations. In the pressure-loss test, one of the main reasons for running the test is to find k. Yet we should know k to use Eq. (6-1) to plan our spacing. The investigator must thus apply some other approximate or specialized method that does not require such a complete knowledge of the experimental function under study.

If the function is expected to be a simple one, it can often be transformed to a linear form, by one or another kind of algebraic transformation. The pressure-loss-versus-velocity function just discussed can be transformed,

$$\ln \Delta P = \ln \frac{k\rho}{2g} + 2 \ln V$$

If we are willing to accept a plot of $\ln \Delta P$ versus $\ln V$, we can have a correctly spaced curve by taking equal increments of $\ln V$ instead of V alone. Furthermore, we do not have to know the value of k, g, or ρ, nor do we have to know that the exponent of V is 2.

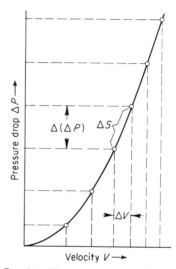

Fig. 6-5. The same curve as shown in Figs. 6-3 and 6-4 only now the points are chosen such that the distance between them along the curve ΔS is approximately equal.

Some other examples of similar transformations are

$$Y = \frac{A + B}{X^2}$$

where we see immediately that correct spacing occurs if we take equal increments of $1/X^2$ rather than X alone, and plot $1/X^2$ versus Y,

$$Y = Ae^{-bX}$$

which becomes $\qquad \ln Y = \ln A - bX$

and we should plot X versus $\ln Y$ taking equal increments of X,

$$Y = A \ln BX$$

or $\qquad Y = A(\ln B + \ln X)$

And we see that Y should plot versus ln X, and ln X should take equal intervals.

In Sec. 9-2 a least-squares plotting method is described that depends entirely on the careful pretest spacing of the independent variable(s). The method allows an investigator to perform a complete least-squares solution entirely on graph paper, using only a compass and straightedge and without resorting to desk calculators or tables of squares. This is one of the many dividends accruing to the test engineer who thinks before he turns the switches on his test equipment.

It must be kept in mind that we are not adjusting the spacing of test points simply to get a "symmetrical" or "pleasing" curve. There is, in fact, one basic reason for considering point spacing at all. It is our desire *to have every part of our experimental curve or map have the same precision as every other part.* We may or may not be able to achieve this ideal in any given test. We should, however, never fail to try to bring it about.

6-2. The Sequence of Experimental Testing

Having spaced the test points through a consideration of precision, we still do not know just what sequence we should follow in putting our apparatus into these chosen configurations. There are many types of experiments in which little or no choice exists as to the sequence of operation. In astronomy and many of the so-called "earth sciences," outside factors force a time and sequence on the investigator. We must observe Mars, not when we might wish, but when the weather is clear, the planet close, and the moon not bright. The usual sequence of seasons may not be particularly convenient for running some planting experiments, but we cannot change them.

In engineering, such a situation is somewhat unusual. More common is the experiment that we will call *irreversible*. This is a test that proceeds irrevocably from past to future without chance of alteration. Most obvious of this class are those tests involving endurance under extreme conditions where the test item suffers continuous and progressive deterioration. Many materials-testing experiments are irreversible. Suppose we plan a test on a steel tensile specimen and decide to apply our preselected load values at random. We apply 6,000, then 1,000, then 900, then 15,000 lb, and so on. Such a plan is certainly defective. The first load that we apply above the elastic limit will permanently deform the piece, and all subsequent readings will be made on a deformed specimen. Other examples of irreversible tests are all tests in which chemical changes (such as corrosion) may occur; all tests involving metal fatigue where this fatigue is significant to the operation of the test; all tests in which high temperatures, radiation fields, or high-gravity forces are progressively changing the crystalline structure of the test piece.

It could be argued that all tests are basically irreversible in the sense that no piece of apparatus ever returns to an identical configuration after use. Usually, the changes wrought by testing are so small as to be below the level of detection, and we say such tests are reversible and maintain that the apparatus can be returned at will to any previous configuration. All such tests admit a choice of point sequence, of which we will discuss two basic kinds. We may start with an independent variable at its upper or lower extreme value and change it in steps until the other extreme is reached. Or we may run the selected points in a perfectly random fashion, now high, now low. The first plan we will call the *sequential plan* and the second, the *random plan*. The fact that the sequential plan is now followed in almost all engineering tests is remarkable since the random plan makes more sense in most reversible experiments.

The sequential plan is obviously essential for irreversible tests of the materials type. There are other, more subtle places in which sequential plans are also desirable. The best example and one familiar to every young engineer is the classic pipe-friction experiment. At first glance it might not be evident why a sequential plan is desired in this case. As it happens, a laminarly flowing fluid, if the Reynolds number is slowly and carefully increased, tends to remain in laminar motion well into the transition region while the opposite (continued turbulence) occurs as the Reynolds number is shifted from high to low values. Figure 6-6 shows the data of a group of college juniors who were told that this effect was possible and could be noted by running in ascending and then descending sequence of Reynolds numbers. Had Reynolds numbers been selected in a random manner, now laminar, now turbulent, it is doubtful that this small effect would have been found. This is an experiment in which *sequence itself is a parameter of the test*. Other simple tests that show similar behavior are any test of an iron-core inductor in which the hysteresis pattern may depend on a previous test point and tests of friction in which transitions are made, from starting to sliding friction and back.

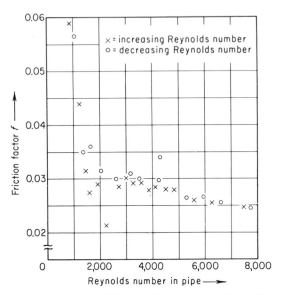

Fig. 6-6. A plot of friction factor versus Reynolds number for the flow of water in copper tubing. The test was run with N_{re} increasing continuously and then decreasing continuously, with the two kinds of points distinguished. Note that in the range 1,500 to 5,000 the decreasing points show higher f values than the increasing ones, suggesting a sequence effect on the test.

The great majority of tests in engineering are best handled by a partially or completely randomized plan. The arguments for such plans are quite convincing, and a few will be advanced at this point.

Natural effects may show a general trend during a test series. The barometric pressure may increase, the surrounding temperatures may rise or sink slowly, the humidity may change. If the controlled variable X is also changing in a regular manner, the dependent variable R may show the effect of both X variation and weather variation. If X is varied in a random manner, there can be no chance of mistaking weather-induced trends for an X effect.

Human activities may show a trend during the test series. Most obvious is increasing skill or, alternatively, increasing boredom among data takers and operating personnel. Are certain effects due to increasing X variable or are they due to sloppy reading as shift change approaches? There need be no confusion due to such factors if the X variable is varied in a random manner.

Mechanical effects may produce a trend with regular X variation.
This is probably the most important reason for using a random
plan. Suppose we have a control, instrument, gauge, or other
device that is sticky. If the previous reading on the apparatus
was a high one, this instrument will stick high, while if a low reading precedes, the device will stick low. Now if we go from low to
high in regular, sequential steps, what is the effect? Every single
reading, except perhaps the first one, will be low, and the entire test
will have a regular and hard-to-spot bias. Suppose instead that
we randomize our point selection so that there are just about as
many points approached from above as from below. The data
may show some scatter, *but they will scatter around the correct values.*
Figure 6-7 shows such a situation. This occurs in test work in a
variety of guises. All sorts of thermal and engine tests will show
errors due to a failure to reach steady state. If a sequential plan
is used, we will always be on the same side of steady-state conditions
(too hot or too cold), and regular errors result. Dirty manometer
tubes behave like sticky instruments, as do orifice lines that are partially blocked or pressure lines with small leaks. Unless the experimenter is very familiar with his system, he risks regular and trouble-
some error by following a sequential plan when it is not necessary.

Perhaps it is not putting the matter too strongly to say that the
only justifications for the sequential plan are (1) an experiment
known to be either irreversible or having some aspect that can only
be shown by taking data in some regular sequence or (2) an experiment of such length, cost, or difficulty that randomization is not
practical. An example of this latter case might be a nuclear reactor with a time to reach thermal steady state that is on the order

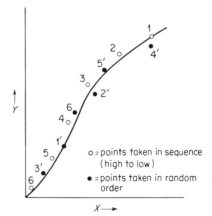

Fig. 6-7. Plot illustrates the effect of
a "sticky instrument." In this
case, the reading is "high" if it follows a higher reading and "low" if it
follows a lower reading. Note that
the random set of points will bracket
the "true" curve, while the sequential plan yields a curve that is
entirely misleading.

of days, so that each change in operating condition must be as small as possible.

In the next sections, we will see how partial and complete randomization can be achieved through special "block" plans. For many experiments, randomization is best obtained by some simple "gaming" method. For example, the chosen runs can be numbered and the numbers drawn from a hat as in a lottery. If two or more dice are available of different colors, we can handle tests of 36, 216, etc., runs. If the red die is units and the green is tens, then green 3 and red 1 is number 31. Runs can be given numbers 11 through 16, 21 through 26, and so on and the plan developed through successive throws of the dice. Alternatively, and perhaps with greater dignity, a set of random-number tables can be obtained and used to assign test-point sequence.[1]

What we are discussing here is *experimental control*, which, with precision, forms the crucial pair of desired aims in all test efforts. Although control and precision are related, it is perfectly possible to have excellent precision and terrible control, or vice versa. Experiments in the social sciences are often very precise in the sense that the numerical counts of occurrences are exactly correct. Yet the control over the behavior of human beings in experimental situations is so difficult as to be an impossibility in many such tests. On the other hand, a test such as the detection of the rotation rate of Venus by spectrographic studies of its light is very imprecise yet entirely free (if the night be clear) of other effects.

6-3. Randomized Blocks: Extraneous Variables

We have so far restricted our considerations in this chapter to those simplest of experiments having one independent or controlled variable X and a dependent result R. We will classify this as a *one-factor experiment*. But, although there may be only one controlled variable or factor, we would be naïve if we did not recognize the possibility of various other uncontrolled or *extraneous* variables. We have already suggested such variables in the form of changing temperature, pressure, or humidity, or changes in the attitudes of data takers. Extraneous variables of this sort change in a continuous manner with time and are best controlled by the simple randomization of test points as described in Sec. 6-2. Other extraneous variables are discrete in character. Examples are groups of men,

---

[1] For example, see K. A. Brownlee, "Industrial Experimentation," pp. 21–22, Chemical Publishing Company, Inc., New York, 1948.

different machines or instruments, different "mill runs" or material batches, different days or weeks or seasons of the year,[1] and so on. All may have definite, though uncomputable, effects.

Since we cannot eliminate the effect of many extraneous variables or allow for their effects by computation, we try to minimize their effects through randomization which will spread extraneous effects more or less equally over all runs. When discrete extraneous variables can be identified, we can use the concept of the *randomized block*, as will be developed in this section.

Suppose we have a new cutting tool which we wish to test in a production situation. We wish to establish the optimum machine speed for this tool to maximize production rate, while not exceeding some rejection percentage. This is then a one-factor experiment with machine speed X as the independent variable and the production rate function R as the dependent result. But such an experiment has one obvious extraneous variable, the machine operator. If we have perhaps 20 machinists, how are we to select a typical or average man to run our test? Obviously we cannot do this. Machinists vary so much in skill, temperament, physical strength, and so on that to select a single "average" man to run the test would be foolish. Let us then, through some chance method, select four men, each of whom will run a given speed over an entire shift. To balance the test, let us select four different speeds, so that each man will run each of the four speeds over a four-day period, and we can average the results of each speed run. This will randomize the test over the extraneous variable machinist. Assigning the speeds numbers 1, 2, 3, and 4 and the men letters A, B, C, and D, a possible plan might be

Man	Shift day			
	Monday	Tuesday	Wednesday	Thursday
A	1	2	3	4
B	1	2	3	4
C	1	2	3	4
D	1	2	3	4

[1] In one case in the author's experience the month of August was a particularly poor time for running heat-transfer and air-flow tests in a temporary building located in a large open field. Thousands of potato bugs were swarming at this time, and they plugged orifice and pressure lines and blocked air passages in the heat-exchanger test units.

Such a plan is surely defective, for it ignores effect of sequence on the test. The enthusiasm, interest, or perhaps dismay generated by a new tool on Monday shift may pall by Thursday, and production may fall for this reason. Alternatively, learning may occur, and production may go up. We have not randomized the extraneous-variable shift day. Suppose that we draw speed numbers out of a hat for each man, thereby randomizing the sequence with which they occur:

Man	Shift day			
	Monday	Tuesday	Wednesday	Thursday
A	4	2	1	3
B	2	3	1	4
C	3	2	1	4
D	1	3	4	2

This is an improved plan, but we can do better. Notice that in this hit-or-miss randomizing method, the speeds 1 and 4 fall mainly in the last two days. Thus a decrease in interest at the end of the test might suggest a peaking in the middle speed range that was not actually due to speed changes at all. Let us completely randomize this test such that each speed appears only once on a given day and no man runs at the same speed more than one day. Such a plan might be

Man	Shift day			
	Monday	Tuesday	Wednesday	Thursday
A	1	2	3	4
B	3	4	1	2
C	2	1	4	3
D	4	3	2	1

where we have constructed a so-called *Latin square*, a special type of experimental plan that is part of the general family of *factorial experiments*, although the words factorial experimentation imply not only the random plans but also the analysis of the results using advanced statistical methods. In engineering, we are usually not interested in the actual effect of extraneous variables on our desired result. Here, for example, we could, through statistical means, investigate the relative strengths of "shift day" and "man" on our production rate and draw certain conclusions about the interaction of these variables, their variance, and so on.[1] Such material may be studied in a variety of advanced statistical works referenced at the end of this chapter and Chap. 8.

But we may be able to improve our machine-tool experiment still further. To let each man stay with a given machine—and machines may show large differences among themselves—might introduce bias due to such machine differences. Taking four machines as W, X, Y, and Z, we wish to distribute the test runs among the machines such that each machine is used only once by each man and is used only once with each speed. Then

Man	Shift day			
	Monday	Tuesday	Wednesday	Thursday
A	$1W$	$2X$	$3Z$	$4Y$
B	$3X$	$4W$	$1Y$	$2Z$
C	$2Y$	$1Z$	$4X$	$3W$
D	$4Z$	$3Y$	$2W$	$1X$

which will permit us to average out the effects of shift day, machine, and machinist using a *Graeco-Latin square*. There could be yet another extraneous variable, such as "steel lot," but the addition of this variable to our plan is left as an exercise. Such "high order" squares have been little used in experimentation probably owing to the great difficulty of getting five or more variables in desired combinations and all at the same number of levels. Interestingly enough, a six-by-six square is possible only with three variables, that is, as a Latin square.

When the four days and the 16 runs are complete, we would very likely be satisfied with a numerical average of the four production figures at each speed, plotted against speed. In Chap. 8, we will see how a *test for significance* can be made on such data for cases when the effect of speed is not obvious from the usual engineering curve.

The square array is not necessarily the most convenient form for

---

[1] For the most concise and understandable presentation of this material in engineering terms see Brownlee, *op. cit.*

many experiments. We might, for example, wish to vary the speed over six increments, yet use fewer men and machines. A great many partial and unbalanced experimental designs are available in literature, coming under the names *Youden squares, lattice squares,* and so on.[1] For common engineering use, multiple Graeco-Latin plans are often sufficient and are easily applied. For example, with speeds 1, 2, 3, 4, 5, and 6; machinists A, B, and C; and machines X, Y, and Z, we can construct two three-by-three squares:

Man	Shift day			Shift day		
	Monday	Tuesday	Wednesday	Thursday	Friday	Monday
A	$1X$	$3Z$	$5Y$	$2X$	$4Z$	$6Y$
B	$3Y$	$5X$	$1Z$	$4Y$	$6X$	$2Z$
C	$5Z$	$1Y$	$3X$	$6Z$	$2Y$	$4X$

where we have distributed the six speeds equally to the first and second blocks, "interlacing" as far as possible. This plan is not so randomized as a single 36-item square including six men, six machines, and six days, but would probably suffice.

Example 6-1. We wish to subject a series of transistor radios to operation at six different temperatures and plot loss of sensitivity at one hundred hours against temperature level. Radios from two different plants, with printed circuits of three kinds of plastic, are to be tested. The humidity is extraneous and cannot be controlled, and only two test chambers are available. What is a good plan?

Solution. A short test will result if we use two three-by-three squares, with each square taking radios from a different plant. Let temperature levels be T_1 through T_6 and types of plastics be P_1 through P_3, and let us set up 100-hr periods A, B, and C. Then

Type of plastic	Plant 1			Plant 2		
	T_1	T_3	T_5	T_2	T_4	T_6
P_1	A	B	C	A	B	C
P_2	B	C	A	B	C	A
P_3	C	A	B	C	A	B

[1] T. Kitagawa and M. Mitome, "Tables for the Design of Factorial Experiments," Dover Publications, Inc., New York, 1953.

might be a plan.   But, although this is about minimum in size for a factorial experiment in this case, the time is long to completion. We can place only a single radio in each of the two furnaces for each 100-hr period, and the entire test will take 900 hr.   We might be satisfied to simply distribute the time periods in a less random manner in the interests of rapid completion.   The design then is not a pair of Latin squares:

Type of plastic	Plant 1			Plant 2		
	T_1	T_3	T_5	T_2	T_4	T_6
P_1	A	C	B	B	A	C
P_2	A	C	B	B	A	C
P_3	A	C	B	B	A	C

Now three radios can be placed in each furnace, and the test totals only 300 hr in length.   We pay for this short time in the poorer control over a humidity effect, for now six radios undergo test simultaneously.   By interlacing, that is, putting temperatures T_1 and T_4, T_3 and T_6, and T_5 and T_2 together, we partially mitigate any effect of humidity on the temperature-versus-sensitivity-loss curve.

6-4. Multifactor Experiments: Classical Plans

Many tests involve two or more controlled and variable factors, and we will refer to them as two-factor, three-factor, and so on, experiments.   In all such experiments, one, two, or many extraneous variables may also be present.   In such multifactor tests, we often have the choice between two types of experimental plans, *classical* or *factorial*.   The classical plan is in almost universal use by engineers everywhere and is perfectly general in application. The factorial plan is often shorter, always more accurate (for a given length of test), but has much less general application.

If we are given a dependent result R which is a function of several independent variables X, Y, Z, etc., the basic classical plan consists in holding all but one of the independent variables constant and changing this one variable over its range, following any spacing plan that we have worked out, and allowing for extraneous variables as just discussed.   If the mathematical relationship among the independent variables is simple, this should reveal the function of R versus the changing variable (say X). Then all but the next variable (say Y) may be held constant, and Y may be varied to find the separate RY function. Essentially, a multifactor classical experiment is simply a series of one-factor experiments. This limited classical approach will find such simple functions as

$$R = AY^n + BX^m$$
$$R = AY^nX^m$$
$$R = AYB^{cX}$$

and so on. For a two-factor experiment with each factor taken over five levels, we can diagram the plan as follows:

<pre>
                    −Y level
                 1 2 3 4 5
           5 ┌   *
           4 │   *
X level 3 │ * * * * *
           2 │   *
           1 │   *
</pre>

where the asterisk marks indicate configurations of the test apparatus that are to be run. When the function is more complicated, such as

$$R = AX \sin \frac{BY}{X}$$
$$R = A + BX^mY^n + CX^oY^o$$
$$R = AX^{bY}$$

it is doubtful that a limited plan of X and Y at one level each would unravel it, and we might have to try X and Y at several levels, for example,

<pre>
                    −Y level
                 1 2 3 4 5
           5 ┌ * * * * *
           4 │ *   *   *
X level 3 │ * * * * *
           2 │ *   *   *
           1 │ * * * * *
</pre>

or we might completely fill this plan and run all 25 test points. The actual establishment of functions from data will be taken up in later chapters. When a classical experiment, either partial or complete, is planned, it does not have to be balanced. That is, we can choose ten X levels and only three Y levels if it is felt that the

R-versus-X function is the more important or more difficult.   In the test of heat exchangers, for example, correlation is often achieved by

$$N_{st} = kN_{re}{}^{a}N_{pr}{}^{b}$$

where the Stanton number N_{st} is the dependent result, and the Reynolds number N_{re} and Prandtl number N_{pr} are the two independent variables.   In most practical situations, the Prandtl number changes very slightly over a wide range of temperatures, while the Reynolds number, which contains the fluid velocity, will show wide variation.   In such a case we would vary the Prandtl number over far fewer levels than the Reynolds number.   In the practical use of the final experimental equation, accuracy in the Stanton-versus-Reynolds-number function is by far the most critical.

6-5. Multifactor Experiments: Factorial Plans

We have already seen how Graeco-Latin-square factorial plans can be applied to the one-factor test with several extraneous variables.   It is also possible to apply these plans to engineering experiments of several factors, providing certain limitations and precautions are observed.   The special advantages of such factorial experiments over the classical types will become evident as we examine the methods.

The most serious restriction on the use of factorial experiments in engineering work is that only two types of general experimental functions can be readily handled.   Furthermore, we must know which class of function we are dealing with before the data are processed.   The first class of these is that in which the dependent result R is a function of the sums of the functions of the independent variables.   This case has the general formula

$$R = f_1(X) + f_2(Y) + f_3(Z) \qquad (6\text{-}2)$$

where f_1, f_2, and f_3 are functions of any level of complexity.   An example of this class of noninteracting relationship is very uncommon in engineering and physical science.   In agriculture, such a relation is often assumed in problems involving such variables as depth of planting, amount of fertilizer, and seed concentration.

The much more usual second class of general relationship that can be handled by a factorial experiment is the case of the result being a function of the product of the individual functions of the independent variables, or

$$R = f_1(X)f_2(Y)f_3(Z) \tag{6-3}$$

This can be treated as a special case of the first class since Eq. (6-3) transforms to the form of Eq. (6-2) if we take logs,

$$\log R = \log f_1(X) + \log f_2(Y) + \log f_3(Z) \tag{6-4}$$

Equation (6-3) is one of the most important general relations in scientific work. It includes the commonly assumed result in dimensional analysis (see Sec. 4-6),

$$R = kX^aY^bZ^c \tag{6-5}$$

as well as a variety of complex forms such as

$$R = kX^ay^be^{cZ}$$

or
$$R = \frac{k}{X} A^Y \sin BZ$$

Examples of functions that are *not* in this class are

$$R = AX^a + Y^bZ^c$$
or
$$R = AX^ae^{bY/Z}$$

and an infinity of other functions having higher-order complexity.

Let us now see how a factorial experiment could be run when the function is known to be of the class defined by Eq. (6-3). We shall consider a balanced experiment involving X, Y, and Z at three levels such that the Latin square is

	Y_1	Y_2	Y_3
X_3	Z_1	Z_2	Z_3
X_2	Z_2	Z_3	Z_1
X_1	Z_3	Z_1	Z_2

Let us assume that we know (from theory, intuition, or past experience) that Eq. (6-3) is the general expression governing the effect of X, Y, and Z on R. Let us write the three equations covering the horizontal X_1 row, but in logarithmic or noninteracting form,

$$\begin{align}
(\log R)_a &= \log f_1(X_1) + \log f_2(Y_1) + \log f_3(Z_3) \tag{6-6a} \\
(\log R)_b &= \log f_1(X_1) + \log f_2(Y_2) + \log f_3(Z_1) \tag{6-6b} \\
(\log R)_c &= \log f_1(X_1) + \log f_2(Y_3) + \log f_3(Z_2) \tag{6-6c}
\end{align}$$

Now let us add these three equations together, obtaining

$$\Sigma \log R_{x1} = 3 \log f_1(X_1)$$
$$+ \log (f_2Y_1 \times f_2Y_2 \times f_2Y_3) + \log (f_3Z_3 \times f_3Z_2 \times f_3Z_1)$$

We can repeatt he same procedure for the middle, or X_2, row, obtaining

$$\Sigma \log R_{x2} = 3 \log f_1(X_2)$$
$$+ \log (f_2Y_1 \times f_2Y_2 \times f_2Y_3) + \log (f_3Z_2 \times f_3Z_3 \times f_3Z_1)$$

and similarly for the top, or X_3, row.   The above equations can be written

$$\log f_1(X_1) = \frac{\Sigma \log R_{x1}}{n} - \text{const} \qquad (6\text{-}7a)$$

and
$$\log f_1(X_2) = \frac{\Sigma \log R_{x2}}{n} - \text{const} \qquad (6\text{-}7b)$$

and so on for the X_3 level; n for a three-by-three square is 3, and for a higher-level square is equal to the number of levels.   What we have done in this proof is to show that, if the logarithms of the results are numerically averaged over a single X, Y, or Z level, the effects of those factors that are changing (Y and Z in the case examined) will remain the same from one X level to the next. Thus, all changes in the log average of the result are wholly due to the effect of X alone.   We could easily continue to show the same result when averaging occurs over the three Y levels and then over the three Z levels.   If yet another variable, say W, were added forming a Graeco-Latin square, the same rule would apply in finding the effect of W on R.

If the experimental function is known before the experiment is analyzed to be a sum type following Eq. (6-2), we obtain the effect of X, Y, and Z on R by *averaging the appropriate R values rather than log R*.   If it is not known which class applies or whether either applies at all, it is recommended that this factorial approach not be used and that a standard classical approach be taken.

The analysis of the various functions can be undertaken using plots of $\log X$ versus $\log R_{\text{avg}}$ or by taking antilogs and examining the X-versus-R_{avg} function or by numerical means.

Suppose that we obtain tabulations or curves of R as a function of X, Y, and Z separately.   Equations (6-7a) and (6-7b) show that such curves or tabulations will yield us

$$R_x = kf_1(X)$$
$$R_y = k'f_2(Y)$$
and
$$R_z = k''f_3(Z)$$

where R_x is the antilog of $\Sigma \log R_x/n$, k is the constant in Eqs.
(6-7a), (6-7b), and so on, made up of the Y and Z portions eliminated through use of the Latin square, and $f_1(X)$ is the function of
the X variable, as noted. If we solve these three equations for
$f_1(X)$, $f_2(Y)$, and $f_3(Z)$ and substitute in Eq. (6-3) we obtain

$$R = K(R_x)(R_y)(R_z) \qquad (6-8)$$

where K is $(kk'k'')^{-1}$. We can evaluate K if we know the final
result R and the individual R's from the X, Y, and Z curves or
tabulations. The following example will show the method.

Example 6-2. A student group wished to study the effects of
speed, load, and cooling-water temperature on the operating characteristics of a 1949 Dodge internal-combustion engine mounted on
a test stand. From their study of internal-combustion engine
testing, they assumed that such characteristics are related by a
products-of-functions type of experimental equation, as in Eq. (6-3),
so that a Latin square is possible with the results log-averaged.
How was this test planned, and what sort of data resulted?

Solution. The students selected a four-by-four square having the
following construction:

Speed, rpm.....	1,400	1,600	1,800	2,000
Dynamometer load, lb	Temperature in square, °F			
87.5	110	135	160	200
66.0	200	110	135	160
44.0	160	200	110	135
22.0	135	160	200	110

after first ensuring that all 16 of these engine configurations could
be met by the test equipment. Note that all Latin squares are not
necessarily possible. A square with the top row having temper-

atures 200, 160, 135, and 110°F reading from left to right was not possible, since the cooling-water flow was insufficient to hold temperature at its minimum (110°F) when load and speed were at maximum.

The 16 runs were then made, and the square was filled with the basic dependent result, which was fuel consumption in pounds of fuel per hour.

21.2	24.5	28	29
14	16	19	22
8	11	14	16
6	8	8	12

Now if the general equation (6-3) governs this test, we must make a logarithmic average and then take the antilog (of fuel consumption) as follows:

					Load varying			
	Log (fuel consumption)				Sum	Avg	Antilog	
T=110°F →	1.326	1.392	1.447	1.462 →	5.625	1.406	25.5	
T=200°F →	1.146	1.204	1.279	1.342 →	4.971	1.243	17.5	
T=160°F →	0.903	1.041	1.146	1.204 →	4.295	1.072	11.9	
T=135°F →	0.778	0.903	0.903	1.079 →	3.664	.916	8.2	
Sum	4.154	4.538	4.775	5.088	4.756	1.189	15.5	(T=110°F)
Avg	1.038	1.135	1.194	1.272	4.650	1.163	14.5	(T=135°F)
Antilog	10.9	13.6	15.6	18.7	4.596	1.149	14.1	(T=160°F)
		Speed varying			4.553	1.138	13.8	(T=200°F)
					Temp varying			

Fuel consumption, specific fuel consumption, and efficiency were then found and Figs. 6-8 to 6-10 plotted to show the results of the test. We cannot use these curves directly to give us, say, the efficiency at a given load, for they represent averages rather than discrete values. Let us take Eq. (6-8) and compute the unknown constant K, and then use this equation for useful interpretation of the curves. The data in the upper row, second column from the left in the Latin square, have the values: load, 87.5 lb; rpm, 1,600; temperature, 135°F; and fuel consumption for this run, 24.5 lb/hr. Now we see, by looking at either the fuel consumption curves or the analyzed square itself, that a load of 87.5 lb gives an average fuel consumption of 24.5 and that this fuel consumption is the direct result of the log-averaging process which we showed would eliminate the effect of rpm and temperature variations. Similarly, the average fuel consumption for 1,600 rpm is 13.6 and for 135°F is 14.5.

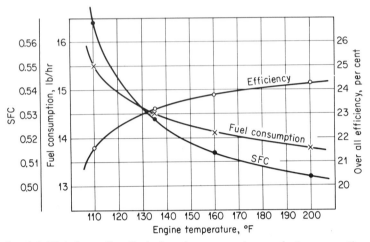

Fig. 6-8. Plot shows the effect of engine temperature on fuel consumption and other operating parameters of the internal-combustion engine discussed in Example 6-2.

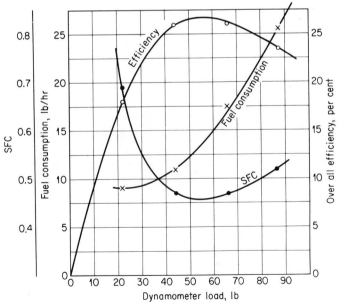

Fig. 6-9. Plot shows the effect of dynamometer load variation on fuel consumption and other operating parameters of the internal-combustion engine discussed in Example 6-2.

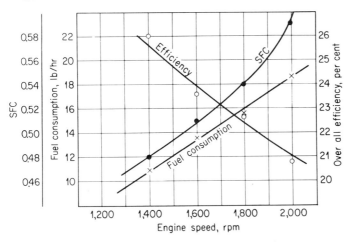

Fig. 6-10. Plot shows the effect of engine speed on fuel consumption and other operating parameters of the internal-combustion engine discussed in Example 6-2.

Thus from Eq. (6-8) we find

$$K = \frac{24.5}{25.5 \times 13.6 \times 14.5} = 0.00488$$

But notice that we can check this K value by repeating this calculation on any other data point of the Latin square. For example, the lower-right-hand run (2,000 rpm, 110°F, 22.0 lb) gives a K of $12/(8.2 \times 18.7 \times 15.5)$ or 0.0051. The following square shows the K values computed for each of the 16 runs:

0.0049	0.0049	0.0050	0.0044
0.0053	0.0043	0.0048	0.0048
0.0044	0.0046	0.0049	0.0050
0.0048	0.0051	0.0052	0.0051

The differences in the various K's are indications of how badly the data deviate from the ideal of Eq. (6-3). These deviations may be a result of the failure of Eq. (6-3) to exactly predict the functional relationships of the test variables or the lack of control in holding the variables at their planned levels, or simple lack of precision in the measurements. The average K for these 16 runs is 0.00485, and the maximum deviation from this is 0.00055 or 11 per cent. In this test, most of this deviation is probably due to the difficulty in control of speed and temperature while fuel-consump-

tion readings are being taken.   Using this average K, we could now
answer a number of questions about the apparatus.   For example,
we note that maximum fuel consumption occurs at maximum speed
(2,000 rpm), minimum temperature (110°F), and maximum load
(87.5 lb).   Then

$$(FC)_{\max} = 0.00485(25.5)(15.5)(18.7) = 35.6 \text{ lb/hr}$$

which is the fuel consumption at 2,000 rpm, 110°F, and 87.5 lb,
a condition that was not actually run.   The uncertainty is about
plus or minus 11 per cent, with this uncertainty figure including
perhaps 90 to 95 per cent of all the data.

A similar type of computation can be made for specific fuel consumption or efficiency.   The material in this example is used in
Example 9-4 to show how further analysis is possible using graphical techniques.

It might be asked just what has been gained by this rather
involved type of plan.   In a balanced, three-level experiment
involving three variables, we can obtain three 3-point curves with
only seven runs, instead of the nine in the Latin square.   These
seven can be represented in three-dimensional space as

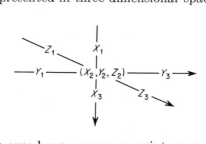

where the three axes have a common point or run.   Even when a
three-by-three Graeco-Latin design is used, a classical test of nine
runs will give the same number of curves and points and handle the
same number of variables.   But notice that each 3-point curve
obtained from a factorial test involves all nine runs.   Each curve
point is actually an average of three separate determinations.
From our discussion in Sec. 2-5 on the improvement in precision
of a mean due to taking increased numbers of readings, we would
expect that each factorial test point would be $3^{1/2}$ or 1.7 times as
precise as each classical test point.   In a four-by-four experiment,
we would have to replicate each run four times in a classical experiment to achieve a precision equal to a 16-run factorial plan.   If

three variables are involved, the basic classical plan would involve
10 runs,

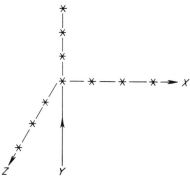

which when completely replicated four times gives 40. Thus,
the main advantage of the factorial multifactor experiment is in
increased precision with little or no increase in the amount of testing. The main disadvantages are the problems associated with
first selecting and then running a large number of test runs with
perhaps imperfect knowledge of the operating envelope of the equipment, plus the fact noted in Example 6-2 that the final curves are
not completely useful alone but must be changed to general functional relationships.

The approach to factorial experimentation taken here is essentially
nonstatistical. In the case of optimizing a machine tool, we did not
care what relationship existed between output and shift day or
operator but only wanted to randomize these effects out of the test.
In the engine test, we knew at the beginning that strong functional
relationships existed between the dependent result and the three
variable parameters of the test. In many situations, we wish to
decide if an effect is present but suspect that such an effect is not as
strong as is suggested in Figs. 6-8 to 6-10. When this is the case,
factorial tests are often used, but the analysis of the result squares
are statistical in nature. Entire books are available on this type of
experimental plan. A short section in Chap. 8 will introduce this
kind of statistical analysis.

Without question, the bulk of engineering experimentation will
continue to be performed along classical lines. In cases where the
function is known to be a product type, where several variables are
involved, and where the precision is thought to be poor, the engineer should always consider the factorial approach.

6-6. Summary

In this chapter we have considered a number of pretest planning methods. Starting with a series of known, independent variables, we first should consider the spacing of our test runs or points over the envelope of the apparatus. The basic concern in such spacing is to ensure that the final plotted curve is equally precise over its range. When an uncertainty analysis suggests that certain portions of a curve or map have less precision than other portions, we try to adjust the point spacing so that more points will fall in the bad precision area. Ideally, we would like to have (approximately) the lack of precision, squared, in these areas so that if the poorest area is one-half as precise as the best area, we would put four times as many test points in the less precise area. This ideal is often not possible to reach.

When the spacing of runs is not dictated by regions of varying precision, we wish to prevent the wasteful "bunching" of test points by setting up an equal data spacing along the curve(s). This can be done exactly using Eq. (6-1), but is seldom possible since an exact spacing requires an exact knowledge of the experimental function. In many cases, where the form of the function is partially known, the investigator can algebraically transform his equation and create a linear form, making the job of spacing quite easy. This approach means, however, that the equation should be plotted in its transformed form, something that is not always desired.

After the actual levels of the independent variables are chosen, the investigator then has the choice of a sequential plan, where the independent-variable changes proceed in a regular increasing or decreasing sequence, or a random plan, where the chosen variable levels are selected at random, following some irregular plan derived from dice throws, card drawings, or the use of random-number tables. The sequential plan, is usually essential for those irreversible tests in which progressive changes or deterioration occurs and in certain special cases where the sequence of data taking is a parameter of the test in its own right. For the majority of reversible engineering experiments, the random plan will average out any regular variations due to surroundings, test personnel, and test apparatus defects and is thus very desirable.

When these extraneous variables of personality, weather, shift day, season, machine, material batch, etc., can be placed in well-defined categories, their effects are best eliminated by using a factorial plan of the Graeco-Latin type, where a variety of extraneous variables are randomly distributed to the different runs. This can be done in balanced or unbalanced plans, although only balanced plans are considered in this book. Often a large block, six, eight, or ten levels on a side, can be replaced by two or more smaller blocks with little loss in randomization.

When an experiment involving several variable factors is to be run, we have the choice of the classical plan, where all but one of the variables are held constant at one level, or the factorial plan, where all the variables are changed in each run as dictated by an appropriate Graeco-Latin square. The classical plan is in universal use by engineers and is general in application and not difficult, but may be lengthy if an experiment has poor precision and must have its data replicated several times. The factorial plan is restricted to cases where the dependent result is equal to the sums of functions of the variables or to the products of functions of the variables, and we must know which. The product-of-functions case is very common in engineering, and if we are sure an experimental function has this form, we need only make numerical averages of the logs of the results to reveal the effect of each variable alone on the results. This is all providing, of course, we have operated the apparatus to follow a randomized plan. The main advantage of using this factorial approach is that the entire set of data is used for each curve, and the precision is therefore at a maximum.

We have barely scratched the surface of test planning. The medical, biological, and chemical sciences have pioneered in sophisticated and complex experimental designs. Much of this material is, for one reason or another, not practical for the mechanical and electrical experimenters in its present form. Still, engineers have lagged behind their colleagues in biology and agriculture, and many radical improvements in engineering test planning can be expected.

PROBLEMS

6-1. In the test of a steam-to-water heat exchanger the relationship among the temperatures, the water-flow rate w, and the over-all heat-transfer coefficient U is given by

$$\frac{\Delta T_{\text{wat}}}{T_{\text{steam}} - T_{\text{wat, in}}} = 1 - e^{-UA/wC_p}$$

where A is 10 ft^2 and C_p is 1 Btu/(lb)(°F). The apparatus will permit a low-water flow of 20 lb/hr which gives a water-out temperature of 130°F. High flow is 500 lb/hr with a water-out temperature of 54°F. Steam temperature and water-in temperature are fixed at 200 and 50°F. Select four intermediate values of w so that log U versus log w will show even spacing, assuming this plot is a straight line.

6-2. The general equation for ship speed versus engine horsepower is hp = $a + bV^3$, where a and b are constants relating to ship form and propeller type. At 5 knots the ship requires 29 hp at the shaft, while at 12 knots, 230 hp is needed. Locate three or four intermediate speeds such that (a) the intervals are equally spaced on a horsepower-versus-speed plot on linear paper, and (b) the intervals are equally spaced on a plot of log (speed) versus log (hp).

6-3. A microwave focusing antenna takes power from a transmitter at distance X and focuses this power on a stationary platform at altitude D. The usual optical equation, $D = X/(a + bX)$, applies. When X varies from 21 to 29 ft, D varies from 32,000 to 6,000 ft. Decide how this test should be run to give a linear plot of X versus D, and place six points between these extreme values to give even spacing on the linear plot.

6-4. A hydraulic transmission is to be tested by applying a known horsepower to one end of the line of pipes and then measuring the useful power (uhp) at the other end. The expected function is uhp = hp $- 1 \times 10^{-5}$ hp³ and we wish to vary hp between 100 and 200. Decide how to vary hp over five steps so that a curve of uhp versus hp suitable for equipment buyers is prepared.

6-5. Devise suitable experimental plans for the following tests:

a. Four types of specimens are to be torsion-tested to find yield point and total angular displacement at fracture. We wish to examine the effect of two different controlled loading speeds on these variables and attempt to minimize the extraneous effects of four different men putting the specimen in the jaws and the four different batches of aluminum that are used.

b. Two internal-combustion fuel-test engines are to be used to check three fuel samples for octane rating. One engine tests one shift, and we have six different technicians available. We wish to completely randomize the effect of technician, shift, and engine. What is the minimum number of shifts needed to accomplish this? Draw a test plan.

c. An airfoil cascade is to be tested over six stagger angles, six incidence angles, and three solidity ratios. Design an experiment to find the effect of these variables on flutter velocity if (i) the function is simple but not a sums or powers type, (ii) the function has very complex interaction, or (iii) the function is of the product-of-functions type and has very poor precision.

6-6. Draw a five-by-five Graeco-Latin square that is *completely* different from the one given in the Appendix. (That is, do not simply change the position of rows or columns.)

6-7. In the example involving a four-by-four Graeco-Latin square considered in Sec. 6-3, we wish to randomize along with shift day, machine, and machinist the extraneous variable "steel lot," the four lots having designations P, Q, R, and S. Draw the new design. Can yet another variable be randomized among the 16 runs of this test?

6-8. Starting with the five-by-five Graeco-Latin square in the Appendix, add new sets of variables F, G, H, I, and J, K, L, M, N, and O, and so on, until no further sets can be added in a randomized manner. How many different extraneous variables could we randomize with a five-by-five square in a one-factor experiment?

6-9. Devise suitable experimental plans for the following tests:

a. The melting point of a variable mixture of five components A, B, C, D, and E follows the function $MP = (a\% \ A + b\% \ B + c\% \ C + d\% \ D + e\% \ E)k$, where a, b, c, d, e, and k are constants to be found. Design an experiment with each component at four different levels plus zero per cent.

b. Suppose that, in the test of rotating equipment, we have as extraneous variables two different shifts and four methods of taking eight levels of rotating speed. Design a test with no more than 32 runs.

c. Suppose that in the test in (*b*) we wish to obtain additional runs at the lowest speed where precision is poor, but we wish to randomize data taking and shift and include the effect of temperature. How many runs are needed for this substitute plan, and what does it look like?

6-10. Prove that when a result R is equal to the sums of individual functions of the variables we can numerically average the result at each level to find the separate functions of R and the variables.

6-11. Can the following physical equations be investigated by a factorial experiment? Show algebraic proof of your answer, and, if it is "yes," explain how the columns should be averaged. Draw a three-by-three square for those equations that are possible in a factorial test.

a. $C = Ak/\ln (d/r)$, where C is capacity, k the dielectric constant, and d and r are geometric variables with A constant throughout.

b. $I = Aw(a^n + b^m)$, where I is the moment of inertia, w is the weight, a and b are body dimensions, and A, n, and m are constant.

c.
$$P = \frac{Ast}{R + t}$$

where P = allowable pressure
s = material working stress
R = inner radius
t = wall thickness
A = a constant

6-12. A machine is operated on a factorial plan with three independent variables: flow w, rotational speed rpm, and back pressure P. The final result of each run is efficiency E. The following points are taken:

Rpm	w	P	E
1,000	14.2	26	12.6
1,260	14.2	158	25
1,590	14.2	63	12.5
1,260	17.8	63	24.8
1,590	17.8	26	12.8
1,000	22.3	63	51
1,000	17.8	158	50
1,590	22.3	158	49.5
1,260	22.3	26	25.5

Arrange this data in a Latin square and decide whether a log average or plain average will give the most logical results. By proper averaging, find the function of E with respect to the three variables. (*Hint:* The functions should all plot straight lines on log-log paper.)

6-13. Two ovens are available to test four different kinds of transistors having two different brands of lead wires. A single test requires a complete day, but the ovens are identical and interchangeable (not extraneous variables). We wish to randomize days of the week, kinds of transistors, oven temperature (four values are ample), and wire type. Design a test plan to do this, and state the maximum number of transistor specimens needed and the minimum number of days.

6-14. A series of automatic, electronic flue-gas analyzers that sense per cent oxygen and per cent nitrogen and read out the per cent excess air E in the combustion chamber are to be tested over their operating range. This test is to be conducted with a series of premixed gas samples containing various amounts of O_2 from 0 to 15 per cent and a single N_2 percentage of 80 per cent with CO_2 making up the remainder. If the governing equation is

$$E = \frac{O_2}{0.264 N_2 - O_2}$$

with the symbols O_2, N_2, and E standing for decimal fractions, and we wish to have a dozen samples to cover the applicable range, what spacing of O_2 should we choose?

REFERENCES

Brownlee, K. A.: "Industrial Experimentation," Chemical Publishing Company, Inc., New York, 1953.

Chew, V.: "Experimental Designs in Industry," John Wiley & Sons, Inc., New York, 1958.

Cochran, W. G., and G. M. Cox: "Experimental Designs," John Wiley & Sons, Inc., New York, 1950.

Fisher, R. A.: "The Design of Experiments," Oliver & Boyd Ltd., London, 1949.

Hicks, C. R.: "Fundamental Concepts in the Design of Experiments," Holt, Rinehart and Winston, Inc., New York, 1964.

Kitagawa, T., and M. Mitome: "Tables for the Design of Factorial Experiments," Dover Publications, Inc., New York, 1953.

Mann, H. B.: "Analysis and Design of Experiments," Dover Publications, Inc., New York, 1949.

Pratt and Whitney Aircraft, Engineering Statistical Methods Group: "Increasing the Efficiency of Developmental Testing, PWA-2236," East Hartford, Conn., July, 1963.

Wilson, E. B.: "An Introduction to Scientific Research," chap. 4, McGraw-Hill Book Company, New York, 1952.

CHAPTER 7

Test-data Checking and Rejection

No matter how carefully the experimenter studies his instrumentation, his variable spacing, his sequence planning, and the suppression of extraneous-variable effects, the chance of serious error sources is always present. These sources may be instruments or controls that malfunction during test, or they may be readings of poorly controlled variables unsuspected during planning, or they may be data-taking or computing errors caused by untrained or careless operation of the equipment or program errors during data processing. The engineer who uses fast electronic computation equipment for test-data reduction (and more do so every month) must beware the systematic program error that can occur in even the most advanced computing laboratory.

The only way to guard against such occurrences is for the engineer to anticipate the ever-present chance of serious error and to plan for one or more checks on the accuracy and reasonableness of his data. In this chapter, we will examine a few of the common analytical checking methods, checks that can sometimes be used to actually identify the fault source.

7-1. Balance Equations

Probably the commonest of all checking equations is the balance or *conservation* equation, more familiar in some of its specialized forms of *energy* balance (or first law of thermodynamics), *mass* balance, *momentum* balance, and so on. Almost every experiment that one can conceive in civil, mechanical, and electrical engineering involves one or more balance equations, although there are many cases where using them as a check would involve far greater instrument problems than the test itself. At other times, the addition of one or two inexpensive instruments will permit a balance check on all data with ease. Some common tests in which balance equations might be useful are:

a. Energy flow in heat-transfer equipment. Here it is usually possible to measure the energy given up by the hot fluid and the amount gained by the cold since such devices are always constructed so that very little energy is lost to the surroundings in transit. The exception to this occurs when one fluid is condensing or boiling. In this type of exchanger, the enthalpy loss or gain can only be computed when the actual weight per unit time of fluid boiled or condensed is found, a measurement that is notoriously difficult in many cases.

b. Current flow in electrical networks. This is really a mass balance since we are assuming that the same number of electrons that enter a network will ultimately leave it. The range of application of this conservation law is very large and covers such systems as simple Kirchhoff networks, vacuum-tube and transistor tests, three-phase problems, and so on. The main precaution is that the analyst must fully understand the phase relationships in his system and be sure that his ammeters are measuring the proper current at whatever point they are inserted.

c. The general mass balance in fluid systems. This is so basic a consideration that it appears trivial; yet it is often overlooked in test-system design. Any time that we place two or more flow-metering devices in the same line, such that one will check the other, we are making use of the basic continuity principle that mass is conserved. This is often done to calibrate an air-flow orifice against a standard nozzle or to calibrate a fluid-flow meter against a weigh-barrel measurement. If it can be conveniently done, permanent installation of two different flowmeters in the same line is far better.

d. Momentum exchange in conservative fluid systems. The use of the momentum balance to check for error is often a rather subtle problem, since momentum is so easily lost in exchange situations through turbulence, friction, and nonelastic collisions. In some tests involving flowing fluids, the investigator can be sure that friction plays a small part so that a momentum balance is possible. In a jet-engine tailpipe, for example, radial and linear velocities will both be present, and momentum will be interchanged between these two forms as the gas travels down the duct. A series of measurements should show the summed momentum to be constant if all is well. Probably the most powerful application of the momentum balance occurs in the study of nuclear tracks on cloud-chamber photos.

There is actually a vast variety of balance equations available to investigators. Charge, voltage, or field strength might be conserved in electrical tests. Enthalpy, free energy, or entropy could be conserved in thermal or chemical systems. Head, pressure, or specific energy might be balanced in certain fluid experiments. When planning a test, the investigator should always ask himself if a conservation equation exists in his test and if it is readily checked by measurement.

In many common tests a balance cannot be applied for various reasons. Some examples follow.

a. Energy balance on an engine, a fan, or a compressor. All such devices essentially transform one form of energy (thermal, electrical, mechanical) into another form (usually mechanical). Interposed between the numerical output and the numerical input is the conversion efficiency, a number usually unknown until basic testing work is complete. Thus we can say that the output cannot exceed the input, but we can say no more than this without knowing a great deal about the device.

b. Combustion tests. Although it is theoretically possible to estimate the stack loss, insulation losses, and so on, of a combustion system and then to estimate the energy release of the fuel through measurement of the flue products, the actual energy balance is of such questionable precision that it can seldom be used to check other measurements with any confidence.

c. Mass balance in large fluid systems. In large fluid-flow tests involving whole rivers, large duct work carrying low-pressure air, and similar cases, it is quite difficult to arrive at mass balances at two different stations that will agree with one another. The main reason is that local velocities across a river or in a duct may vary radically from point to point, so that very many careful velocity checks must be made at a variety of locations at a section. When a temperature gradient is also imposed on a velocity profile, with energy of the stream to be computed, the problem is compounded in difficulty.

The use of a balance check in testing work is often overlooked or ignored by engineers simply because they do not see any great use for it.   In problems involving a difficult flow measurement, such as liquid-metal flow in a closed system, the engineer may reject two flowmeters, saying, "Which one should I use?   Should I average them?"   Both might be averaged if they read close to each other without one being consistently high or low.   If they disagree by 20 or 30 per cent, we should certainly not use either, at least until we have decided just what is the matter.   If this is a measurement that is accurate but very imprecise, we could reject all data which did not show a flow balance to within, say, 5 per cent (see Sec. 7-5).

Example 7-1.   A weigh barrel measures 15 lb of water ($\rho = 62.5$ lb/ft^3) in one minute, while a volume flowmeter in the same line registers 0.27 ft^3/min.   What is the amount of imbalance, and what is the per cent error, assuming the weigh-barrel measurement is correct?

Solution.   The conservation (of mass) equation in this case is

$$\text{Time} \times \text{weight} = \text{volume flow} \times \text{density}$$

or
$$1 \times 15 \overset{?}{=} 0.27 \times 62.5$$
$$15 \neq 16.9$$

So, the imbalance is $16.9 - 15.0$ or 1.9 lb/min, and the per cent error is $1.9/15 = 12.7$.

7-2. Location of Error Sources by a Balance Equation

In Chap. 2 we noted that instrument errors can be divided into classes of precision errors and accuracy errors, and we then said that the accuracy error could be found through calibration and easily corrected if it is known to exist.   In many tests, accuracy error may be negligible at the start of testing, but, owing to instrument malfunction, may suddenly become excessive.   In this section we will see how it may be possible to use a balance equation not only to check whether or not such a malfunction has occurred but also to locate the offending instrument.

Consider a test in which we measure four variables, A, B, X, and Y, which we know to be related through a balance equation of the form

$$AB = XY \tag{7-1}$$

where A and X might be flow rates of two heat-exchange fluids and

B and Y the respective temperature changes, or A and X might be gas density at two points in a constant-area duct and B and Y might be the gas velocity at these same points, and so on. Now let us subdivide our accuracy error into two subclasses. First, we define a *sum-type error* where we will say that a true quantity A errs by the amount $f(A)$ so that the *apparent value* is $A + f(A)$, where f is some function of the measured variable A. Next is a *product-type error* where the apparent value is $Af(A)$. An example of the sum-type error might be any instrument in which the input differs from the scale reading by a constant amount because of the scale slipping. A product-type error could result whenever the input is reduced by some proportion before it is sensed, such as might occur in a partially blocked manometer. Errors can, of course, take almost any functional form. For example, there could be a combination type $f_1(A)A + f_2(A)$, but we would expect any rule that held for a pure product or pure sum type to hold here as well. Remember, however, that we are talking here about pure accuracy errors, so that, should a given incorrect instrument be reread, it will give the identical (and still incorrect) value.

Taking first the sum-type error, let us assume that our variable A in Eq. (7-1) has such an error and that the other variables B, X, and Y are exactly correct. Let us then form the per cent error ($\% R$) from Eq. (7-1),

$$\% R_1 = \frac{[A + f(A)]B - XY}{[A + f(A)]B \text{ or } XY} \tag{7-2}$$

Actually, the denominator should be simply XY, which is the true product, but in a practical case we would not know this and might just as likely use the $[A + f(A)]B$ product instead. In this derivation we will retain both as alternatives. Now, Eq. (7-1) in (7-2) gives

$$\% R_1 = \frac{Bf(A)}{[A + f(A)]B \text{ or } XY} \tag{7-3}$$

Now imagine that we operate our apparatus such that all the variables but A are changed. If we change X to mX, Y to nY, and hold A the same, Eq. (7-1) shows that B must become mnB, and the new per cent error in the balance ($\% R_2$) becomes

$$\% R_2 = \frac{[A + f(A)]mnB - mXnY}{[A + f(A)]mnB \text{ or } mXnY} \tag{7-4}$$

The true balance equation for this new configuration of the apparatus is $AmnB = mXnY$, so that Eq. (7-4) becomes

$$\% R_2 = \frac{mnBf(A)}{[A + f(A)]mnB \text{ or } mXnY} \tag{7-5}$$

Let us now compare $\% R_1$ with $\% R_2$ by subtraction,

$$\% R_2 - \% R_1 = \frac{mnBf(A) - mnBf(A)}{[A + f(A)]mnB \text{ or } mXnY} = 0 \tag{7-6}$$

so that $\% R_1$ equals $\% R_2$ whatever $f(A)$ happens to be. Notice that the choice of denominator has no effect, and we will henceforth ignore it. Let us continue but now run a third test point in which we hold only B constant. Then

$$\% R_3 = \frac{[mnA + f(mnA)]B - mXnY}{[mnA + f(mnA)]B}$$

or, since $mnAB = mXnY$,

$$\% R_3 = \frac{Bf(mnA)}{[mnA + f(mnA)]B} \tag{7-7}$$

Again, forming the difference of $(\% R_3 - \% R_1)$, we get

$$\% R_3 - \% R_1 = \frac{Bf(mnA)}{[mnA + f(mnA)]B} - \frac{Bf(A)}{[(A + f(A)]B}$$

or $\quad \% R_3 - \% R_1 = \frac{A[f(mnA) - mnf(A)]}{[mnA + f(mnA)][A + f(A)]} \tag{7-8}$

Thus $\% R_3$ *does not* equal $\% R_1$ for any function $f(A)$ except when $f(mnA)$ equals $mnf(A)$. This occurs when $f(A)$ equals kA where k is constant. The most common sum-type error is the simple case $A_{\text{false}} = A_{\text{true}} \pm k$, where k is constant for any A value. This is easily detected through this method. Let us continue to a fourth determination in which X is held constant. This gives, when A goes to mA, B to nB, and Y to mnY,

$$\% R_4 - \% R_1 = \frac{A[f(mA) - mf(A)]}{[mA + f(mA)][A + f(A)]} \tag{7-9}$$

where again the per cent errors will be equal only when $f(mA)$ equals $mf(A)$ as before. The same result can be found for the final case of Y held constant. We have, then, proved a general rule to the effect: "If one of the variables in the equation $AB = XY$ suffers an accuracy error of the sum type, we can detect the offending variable by holding each constant in turn. Then, that variable that shows no change in per cent error when held constant is the reading in error. The single exception is the case of a variable in error by $(A + kA)$, in which case it cannot be detected by this method."

Let us now examine the same balance equation (7-1) but for the case of a product-type error. In this case,

$$\% R_1 = \frac{f(A)AB - XY}{f(A)AB \text{ or } XY} \tag{7-10}$$

and after variation with A held constant,

$$\% R_2 = \frac{f(A)AmnB - mXnY}{f(A)mnAB \text{ or } mXnY} \tag{7-11}$$

and $\% R_2 - \% R_1$

$$= \frac{f(A)AmnB - mXnY - f(A)AmnB + mXnY}{f(A)AmnB \text{ or } mXnY} = 0$$

With B held constant we find

$$\% R_3 - \% R_1 = \frac{f(mnA) - f(A)}{f(mnA)f(A)} \tag{7-12}$$

This is nonzero for all functions except the case of $f(A)$ equaling $f(mnA)$, which occurs when $f(A)$ is a constant for all A's [that is, $f(A)A = kA$]. This is, unfortunately, a type of product error which is quite common. Thus, the same rule applies in locating a product-type error as in a sum type, but the exception to the rule is different.

It is easily seen that all we have said so far will apply to balance equations of the types

$$AB = X \qquad ABC = XYZ \qquad \text{or} \qquad \frac{A}{B} = \frac{X}{Y}$$

rewritten $AY = BX$, and so on   The case

$$X = Y$$

cannot be used for error detection.

Experiments involving situations where energy terms, electric currents, or flows are added together lead to the other general form of balance equation

$$A + B = X + Y \tag{7-13}$$

which is also amenable to similar manipulations. It will be left as an exercise (Probs. 7-4 and 7-5) to prove that for an equation of the form of (7-13), "An accuracy error of the sum or product type can be found by holding each variable constant, in turn, and the variable in error will be the one that shows no change in the *imbalance error* defined as $\Delta R = X + Y - A - B$." Also left as an exercise is the establishment of exceptions similar to those already noted.

The application of these balance checks will seldom reveal the error source when:

1. One or another of the variables has a large precision error.
2. The error is one of the exceptions already noted.
3. The control of the variables is too uncertain to hold the chosen variable truly constant.

Point 1 above will prevent the successful location of error in most cases. However, when poor precision alone is the problem (the variation centers around the true value), some of the data may be salvaged by simply rejecting all points with imbalances beyond some preset maximum and keeping the others. Such a selection method is entirely valid and is one of the major reasons for ensuring that a balance check can be made on the apparatus. It is, in fact, one of the very few places in experimental work where throwing out data is entirely justified.

Example 7-2. A water-to-water heat exchanger has a heat-balance equation $C_p w_c \, \Delta T_c = C_p w_h \, \Delta T_h$, where the C_p's are the same for each side. The balance is poor and a series of runs are made that give the following results (w in pounds per minute, ΔT in degrees Fahrenheit):

Run no.	w_c	ΔT_c	w_h	ΔT_h	$\% \ R^*$
1	1	50	3.25	20	30
2	2	15	1.75	30	75
3	2.2	40	2.25	58.5	50
4	1	30	2.3	18	38
5	1.9	40	3.25	30	30

* $\% \ R = (w_h \, \Delta T_h - w_c \, \Delta T_c)/w_c \, \Delta T_c$.

Which reading is probably causing these poor balances?

Solution. If the error is a sum or product type and not one of the exceptions, we expect that quantity in error to show no change in $\% \ R$ when it is held constant and all other variables are changed. Runs 1 and 5 show about the same $\% \ R$, and the hot-fluid flow rate w_h was constant for these two runs. Thus, we expect this to be the measurement error.

7-3. Error Checking by Extrapolation

Although the shape and magnitude of experimental curves are often not known before testing, it is often possible to estimate their terminal points through theoretical or common-sense reasoning. Thus the efficiency of any machine under zero load is *always zero* no matter what value it may take in other situations. We know that when an alloy or mixture is varied as to components A and B, its properties will always extrapolate to the known properties of A as the percentage of B decreases, and to the properties of pure B as the amount of A is reduced. In any type of flow-measuring device depending on head measurement, head versus flow must pass through the origin. In turbulent flow, the heat-transfer coefficient h is often a function of the mass flow per unit area G to the 0.8 power. If we plot $1/h$ versus $1/G^{0.8}$, we have a curve (if all is well) that should pass through the origin. When Ohm's law applies, the current is zero when the voltage is zero, while a plot of viscosity^{-1} versus temperature for a liquid should pass through zero at the liquid's freezing point. In spite of the uncertainties and potential errors involved in any extrapolation, this is often a good method for checking the over-all consistency of numbers of data. Bad data might still extrapolate to the correct point, but failure to show a proper extrapolation will at least raise suspicions.

In order that the check be as meaningful as possible, the investigator must make his plot as error-free as possible. The most obvious way to achieve a good indication is to choose graphical scales or algebraic functions that result in straight-line plots, or at least suppress any large curvature near the origin. Linear, log-log, or semilog scales are usually available, and the plot can be of the inverse of one or both variables, the square, square root, or whatever other transformation will give an easily plotted line. The main danger in extrapolation lies in the potential failure to recognize changing curvature beyond the range of the data. Such a mistake, as shown in Fig. 7-1, is often hard to detect and can best be

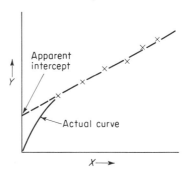

Fig. 7-1. Sketch illustrates how failure to obtain the lower XY points might incorrectly lead to an erroneous intercept from extrapolation.

avoided by a thorough knowledge of the theory of the experiment and the reasonable expectations of the result.

Note that the log-log and semilog plots have no zero origin. If extrapolation to zero-zero is desired, the data can first be plotted on the logarithmic coordinates to see whether a straight line results. Then the function can be found, and the variables replotted after transformation yielding a straight line on linear paper. The following example will make some of the commonest techniques clear.

Example 7-3. A weir box having a triangular notch is calibrated by groups A and B. The following data result:

Group A					
Flow, lb/sec............... 0.228	0.540	0.890	1.54	2.07	3.00
Head, in. over notch...... 0.557	0.833	1.197	1.548	1.792	2.047

Group B							
Flow, lb/sec............... 0.054	0.822	1.40	1.82	1.95	2.78	3.95	6.25
Head, in. over notch....... 0.418	1.349	1.691	1.966	2.060	2.292	2.630	2.896

We suspect that at least one of these data sets is in error, since the B data sheet indicates a zero reading for the hook gauge of 7.090 in. (the scale reading as flow just starts) and the A data sheet shows 7.293 in. for the same quantity. Which of the two sets of readings is true (if either), and how dependable is the better set?

Solution. We know that head h and flow Q in a weir of any sort follow the general relation $Q = kh^a$, and that at zero head we must have zero flow. Thus an extrapolation to the zero-zero origin is the obvious way of checking these data. We first plot the two data sets on log-log paper to obtain the value of the exponent a and to enable us to transform the data into a straight-line form. This is shown in Fig. 7-2. From these curves we see that the relationship for either set is $Q \approx h^{2.2}$ approximately,[1] and we can now tabulate $h^{2.2}$ and plot it versus Q on linear coordinates. This is done in Fig. 7-3, and we see that group A's data fail to pass through the origin, while group B's extrapolation appears to very closely strike the zero-zero point. To bring the A curve up so that its extrapola-

---

[1] It is assumed that the reader understands the finding of exponents from a log-log, straight-line plot. The method is explained in any engineering graphics textbook or handbook.

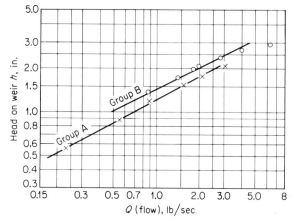

Fig. 7-2. A log-log plot of the weir data discussed in Example 7-3, showing that each set has about the same exponent but that the two are displaced from each other.

tion is correct, we would have to add $(\Delta h)^{2.2} \approx 0.15$ or $\Delta h \approx 0.23$ in. to all A data. We noted that the A zero reading is about 0.2 in. higher than the B reading so that if B data are true, A data are about 0.2 in. too small in all head readings, as predicted by our extrapolation. We can thus say with some assurance that the B data are the preferred set. An investigator might be satisfied at this point to accept the B data without further analysis or question. Interestingly enough, these actual data from two student laboratory reports reveal another and somewhat more subtle error of head measurement, as we will now prove.

We would expect that if the head on a weir is increased to very

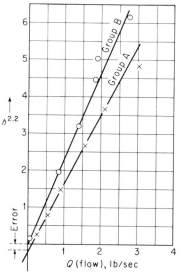

Fig. 7-3. A plot of the data from Example 7-3 after they have been "rectified" (made to plot as straight lines), showing that the group A data do not satisfy the requirement of extrapolation to the origin.

large values, the flow will correspondingly increase and that infinite head and infinite flow will occur together.   We can check this other end of the curve by plotting reciprocals of Q and $h^{2.2}$.   (If Q versus $h^{2.2}$ is a reasonably straight line on linear coordinates, $1/Q$ versus $1/h^{2.2}$ will also be straight.)   We expect, if all is well, that the curve will extrapolate through the origin.   Let us first add $(7.293 - 7.090)$ or 0.203 in. to each A reading, thereby correcting for the already established group A error in zero reading.   Then we can tabulate:

Group A				
h (meas), in.	h (meas), +0.203 in.	$h^{2.2}_{\text{correct}}$	$(h^{2.2})^{-1}$ correct	Q^{-1}, sec/lb
0.557	0.760	0.5	2	4.4
0.883	1.086	1.2	0.83	1.85
1.197	1.400	2.1	0.476	1.12
1.548	1.751	3.4	0.295	0.65
1.792	1.995	4.57	0.22	0.485
2.047	2.25	5.9	0.17	0.333
Group B				
0.418		0.125	8.0	18.5
1.349		1.93	0.519	1.13
1.691		3.18	0.315	0.71
1.966		4.42	0.226	0.55
2.060		4.95	0.201	0.51
2.292		6.17	0.162	0.36
2.630		8.40	0.119	0.253
2.896		10.3	0.097	0.16

Figure 7-4 shows the plot of the last two columns in this tabulation.   Although the resulting curve has some curvature at its lower end, the extrapolation is clearly not to the origin.   Instead, this plot indicates that the flow will reach infinity at some finite head, a physical impossibility.   Thus the data from both A and B determinations are defective, and we should logically suspect the head readings, which are usually more difficult to get accurately than the flow rate.   Investigation of the particular weir box in question revealed the difficulty and its cause.   The hook gauge used to measure head was located so close to the outfall of the weir that at high rates of flow it read something less than true head, and

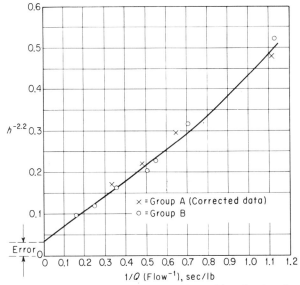

Fig. 7-4. This plot shows the curve formed by plotting the corrected reciprocals of the data graphed in Fig. 7-3. The failure to extrapolate to the infinite-flow, infinite-head condition is clearly evident.

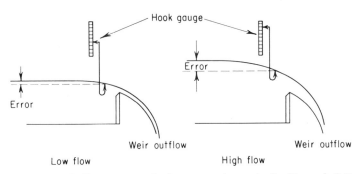

Fig. 7-5. This diagram reveals the source of error in the Example 7-3 weir test. As flow increases, the water surface curvature increases. This in turn causes the hook gauge, located too close to the outfall, to read depth in ever greater error.

this error grew progressively larger as flow increased, as shown in
Fig. 7-5.   The final result was, as shown in Fig. 7-4, a progressive
error in h that had the cumulative effect of giving an improper zero
intercept.   A little thought should convince the reader that adding
larger and larger amounts to the apparent h readings will indeed
straighten out the $1/h^{2.2}$ versus $1/Q$ curve and cause it to pass
through, or at least closer to, the origin.

The calibration of a simple weir is one of the standard short
experiments demanded of many student engineers and is often
viewed with mild boredom by student and instructor alike.   Yet
even in such an apparently limited test can lie a rich store of material for the exercise of imagination, technique, and ingenuity.

7-4. Replication and Aging Error

The most common method of checking the consistency of test
data is replication of previous test configurations.   As we noted in
Chap. 2 and again in Chap. 6, reruns may be necessary when the
precision of measurement (or control of a variable) is poor.   Running the same configuration as a check on apparatus function is
standard practice in most test programs.   The failure of a second
run to confirm the first suggests that precision or control is now
poor or that the apparatus suffers malfunction or *aging error*.   Such
aging error is commonly observed in:

1. Heat-transfer tests where passage fouling or fin deterioration
may occur progressively
2. Nuclear-equipment tests in which radiation damage occurs
3. Test of equipment involving vacuum tubes whose characteristics gradually change with age
4. Tests involving any equipment which may suffer from creep,
metal fatigue, mass transport in corrosive-fluid systems, crystal-
grain growth at high temperature, etc.

Aging error is really a progressive malfunction that occurs gradually instead of spontaneously.

When such effects are known to be important to a device, we
usually plan the special yet important *endurance, life,* or *fatigue*
tests in which the primary independent variable is the time of operation.   Such tests are easily planned following the methods in the
previous chapter, providing the investigator knows what he wants
to do.   That is, he should be perfectly clear as to whether he wants
to subject his item to some kind of "use" test, such as is often

done with consumer items placed in "selected homes," or a simple endurance test in which the item is subjected to certain carefully controlled conditions until failure or performance degradation is detected. The former situation is very similar in purpose and plan to the machine-tool problem discussed in Sec. 6-3 and might require a relatively large number of tests and possibly some statistical manipulation of the results (as will be discussed in Chap. 8). The latter case is a more basic type of test and will yield more general, and probably more precise, results.

Even though an investigator may not anticipate aging error, he should still rerun certain portions of his testing plan. For example, using a limited classical plan:

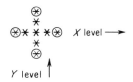

where the circled marks indicate replicated points, we might select all test points at random, including the replications. Probably a better way is to randomize the basic series of runs and then insert the replicated runs at equal intervals. For example, we might randomize the above plan. First, we assign numbers to the runs:

$$1$$
$$2$$
$$67389$$
$$4$$
$$5$$

Then these are randomized by a gaming method or by random-number tables (see Sec. 6-2). For example, 6, 2, 8, 4, 9, 5, 1, 3, 7. We have 1', 6', 9', and 5' to add so the final plan might be: 6, 2, 1', 8, 4, 6', 9, 5, 9', 1, 3, 5', 7, which should suffice as a general check. If certain regions of measurement are of doubtful precision, it might be more practical to replicate a single test configuration four times, thereby obtaining both a check against aging error and additional readings in the doubtful region. For example, the lowest X level might be quite doubtful. Then our plan would be 6, 2, 6', 8, 4, 6'', 9, 5, 6''', 1, 3, 6'''', 7. The trouble with this plan is that we are using the reading with poorest precision as a check, and it might

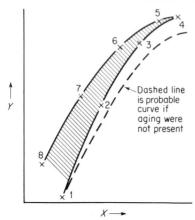

Fig. 7-6. A possible set of data resulting when either X or Y or both are undergoing aging changes. Since the obvious effect of aging here is to raise the Y value, we suspect the true or nonaging curve to be generally lower than either of the data curves, as suggested by the dashed line.

be difficult to separate precision difficulties from true aging error. Then point 3 or point 9 might be replicated four times instead. The experimenter might now say, "Suppose the four readings show a progressive variation." No general answer can be given. If the item is in the "production" or "pilot" stage, we might infer that it was insufficiently tested and should be returned to a more thorough series of "life" or "destructive" tests. If protracted life tests are not to be undertaken until a preliminary performance check is made, the investigator may wish to proceed with his work, in spite of aging, and process the data as best he can. In some situations, and nuclear technology is full of them,[1] the investigator knows his test piece will suffer changes with time, but he decides to go ahead on performance testing anyway. In such an uncertain situation, the experimenter realizes that he must take his data as rapidly as possible, perhaps using automatic recording gear. Of primary importance here is complete planning before the apparatus is set in motion.

Tests having aging error are often thermal energy experiments of one sort or another, and the investigator is faced with two counter-working effects. He desires to make his variable changes as rapidly as possible to cut down the effect of time, and he also wishes to randomize his variable levels so as to distribute the aging effect randomly. These two desires are not compatible, since a random plan requires large changes in variable spacing, while data-taking speed in thermal devices requires small changes if the time to reach steady state is not long. No general resolution is possible, since

---

[1] The nuclear experimenter is continually faced with delay in material procurement. So rapid are technological innovations here that the fabrication of production lots of new metals and ceramics lags the tests that should use these new materials. Thus the engineer is often running second-generation tests with first-generation metals.

each test is unique, but one possible compromise is interlacing which, while not a random plan, will distribute the age effect over the whole experiment in a regular and easily identified manner. If, for example, we wish to vary X over eight levels X_1 to X_8, we might follow the sequence X_2, X_4, X_6, X_8, X_7, X_5, X_3, X_1. This plan has the advantage of taking the high X values together and the low X values at the beginning and end, thereby making an age effect stand out. If aging error were present, such a plan might yield the curves shown in Fig. 7-6, where the shaded region immediately shows us how serious are the changes produced by aging. The distance between the two curves is representative of the effect "time," and if time is recorded as part of the data, we might approximately estimate its numerical effect.

Example 7-4. We wish to obtain performance curves of an electromagnetic pump used to pump liquid sodium. The pump throat is expected to gradually accumulate oxide and transferred mass during the test. The variables are back pressure (six levels), input voltage (three levels), and magnetic field resistance (five levels). We are interested in the effect of operating time on performance as well as the other variables. What is a possible plan?

Solution. Let us assume first that we have investigated this pump from the standpoint of dimensional analysis and find that no reduction of variables beyond those three listed is possible. We probably wish to run the most limited classical plan possible, assuming that the effects of pressure, voltage, and winding resistance are not complex. Then

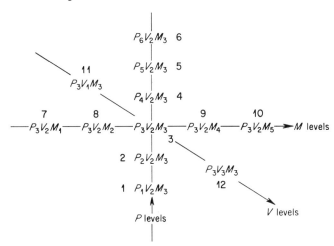

is the layout of the points to be taken with each point numbered. Since this is not a device in which large changes in variable level take more time than small, we can randomize our point sequence. To detect the effect of age, let us replicate a single run, say (3). Thus, 3, 11, 7, 10, 3′, 12, 5, 9, 3″, 6, 1, 4, 3‴, 2, 8, 3⁗ might be a reasonable sequence.

7-5. Rejection of the Outlier

It is an unusual test that does not produce at least one "outlier" or "wild point" which is immediately suspected of being in error. Opinions on the treatment of such faulty observations vary,[1] but it is often felt that they should be thrown out providing some criterion for rejection different from "hunches" or a "desire for symmetry" can be found. Once a criterion is chosen, it must be applied to every test point, even those that look all right. If there is any doubt, the point stays in the data set.

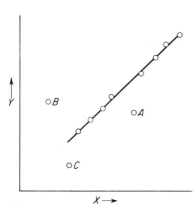

Fig. 7-7. Illustrating some types of outliers: *A* is very probably a doubtful point, while *B* might be bad but could be the most important data point of all. Since *B* may represent a real physical effect, *C* should also be retained until more data are added to the plot.

In this regard, it is well to distinguish between *end points* and *center points*, since these must be viewed differently. In Fig. 7-7, point *A* is quite obviously an outlier, and assuming we have a rejection criterion that so orders, we should throw it out. On the other hand, point *B* may not be a wild point at all, but merely the beginning of a new portion of the curve (transition to turbulence, passing the yield point, change of phase, etc.), and to omit it will deny us the most significant portion of the test data. Even point *C* may be both correct and important. We cannot, in any case, tell without taking more data at low *X* values. Thus it seems to the writer that a reasonable compromise between those who would throw out everything that looks

[1] For a concise statement of two divergent opinions, see the book review of "An Introduction to Scientific Research," by J. W. Dumond in *Am. J. Phys.*, **21**(5):393–394 (May, 1953).

slightly off and those who would never drop a data point is given in the following simple rule: *Outliers should be rejected, following a statistical criterion, only if they are center points.*

The reader may wonder why, if we run the risk of throwing out important discoveries, we wish to reject any points at all. The reason, of course, is that a few very inaccurate test points may needlessly prejudice the final results. Averages will be thrown off, curves fitted poorly, and statistical tests upset.

Let us list some major criteria for data rejection of both a *physical* and a *statistical* nature:

a. Obviously defective control. In most tests we will be taking a great deal of data that are not directly concerned with the machine or effect under investigation. Such variables as barometric pressure, line voltage, humidity, oil pressure, coolant flow, and so on, are not expected to exhibit any radical variation but are monitored just in case. Thus, if a wild point occurs at the same time that the data sheet shows a line-voltage surge, rejection of this point is entirely reasonable.

b. Obvious instrument malfunction. If the last several points taken on a given day or test series are all wild, and, furthermore, they are distributed at random among the other points (as they will be if the test sequence is randomized), we expect that a measurement malfunction has occurred, and we should reject these points.

c. Imbalance beyond a preset criterion. If a balance equation (Sec. 7-2) can be used to check each data point, we can decide on some maximum amount of imbalance and reject all points that exceed it. Notice that all such points may not necessarily be outliers, but we must not selectively reject if consistency is to be maintained. All or none is the rule here.

d. Exceeding a statistical criterion. There are a number of ingenious statistical means of setting limits for point rejection.[1] We will consider only one, the so-called *Chauvenet's criterion*, and we will assume that our errors are normally distributed so that Table 2-1 can be used to find probability values. For other criteria and for nonnormal error distributions the reader should consult the various footnoted and end-of-chapter references.

This rule states that any reading out of a series of n readings shall be rejected if the magnitude of its deviations from the true or

[1] See F. Proschan, *Am. J. Phys.*, **21**(7):502–525 (October, 1953); C. A. Bennett and N. L. Franklin, "Statistical Analysis in Chemistry and the Chemical Industry," pp. 665–668, John Wiley & Sons, Inc., New York, 1954.

mean value is such that the probability of occurrence of such a deviation does not exceed $1/2n$. Suppose we have an apparatus which we have computed will give horsepower with a probable error of ± 0.05 hp (perhaps by following the methods of Chap. 2). We make eight readings of horsepower and obtain one that deviates from the mean by 0.12 hp. Should it be rejected? Let us first obtain the modulus of precision h knowing the probable error. Equation (2-10) shows that $h = 0.477/p$; so $h = 9.55$ hp^{-1}, and $1/2n = 0.0625$. Thus we must find whether a normally distributed set of readings with h of 9.55 will give more or less than 6.25 per cent of its readings outside the range 0.12 hp; hx here is 9.55×0.12 or 1.14. The probability of any reading falling outside this hx value is (from Table 2-1) $1.000 - 0.893$ or 10.7 per cent. Applying Chauvenet's criterion, we see that 10.7 per cent of our deviation can exceed ± 0.12 hp by chance. This exceeds the $1/2n$ figure of 6.25 per cent, so that we should not reject this measurement. We might wonder how large a deviation would just be rejected by this criterion. Any deviation that fell outside the probability range of $1.000 - 0.0625$ or 0.9375 would be out (if n stays at 8). From Table 2-1, hx is 1.31, or x will be $1.31/9.55$ or 0.138 hp.

The following table summarizes the requirements of Chauvenet's criterion for selected numbers of data (n):

No. of items (n)	4	5	6	10	15	25	50	100	300
Ratio of maximum allowed deviation to s' [Eq. (2-16)]	1.54	1.65	1.73	1.96	2.13	2.33	2.57	2.81	3.14

Rejection of points when less than four data exist seems unwise, particularly considering Fig. 7-7.

One disturbing thought usually occurs to engineers who find any idea of point rejection abhorrent. Suppose one or two data are thrown out following a statistical criterion, and a new standard deviation and probability limit are computed, which necessitates throwing out still more points. In theory, we might continue until almost all the data lay outside our acceptable limits. A rule of thumb to prevent such a disturbing (and almost unheard of) occurrence is to apply a statistical rejection criterion *only once*. Actually, if data were so strangely scattered as to produce this kind of mass rejection, statistical inferences should probably give way to a practical reevaluation of the test and instrumentation.

The idea of assigning a limit to a deviation using a reasonable statistic has applications in experimentation beyond the simple rejection of wild points. In a variety of tests, such as stress-strain experiments using testing machines, a straight-line function is assumed to govern the test behavior up to some fixed but unknown limit. Detection of significant deviation from a straight-line law can be put on a firm basis using Chauvenet's criterion. A straight line through the data points (using least-squares methods as discussed in Chap. 9) will enable the experimenter to compute a standard deviation and, assuming the deviations are normally distributed, assign a limit to the nth deviation. When the test indicates two points in a row that exceed the Chauvenet limit, the experimenter may logically assume that the limit of the straight-line law is reached. Since the computation must be performed after each new data point is added, it is best to obviously exceed the straight-line region and then process the data, point by point, on a computer to find exactly where the deviation began.

7-6. Summary

In this chapter we have examined a few of the ways in which developing test data can be checked for consistency, accuracy, and reasonableness. Much of the success of these methods depends, again, on pretest planning rather than on some "fix" begun from scratch halfway through a test series when suspicions belatedly arise. The generation of test data in the modern laboratory, using automatic sensing equipment that can instantly transfer its readings directly to cards or magnetic tape, is astonishingly rapid. One of the most effective uses of this new speed and processing ease can be better and more complete cross-checking carried out as the test proceeds.

One of the commonest checking methods occurs in the use of a balance or conservation equation in which we equate the "in" to the "out," where these quantities can be mass, energy, momentum, velocity, voltage, charge, current, and so on. The main difficulty with the use of such equations occurs when some of the "conserved material" is "leaked away" through poor insulation, friction, sneak circuits, etc., or when the in or out measurement is difficult to make with any accuracy.

When the balance equation can be used, it is sometimes possible to detect the error-producing term. If the balance is made up of products, we hold each variable constant in turn and suspect that variable that shows no change in the *per cent error*. When the balance equation is made up of sums, we follow the same procedure but now suspect that quantity which, when held constant, produces no change in the *imbalance magnitude*. Unfortunately, exceptions exist to both rules, and the indications are confused if large precision errors are present. This location method is thus good only for pure accuracy error in a single variable in the balance equation.

When several pieces of data have been collected, they can be checked for over-all consistency using extrapolation, provided the end point(s) of the curve(s) is (are) known and the data sufficiently representative of the function to delineate it. Best results are obtained when the variables are transformed through the taking of reciprocals, powers, or other functions that yield straight-line plots. This may require initial plotting on log or semilog paper. Sometimes a double check is possible by checking both ends of the curve independently.

Probably the most basic and general checking method is simple replication of previously run test configurations. Deviation in the first and second trials may be due to generally poor precision or aging error, a general name we give to any progressive and irreversible malfunction of the test piece, apparatus, or instrumentation. When aging error is anticipated, the test sequence may be randomized or some interlacing scheme may be practiced. In any event, aging errors are detectable by periodic replications of a selected configuration, and this should always be considered when test planning is undertaken.

In almost every set of data will be one or more outliers, which should be rejected if they can be shown to exceed some preset criterion of control, instrument accuracy, imbalance, or statistical chance. Chauvenet's criterion, a statistical method of setting up rejection standards, can be followed, providing the probable error or some other precision index is known or can be computed, and providing we do not use it to reject end points of a curve where function change may be indicated.

These checking and error-location methods are only a few of the many available. Many specialized tests and checks have been devised for specific technical fields. The general principles can be seen from our discussions. We wish to check the data point for accuracy of measurement on an individual basis. We wish to check a set of points for scientific reasonableness and consistency. We wish to detect as rapidly as possible any sudden malfunctions or aging alterations. We wish to keep every point that can yield useful material for our final conclusions and reject every point that will lead us to incorrect averages or curves. All these aims can seldom be met, but they remain, in their total sense, the goal of sound test operation.

PROBLEMS

7-1. Prove that we can detect the special sum-type error $(A + kA)$ if we examine the *imbalance* in a product-type balance equation $(AB = XY)$, defined as $\Delta R = (A + kA)B - XY$ instead of the per cent error. Follow the same method as in the text, and note what the indication is for A in error in this manner.

7-2. A series of electric heating elements having voltage V and current I is tested as to rapidity of heating a liquid metal of C_p 0.19 Btu/(lb)(°F), mass M, and temperature rise in one hour, ΔT. The entire system is carefully insulated, and these data result:

V, volts........	10	10	10
I, amp.........	1	3	4
M, lb..........	2	4	4
T, °F..........	95	140	179

Decide whether further tests should involve larger currents and temperatures or smaller values of these quantities. What is the per cent of error of each balance?

7-3. A small, solid-fuel-rocket test stand measures thrust by permitting a piston to travel some distance D against a measured force F. We can also measure the mass of ejected material at any instant M and the kinetic energy of the ejected material $V^2/2g$. The balance equation is $FD = mV^2/2g$, and we assume that D is without error. A series of readings are made in Latin-square form as follows:

m, lb	$V^2/2g$, ft	F, lb	D, ft
7	18	500	0.18
10	18	300	0.48
13	18	200	0.99
7	23	200	0.58
10	23	500	0.37
13	23	300	0.84
7	28	300	0.47
10	28	200	1.1
13	28	500	0.5

where D, since it is known to be correct, serves as the dependent variable. Arrange this in a square form, and, using the % R, decide which of the three doubtful variables is causing the imbalance.

7-4. Suppose we are given a balance equation of the form $A + B = X$, and A has a general sum-type error $[A + f(A)]$. How should we locate this error using the imbalance ΔR equal to $X - [A + f(A)]B$? What exceptions occur in this location method?

7-5. Given the same equation as in Prob. 7-4, how should we detect a product-type error $Af(A)$, using the imbalance? What exceptions occur in this case?

7-6. Four ammeters, A, B, X, and Y, are located such that $A + B = X + Y$. The following results occur:

A	B	X	Y
2.2	3.1	2.5	2.6
1.7	4.4	2.5	3.5
2.2	2.0	1.1	2.9
4.4	2.0	4.7	1.3
3.2	1.1	0.5	3.5

Using the rules developed in Probs. 7-4 and 7-5 above, decide which of the instruments is in error.

7-7. How would you check the following experiments by extrapolation? Sketch the type of plot you expect to get, and indicate how bad data might be revealed.

a. A jackscrew gives a continuously increasing efficiency with load and follows the general formula $E = 100(1 - 1/L^n)$, where L is the load, and n some constant.

b. A set of data on the viscosity of a fluid versus temperature is given. The freezing and boiling points are known without error, and viscosity of the vapor is one-thousandth that of the liquid at the pressure of the test. Show how both ends of the curve can be checked.

c. Two different Orsat-type analyzers give per cent CO_2 (unit A) and per cent O_2 (unit B). The amount of CO is known to be zero. We check several samples of flue gas with each of the units in turn and obtain various percentages.

7-8. A test of a thermocouple gives the following data:

T, °F...........	20	40	60	80	100
m, volts.........	0.42	0.81	1.15	1.54	1.93

Are these data consistent?

7-9. A ventilating fan is operated at constant conditions, and a series of probings are made at various distances from its outlet, and average velocity is obtained for each position.

| Velocity, ft/min........... | 3,000 | 1,000 | 500 | 400 | 250 | 100 |
| Distance of probe, in...... | 0 | 12 | 27 | 33 | 45 | 68 |

Are these data consistent?

7-10. A 116-volt tungsten lamp is tested at reduced voltages. (It does not follow Ohm's law owing to temperature effects.)

| Volts........ | 4 | 6 | 10 | 18 | 27 | 34 |
| Amperes..... | 0.0245 | 0.0370 | 0.057 | 0.0855 | 0.1125 | 0.1295 |

Are these data consistent?

7-11. Lead and zinc alloys are tested for melting point with various percentages of lead.

| Per cent of lead...... | 50 | 60 | 70 | 80 | 90 |
| Melting point, °C.... | 205 | 226 | 250 | 276 | 305 |

Are these data consistent?

7-12. A sodium-loop system is to be run at eight temperature levels and four levels of system pressure. Progressive oxide build-up is expected, and making large temperature changes is a long process. Design a test that will allow us to periodically check the effect of oxide build-up.

7-13. The test of a centrifugal fan gives the following results:

| Flow, lb/sec...... | 3.76 | 3.38 | 2.92 | 2.51 | 1.64 | 1.24 | 0.587 |
| Efficiency, %..... | 10.5 | 8.2 | 7.3 | 6.5 | 4.9 | 3.1 | 2.1 |

The probable error in efficiency is estimated to be 0.2 per cent. Decide which, if any, points should be rejected by drawing the best line and assuming that all error is in efficiency. (Assume that the best line is given by: efficiency equals 2.77 times flow.)

7-14. Thorton's data show that the bacteria in a closed dish multiply following the law

$$A = \frac{k_1}{10^{-k_2(T-k_3)} - 1.0}$$

where A is the plate area covered by bacteria at any time T after the start of the experiment and the k's are known constants except for k_1, which is unknown to the experimenter. How could data following this law be checked using straight-line extrapolation to known end points? If A_{total} is the area of the dish, what is its value in terms of the equation parameters?

7-15. Trevan's experiment with digitalis injected into frogs shows that the death rate D is related to the number of cubic centimeters injected x by

$$D = k_1 e^{-cx^2}$$

where k_1 and c are unknown constants. As in Prob. 7-14, show how data governed by this equation could be checked by straight-line extrapolations to known points or intercepts. In addition, give the expression using the test parameters noted for the number of frogs that will die during the test period of natural causes unrelated to digitalis injection and the number that can withstand massive doses of the drug.

7-16. A pressure-measuring device is expected to follow the equation

$$\Delta P = K_1 H \frac{AB - K_2}{B}$$

where ΔP is the dependent variable or output, K_1 and K_2 are unknown constants, and A, B, and H are adjustable dimensions of the apparatus. What sort of straight-line extrapolation checks could be used for the following tests?

a. ΔP versus H with A and B held constant
b. ΔP versus A with H and B held constant
c. ΔP versus B with H and A held constant

7-17. A device is on test which follows a law of cooling of the form

$$T = 490e^{-0.107\theta}$$

where T is the temperature in degrees Fahrenheit and θ is the time from the start of cooling in minutes. This law is obtained from the following data using a least-squares analysis:

$\log_e T$	5.5	5.25	4.8	4.0	3.5
θ, min	5	10	15	15	25

Find the standard deviation of $\log_e T$ from the least-squares predicted line. Decide if any of the data points should be rejected using Chauvenet's criterion. When time was zero, the apparatus was known to be at 570°F. Does extrapolation, allowing for the scatter expressed by the standard deviation figure, seem to confirm this figure?

7-18. The thermal conductivity of granite is measured a number of times, and the standard deviation is based on the deviations of the data from the average. Of the following ten readings, 0.23, 0.27, 0.25, 0.23, 0.2, 0.24, 0.31, 0.22, 0.25, 0.21, should one or more be rejected? If so, which one(s)?

7-19. In the test of a pressurized container, the law

$$P = \frac{Ast}{r + t}$$

is assumed to govern the specimens where P is the failure pressure, r is the inner radius before the test and exactly known, t the wall thickness and independent variable, and s and A are unknown constants. How could data from such a test be checked by straight-line extrapolation?

7-20. The normal stress P due to a shrink fit of a collar of measured inner diameter b, outer diameter c, and interference when cold i is

$$P = \frac{Ei}{kbc^2} (c^2 - b^2)$$

Explain how an experiment in which collars of several b values are tested and P is measured by strain gauges can be checked by extrapolation methods using straight lines if E is an average (but unknown) modulus of elasticity and k is an unknown fitting constant.

REFERENCES

Bennett, C. A., and N. L. Franklin: "Statistical Analysis in Chemistry and the Chemical Industry," chap. 11, John Wiley & Sons, Inc., New York, 1954.

Deming, W. E.: "Statistical Adjustment of Data," chap. 9, John Wiley & Sons, Inc., New York, 1943.

Doolittle, J. S.: "Mechanical Engineering Laboratory," chap. 15, McGraw-Hill Book Company, New York, 1957.

Proschan, F.: Rejection of Outlying Observations, *Am. J. Phys.*, **21**(7):520–525 (October, 1953).

Schenck, H.: "Heat Transfer Engineering," chap. 11, Prentice-Hall, Inc., Englewood Cliffs, N.J., 1959.

Worthing, A. G., and J. Geffner: "Treatment of Experimental Data," chap. 6, John Wiley & Sons, Inc., New York, 1943.

CHAPTER 8

Statistical Data Analysis

Let us now assume that we have gathered sufficient data, suitably error-free and consistent, for us to undertake one or more kinds of analysis. In engineering, such analysis can take the form of *data reduction*, then *graphical plotting* and perhaps numerical or analytic study as well. In the past few years, mechanical, electrical, and civil engineers have recognized that some form of statistical study is often possible and desirable. If the control of the test or the numbers of data available are insufficient for reasons of expense or equipment failure, general statistical conclusions may be the only possible end products of the work. In other cases, the usual engineering curve or table may be buttressed with statistical figures.

This is a very broad topic, and the writer has culled from basic statistical writings a few ideas that seem to have the broadest application in general engineering. The reader will recognize that far more intricate, elegant, and powerful methods exist than are covered in this survey. Most of these more advanced methods require special tables, special precautions, and extensive computations. This is the reason why the numbers of professional statisticians are increasing year by year in industrial and research establishments.

In this chapter we will consider methods of answering the following simple and important questions: Given two or more sets of data, do they come from the same population or not? Given a series of occurrences, are these the result of many random effects or does their distribution in time or space suggest or follow a pattern? A little thought should convince the reader that these questions will relate to a huge variety of important engineering experiments.

8-1. Statistical Terminology: Two Kinds of Inference Error

In Chap. 2 we discussed such important ideas and terms as the population and the sample, the normal law, deviations, the mean value, and so on, most of these being statistical conceptions. We will now use statistical ideas, not as ways of finding and specifying precision error in instrument systems, but as full-fledged means of analyzing the entire test, and some additional terminology must be considered. Most important is the idea of the significance of a test or test result. In engineering terms, we might say that a test showing that 20 samples of steel A failed at $60,000 \pm 5,000$ psi while 20 samples of steel B failed at $80,000 \pm 5,000$ psi was highly significant in that it proves steel B to be stronger. The statistician would not disagree in this case, although he might suggest *tests of significance* which will allow us to represent this highly significant result by a number. Should the 20 samples of B show a strength of $63,000 \pm 5,000$ psi, we might begin to wonder whether we have proved B to be the stronger, and a statistical approach becomes more necessary. Once we make such statistical tests, and several will be described in the following sections, we admit the possibility of two kinds of inference errors. *Errors of the first kind* or *type 1 errors* result if we ascribe a real effect to differences where no real effect, in fact, is present. Thus, we might say that sample B (with strength $63,000 \pm 5,000$ psi) is definitely stronger than A and proceed to buy only type B steel and use it. Later work (larger test samples) might show that there is actually no real difference between the steels, so that our choice of B on the basis of the original 20-item sample was an error of the first kind. We can reduce the chance of type 1 errors by demanding that our test results be very significant, but we then increase the risk of *errors of the second kind* or *type 2 errors*, which occur if we miss a real effect or difference that does, in fact, truly exist. We might, for example, decide that the difference between A and B steel lots is not significant and use the two indiscriminately. Later tests might then show that B is unquestionably stronger than A, and we have made a type 2 error.

These ideas may seem rather obvious, but they bring out an important aspect of statistical inference, especially in engineering situations. Most engineering testing will lead, eventually, to action, and there is no hard-and-fast rule we can make regarding the relative undesirability of type 1 versus type 2 errors.   If we are running tests on parachute-opening devices, basic humanitarian motivation should force us to reject the possibility of type 2 errors (which would be the failure to select the truly best device) while a type 1 error (selecting the most costly device which seemed to, but did not, behave more dependably than the others) is not so serious. Conversely, when we are choosing among several kinds of electrical relays to place in a cheap child's toy, a type 2 error (failure to select the best relay) is probably not so serious as a type 1 error (choosing a specific relay design that is not really better than the others but is more expensive).   These ideas will become clearer as we take up concrete methods and problems in the following two sections.

8-2. The Chi-squared Test for Significance

There are many test situations from which we obtain data in the form of *numbers of items*.   Some numbers of parts pass or fail inspection, complete or fail to finish life test, sell or are returned unsold.   Inspection methods may miss some number of reject parts and find some other number, or they may reject some good parts and pass some other number of good parts.   Shifts, men, machines, assembly lines, production methods, etc., may produce different numbers of items over a given period.   Cosmic-ray counts, numbers of tests, vehicles, or parapsychologically guessed card faces may vary from person to person, day to day, shift to shift, location to location, etc.   Many of these kinds of tests can be analyzed for significance using the *chi-squared test*.

The derivation of the chi-squared (χ^2) distribution (which is somewhat different in shape from the normal distribution discussed in Chap. 2) will not be given here, but can be found in most complete statistics textbooks.[1]   To apply this distribution, we first compute χ^2 from the equation

$$\chi^2 = \sum \frac{(O - E)^2}{E} \tag{8-1}$$

where O represents the *observed* number of occurrences (i.e., failures, sales, rejects, items made, counts, correct guesses, etc.) and E represents the *expected* number of these same occurrences.   Now the minute we talk about an expected number, we introduce the idea of

[1] For example, A. M. Mood and F. A. Graybill, "Introduction to the Theory of Statistics," 2d ed., McGraw-Hill Book Company, New York, 1963.

the hypothesis which we are trying to prove true or false. Suppose, for example, we wish to find out whether an old or new lathe will give more good parts. We make the same number of parts on each lathe, and then our hypothesis to be tested might be: "Both lathes turn out the same number of good parts." Or, from our previous experience we might choose: "The new lathe turns out one-third more good parts than the old one." Either hypothesis could be tested by an appropriate χ^2 computation. Before seeing how this is done, however, we must consider one additional new term. Any tabular or graphical representation of the χ^2 distribution requires a knowledge of the number of *degrees of freedom* present in the test. The degrees of freedom are the number of *independent* groups of observations that can be hypothesized. This is always puzzling to beginners, and it is worthwhile here to give some examples.

A buyer has fractional-horsepower motors installed, half from company A and half from company B. After some period of time, F_a failures have occurred in the A motors and F_b have occurred in the B motors. The total number of motors in the failure sample is fixed and equal to $(F_a + F_b)$. Suppose we wish to test the hypothesis that motor failure rates are the same. Then our expected F_a can be chosen as $(F_a + F_b)/2$ and the expected F_b must take the value $(F_b + F_a)/2$. Since we are able to choose only one number, we have one degree of freedom and χ^2 becomes[1]

$$\chi^2 = \frac{[F_a - (F_a + F_b)/2]^2}{(F_a + F_b)/2} + \frac{[F_b - (F_a + F_b)/2]^2}{(F_a + F_b)/2} \qquad (8\text{-}2)$$

A test is operated around the clock. Shift 1 takes half of all the points and makes N_1 reading errors; shift 2 takes one-third of all the points and makes N_2 reading errors; shift 3 takes one-sixth of all the points and makes N_3 reading errors. There are N errors made in all, and we wish to test the hypothesis that there is no difference between the shifts in making errors. If such a hypothesis is correct, the chosen expected number of errors for shift 1 is $N/2$, since taking half the points should result in shift 1 making half of all the errors. We choose for shift 2 an expected error number of $N/3$, and this

---

[1] When one-degree-of-freedom situations occur, the practice is to subtract 0.5 from each $(O - E)$ term before squaring. Failure to do this results in a slightly high χ^2 value, but produces small error in most engineering computations. Since we are seldom sure just how "significant" we want to be, this slight correction will not be included in the examples that follow.

leaves shift 3, $N/6$ errors, since these are what is left of the N total. Thus two degrees of freedom fit here and χ^2 becomes

$$\chi^2 = \frac{(N_1 - N/2)^2}{N/2} + \frac{(N_2 - N/3)^2}{N/3} + \frac{(N_3 - N/6)^2}{N/6}$$

Sometimes we have data on two populations or sets of occurrences in which some factor is changed between them, and we are interested in whether the failures or rejects are significantly different in the two cases. Thus, samples of a steel lot are case-hardened (A many) and left alone (B many). These data are most easily handled in a contingency table as follows:

Observed Data

	Passed	Failed	Total
Case-hardened............	$A - X$	X	A
Left alone...............	$B - Y$	Y	B
Total.................	$A + B - X - Y$	$X + Y$	$A + B$

Now if our hypothesis is: "Case hardening has no effect," we draw up another table as follows, which reflects the expected values of each of the entries or *cells* in the table.

Expected Results

	Passed	Failed	Total
Case-hardened.....	$A - \dfrac{A}{A + B}(X + Y)$	$\dfrac{A}{A + B}(X + Y)$	A
Left alone.........	$B - \dfrac{B}{A + B}(X + Y)$	$\dfrac{B}{A + B}(X + Y)$	B
Total..........	$A + B - X - Y$	$X + Y$	$A + B$

Notice that in filling our expected-result table, we are restricted by the need to keep the four totals the same as in the observed-data table. This restriction, examination will reveal, allows us to choose only one of the four cell values, since once we choose one, the fixed totals force the values of the other three upon us. Thus one degree of freedom holds for this case, and χ^2 is summed from the four terms derived from the expected and observed cell values and Eq. (8-1).

Once the reader has obtained these two crucial quantities, the number of degrees of freedom and the value of χ^2, he enters an appropriate table[1] or Fig. 8-1 of this book and reads out *the probability that the χ^2 value can be equal to or greater than the one found, owing to chance.* If this probability figure is, say, 10, 20, or 30 per cent, this means that the hypothesis is reasonable (*not* proved, however). In any event, such a probability value suggests that our experimental values and the values based on our hypothesis are not from different populations. A probability figure of 5 per cent or less, on the other hand, begins to cast doubt on the hypothesis. The 5 per cent figure, for example, suggests that our experimental distribution, or one that is even more distorted, could not occur by chance from our hypothesized distribution, data, or sample more than once in twenty times. For a *significance level* of 1 per cent, the chance of occurrence shrinks to one in a hundred times, and so on. What level of significance is appropriate is a knotty question that depends on the test, its use, and the number of data available. Speaking generally, 5 per cent raises doubts, and 1 per cent approaches certainty. Notice in this discussion that we are most often attempting to disprove the hypothesis.

Suppose that, in the first of the three examples (dealing with motors), we note five failures from A-company motors and nine from B-company motors. Then Eq. (8-2) gives

$$\chi^2 = \frac{(5 - 7)^2}{7} + \frac{(9 - 7)^2}{7} = 1.14$$

Entering Fig. 8-1 with this value and one degree of freedom (n of 1), we find a probability definitely greater than 10 per cent, and our hypothesis is not disproved. Suppose more time passes, and the same ratio of A-to-B failures continues until we note 15 A failures and 27 B failures. Chi squared is now 3.43, the degrees of freedom are unchanged, and the probability of this value (or of a greater one) has dropped to almost 5 per cent. Although this still does not definitely disprove our hypothesis, our suspicions should be aroused. Further operation and failures at this same rate will suggest with increasing assurance that our hypothesis is false and allow us to say

[1] For example, K. A. Brownlee, "Industrial Experimentation," Chemical Publishing Company, Inc., New York, 1953.

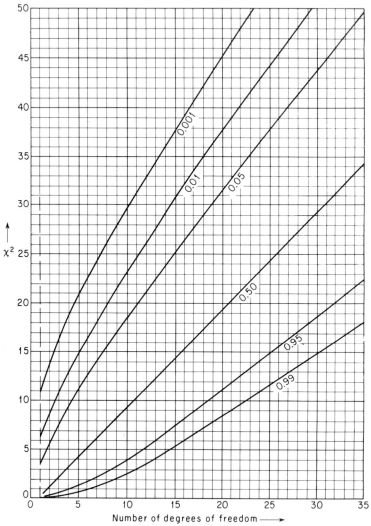

Fig. 8-1. A plot showing χ^2 as a function of the number of degrees of freedom and of the probability of occurrence of a given chi-squared value. Note that zero degrees of freedom are not considered.

what we felt all along, namely, that A's motors are better.[1] Thus the χ^2 test is quite sensitive to the size of the sample, and often more data are needed before real significance is attained.

One other precaution might be mentioned here. *The minimum size of the expected frequency in a cell is five units.* Thus, if $(A + B)$ motor failures had not reached the number 10, we could not properly have used the χ^2 test. The following example will make this and certain other aspects of this test more evident and, it is hoped, more interesting

Example 8-1. The following table compares the percentage of cracks, roads, or canals that form junctions on, respectively, an aerial photo of limestone cracks in the Sahara desert, a railroad map of Ohio, and the astronomer Trumpler's map of "Martian canals." Trumpler's map shows 158 such junctions.

Cracks, roads, and canals per junction	Sahara cracks, %	Ohio railroads, %	Trumpler's canals, %
1	23.3	1.4	8.2
2	*	*	*
3	51.2	10.9	20.5
4	19.9	47.2	42.9
5	4.1	13.7	16.3
6	0.7	9.0	8.2
7	0.0	5.8	3.5
8 or more	0.7	12.0	0.4

* Not counted for any of the distributions.

One crack, etc., per junction simply means that the crack, etc., ends. Two per junction are not counted, since in the Sahara and Martian cases it was impossible to say whether these are true junctions or simply sharp bends in a continuous line. According to the tabulator,[2] the Ohio railroad distribution is typical of man-made distributions (i.e., airline routes, road-map networks, etc.), while the Sahara crack distribution is typical of natural distributions (i.e., lines in crazed surfaces, cracks in baked-mud flats, etc.).

[1] It is assumed here that motor test is done *with replacement;* that is, when a motor fails, it is immediately repaired and put back in use so that the half-and-half division is maintained. If a failed motor is not replaced or repaired, the A motors will gradually become the majority, and their failure rate, compared with B motors, will increase. This is too subtle a case for elementary treatment.

[2] See *Sci. Monthly,* November, 1957, pp. 268–271.

Which of these typical distributions of junctions most closely resembles the Martian distribution, or does either?

Solution. The χ^2 value requires actual numbers, not percentages; so we must construct a table based on 158 items in each distribution:

Cracks, roads, or canals per junction	Sahara cracks	Ohio railroad	Trumpler's canals
1	37	2	13
3	82	17	31
4	31	75	68
5	6	22	27
6	1	14	13
7	0	9	5
8 or more	1	19	1
Total............	158	158	158

Obviously it does not matter how many railroad or stone-crack junctions there actually were. We are simply treating these distributions as typical so that the above table is adjusted to make the number of such cracks or railroad junctions sum to 158. Let us now test the hypothesis: "The Trumpler canal distribution is a finite approximation of the distribution represented by the Sahara crack figures." We have four cells (since the crack distribution is such that numbers 5, 6, 7, and 8 must be gathered into one cell to meet the five-or-more requirement on the χ^2 test), and the crack distribution is the expected one,

$$\chi^2 = \frac{(13-37)^2}{37} + \frac{(31-82)^2}{82} + \frac{(68-31)^2}{31} + \frac{(46-8)^2}{7} = 309.3$$

Once we fill three cells, the fourth is forced upon us owing to the fixed number of canal junctions considered. Thus three degrees of freedom apply, and the probability that this distribution of canal junctions stems from a parent distribution approximated by the Sahara crack distribution is so tiny as to be unreadable on any but the most extensive tables. It is far, far smaller than 0.1 per cent. We can thus say with some assurance that these are not similar distributions.

Now change the hypothesis such that the Ohio railroad network represents the expected distribution. Numbers 1 and 3 must be combined, and we have six terms and five degrees of freedom,

$$\chi^2 = \frac{(44-19)^2}{19} + \frac{(68-75)^2}{75} + \frac{(27-22)^2}{22} + \frac{(13-14)^2}{14}$$
$$+ \frac{(5-9)^2}{9} + \frac{(1-19)^2}{19} = 55.2$$

From Fig. 8-1 it is apparent that the Martian canal distribution would be expected to come (owing to chance) from a parent distribution approximated by the railroad data much less than once in one thousand times. Thus, we have good grounds for saying that the Martian canal distribution is not adequately represented by either of the others and that all three represent unique and unrelated sets of numbers.

Have we proved that the Martian canals are definitely not of intelligent origin? Obviously we have not. What we have done is to suggest that the superficial resemblance between the canal network and the Ohio rail distribution (both have a maximum of four meeting at a junction) is not very significant. Of great importance is the large number of canal junctions of 1 and 3, and the very different railroad distribution having large numbers at 7 and 8 or more. It is difficult to see how these differences could arise from errors of measurement or bad "seeing," and we are probably wise to reject this type of proof of intelligent life on Mars unless better data are made available. Statistical investigation of data is never an end in itself. It can seldom do more than make loose or partly formed ideas and impressions jump into focus or slip away completely.

8-3. The Student's t Test

The χ^2 test is excellent when we have whole numbers of items with which to work. With the "Student's t test"[1] percentages, fractional values, and so on, are readily handled as well. The test is applicable to several types of hypotheses, but we will consider the one having greatest use in general engineering work, namely, "The means from two samples of data come from the identical population." Examples of the use of this hypothesis might be:

---

[1] "Student" was a chemist, employed by the English brewery firm of Guiness, whose real name was W. S. Gosset. Unable to publish under his own name, he adopted the pseudonym of Student and proceeded to establish almost single-handedly the statistics of small samples. Since modern engineering most frequently gives samples of data that are "small" (less than 30 items or so), Student's work is of great value and importance.

"Ten resistors from box A have a mean value of 12,400 ohms while ten resistors from box B have a mean value of 11,900 ohms. The two boxes contain resistors of the same value." "Over a 100-mile course with measurements of gas consumption made every mile, car A has an average consumption of 19.3 mpg and car B has a consumption of 18.4 mpg. There is no difference in gas consumption between A and B."

For this hypothesis, in which we test for the difference between two means, the formula for t is given by

$$t = \frac{\bar{X}_a - \bar{X}_b}{s_{\text{total}} \sqrt{1/n_a + 1/n_b}} \qquad (8\text{-}3)$$

where $\bar{X}_a$ is the mean of sample A and equal to $(X_{a1} + X_{a2} + \cdots + X_{an})/n_a$ with n_a the number of X_a items, $\bar{X}_b$ the mean of sample B and equal to $(X_{b1} + X_{b2} + \cdots + X_{bn})/n_b$ with n_b the number of b items, and s_{total} the familiar standard deviation based on both samples taken together and found from

$$s_{\text{total}} = \left(\frac{\Sigma x_a{}^2 + \Sigma x_b{}^2}{n_a + n_b - 2} \right)^{\frac{1}{2}} \qquad (8\text{-}4)$$

which may be compared with Eq. (2-16).

For this type of hypothesis, the number of degrees of freedom is simply $(n_a + n_b - 2)$, and with this value and t, we enter Fig. 8-2 and read out the probability that the given value of t (or a larger one) could occur with the two means coming from the same population. In other words, a probability of 0.05 means that the value of t found (or a larger one) will occur by chance once out of 20 times with the two samples coming from the same parent distribution. A 0.01 probability means that the chance of this happening is only 1 in 100. The same comments on these significance levels apply that fitted the χ^2 test. A 1-in-20 chance makes us suspicious of the hypothesis, while a 1-in-100 chance strongly suggests that the two samples do indeed come from different populations. Chances of 1 in 1,000 or more approach a "sure thing" disproof of the hypothesis.

Example 8-2. Concrete is taken from a batch mixed on May 25 and formed into eight samples which undergo compression test. The resulting compression-strength values are 4,346, 3,852, 4,240, 3,109, 3,887, 3,852, 3,263, and 3,781, all in pounds per square inch. From a batch mixed on June 4, seventeen samples are withdrawn and tested, giving values of 4,240, 3,746, 4,099, 4,134, 4,664, 4,311, 3,956, 4,211, 4,488, 4,134, 4,523, 3,852, 4,346, 4,558, 4,170, 4,060, 4,488, again in pounds per square inch. The concrete mixture and method of testing are unchanged as far as is known. Can we decide whether these two sets of data belong to the same population?

Solution. The t test applies in this case. The mean of the May samples $\bar{X}_m$ is 3,791 psi, and the mean of the June samples $\bar{X}_j$ is 4,234 psi. Let us tabulate to find the total standard deviation from Eq. (8-4).

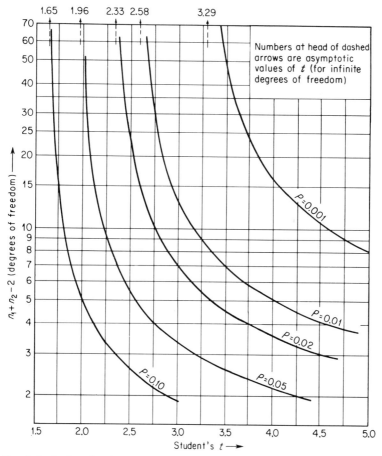

Fig. 8-2. A plot showing the relationship between "Students's t," the term $n_1 + n_2 - 2$, and the probability P of obtaining a given value of t (or a larger one) if both data sets come from the same populations.

X_m, psi	$(\bar{X}_m - X_m)^2 = x_m^2$	X_j, psi	$(\bar{X}_j - X_j)^2 = x_j^2$
4,346	308,025	4,240	36
3,852	3,721	3,746	238,144
4,240	201,601	4,099	18,225
3,109	465,124	4,134	10,000
3,887	9,216	4,664	184,900
3,852	3,721	4,311	5,929
3,263	278,784	3,956	77,284
3,781	100	4,211	529
	$1,270,292 = \Sigma x_m^2$	4,488	64,516
		4,134	10,000
		4,523	83,521
		3,852	145,924
		4,346	12,544
		4,558	104,329
		4,170	4,096
		4,060	30,276
		4,488	64,516
			$1,054,769 = \Sigma x_j^2$

From Eq. (8-4)

$$ s = \left(\frac{1,270,292 + 1,054,769}{8 + 17 - 2} \right)^{\frac{1}{2}} = 310 \text{ psi} $$

which is the standard deviation based on both populations taken together. Notice that the May determinations show a much larger precision error than the June readings, indicating that the control of variability during the May series was poor. Now let us find t from Eq. (8-3):

$$ t = \frac{4,234 - 3,791}{310 \sqrt{\frac{1}{8} + \frac{1}{17}}} = 3.3 $$

The number of degrees of freedom is $(n_m + n_j - 2)$ or 23. Entering Fig. 8-2 with these values, we see that the chance of this t or one even larger occurring if the two data sets are from the same population is less than one out of one hundred but greater than one out of one thousand. Thus, we can say that this t might happen by chance once in perhaps five hundred times, and thus the hypothesis that these two concrete batches plus the testing operations are identical is in great doubt.[1]

[1] Data from A. Cummings, Strength Variation in Ready-mixed Concrete, *J. Am. Concrete Inst.*, **26**(8):765–772 (April, 1955). These two sets are part

8-4. The Analysis of Variance

The t test allows us to compare two means. In some cases, we may be more interested in comparing the variabilities or "spreads" of two or more data samples. We might, for example, compute the *variance* (or standard deviation squared) of the two concrete samples in Example 8-2 separately from Eq. (2-16). For the May data we obtain 1,270,292/7 or 191,470, and for the June data, 1,054,769/16 or 65,900. Are these variances significantly different? The question can be answered by application of the so-called "F ratio" test (named after the English statistician R. A. Fisher). The F ratio is simply the ratio of two variances computed or obtained in different ways. In this case, we will ratio the May variance to that of the June data, obtaining 191,470/65,900 or 2.91.

The chance of obtaining any given F ratio if the two variances are not, indeed, different is expressed in tables as a function of the degrees of freedom of the two data samples from which the ratio is computed. Table 8-1 gives the expected F ratios for the case of 5 per cent probability. The May set had eight measurements. Having selected seven, however, the eighth is fixed by the over-all mean value of the data set so that n for May is 7 and for June, 16. Notice that Table 8-1 is based on the assumption that n_1 refers to the data set having the *largest* of the two variances. Entering Table 8-1 with n_1 of 7 and n_2 of 16 we see that F would be 2.6 for there to be only a 1-in-20 chance that these two variances come from the same population. Since this ratio is even larger, there is a reasonable suspicion that these two variance values do not come from a single parent population. We conclude not only that the concrete shows clear strength deviations from day to day but that the variability about the daily means changes too.

The analysis of variance has important application to Latin-square experiments of the sort described in Chap. 6. In such experimental plans, effects such as shift day, machine, and machine operator can be examined to see if they significantly change output. Antiknock additives, engine speeds, test personnel, and a variety of other parameters can be studied in a single test series. Whereas in Chap. 6 we were concerned with the establishment of an XY function, the analysis of variance is usually applied in experiments where the purpose is, more modestly, to see if X has any effect at all on Y.

---

of a number of daily test sets which were treated as part of a single population. From the data taken on these two days, however, it is apparent that control of the quality of concrete was not perfect.

Table 8-1
F Ratio for 0.05 Probability

$n_1 =$	1	2	3	4	5	6	12	24	∞
n_2									
1	164	200	216	225	230	234	235	249	254
2	18.5	19.2	19.2	19.3	19.3	19.3	19.4	19.5	19.5
3	10.1	9.6	9.3	9.1	9.0	8.9	8.7	8.6	8.5
4	7.7	6.9	6.6	6.4	6.3	6.2	5.9	5.8	5.6
5	6.6	5.8	5.4	5.2	5.1	5.0	4.7	4.5	4.4
6	6.0	5.1	4.8	4.5	4.4	4.3	4.0	3.8	3.7
8	5.3	4.5	4.1	3.8	3.7	3.6	3.3	3.1	2.9
10	5.0	4.1	3.7	3.5	3.3	3.2	2.9	2.7	2.5
12	4.8	3.9	3.5	3.3	3.1	3.0	2.7	2.5	2.3
16	4.5	3.6	3.2	3.0	2.9	2.7	2.4	2.2	2.0
20	4.4	3.5	3.1	2.9	2.7	2.6	2.3	2.1	1.8
30	4.2	3.3	2.9	2.7	2.5	2.4	2.1	1.9	1.6
60	4.0	3.2	2.8	2.5	2.4	2.3	1.9	1.7	1.4
∞	3.8	3.0	2.6	2.4	2.2	2.1	1.8	1.5	1.0

Note: $F = s_1^2/s_2^2$.

Unfortunately, the application of the analysis of variance to multifactor experiments is tricky and fraught with potential errors. A full understanding of the principles of variance analysis is essential for even the simplest application. Failure to grasp the limitations of the method may lead to incorrect estimates of variance or of the number of degrees of freedom needed in the F ratio table. Thus the reader who sees a need for this type of experimentation should carefully read through an appropriate statistics text or, better, register for a course in applied statistics.

8-5. The Poisson Distribution

There may be cases in manufacturing or experimental work where certain occurrences happen by chance, now in profusion, now hardly at all. Cosmic-ray counts, bacterial densities, traffic accidents, and equipment malfunctions might be examples of such occurrences. On the other hand, there may be occurrences which seem to have a random character, but which actually are following some deterministic scheme or pattern. The number of static bursts per hour on a radio monitor could be an entirely random matter, but might be effected by rush-hour traffic or by local television habits. The failure rate per day of pay telephones in Grand Central Station might be a truly random distribution but could perhaps be a function of commuter-train schedules or even police-surveillance patterns. When a set of occurrences or counts is suspected as being a purely random group, a common test for such a hypothesis is to compare the experimental distribution with an appropriate form of the *Poisson distribution,* a nonnormal distribution derived either from assumptions of chance effects[1] or from yet another distribution known as the binomial, which we will not consider. Should the experimental distribution be very close in form to the expected Poisson type, we suspect that occasional large numbers in the distribution are not freaks but simply samples from a proper Poisson-type population. Such a conclusion thus saves us from examining the periods or tests in which such large numbers occur, in hopes that we may find some special and intermittent effect producing them. The usual normal distribution is inappropriate here since we are often dealing with periods of time or regions on microscope slides, maps, or graphs, in which there may be zero counts or occurrences, and with situations in which zero is a lower bound to the distribution. The normal distribution discussed in Chap. 2 is symmetrical about its central point with tails extending to plus-or-minus infinity. Thus the Poisson distribution is a skewed but still a chance distribution.

If P is the total number of occurrences, counts, malfunctions, or accidents, and N the total number of time periods, or slide, map, etc., regions considered (some of which may have zero occurrences or counts), let the average occurrence (or count) per time period (or region) be m and equal to P/N. Then the following table will give the expected probability of occurrence per period based on the Poisson distribution:

Number of incidents or counts in one time period, region, etc.	Probability of this number of time periods
0	e^{-m}
1	$me^{-m}/1!$
2	$m^2e^{-m}/2!$
3	$m^3e^{-m}/3!$
n	$m^ne^{-m}/n!$

This set of terms forms a Poisson series summing to unity. Thus, each term represents the probability that the given number of

[1] See H. Cramer, "The Elements of Probability Theory," pp. 102–108, John Wiley & Sons, Inc., New York, 1955.

occurrences, counts, or malfunctions will occur. When m is less than unity, the Poisson distribution has a maximum probability at zero occurrence of count. It peaks at one occurrence with m between 1 and 2, and so on. The Poisson distribution is usually checked for by finding m, computing each cell value, and comparing these term by term with the observed distribution, using a χ^2 test similar to the approach in Example 8-1. For rough engineering purposes, we might prefer a graphical test similar to the check for normality using probability paper.

Ignoring the zero occurrence term for the moment, we see that the actual number of expected time periods or regions for the nth term E_n is (with N, as noted, the total number of such periods)

$$E_n = \frac{Nm^n}{e^m n!} \tag{8-5}$$

This expression can be transformed to

$$\log E_n = n \log m + \log N - m - \log n!$$
or
$$\log (E_n \times n!) = C_1 n + C_2 \tag{8-6}$$

where C_1 is a constant equal to $\log m$ and C_2 a constant equal to $(\log N - m)$, with neither being a function of n, the term number. Equation (8-6) is then the familiar equation of a slope-intercept straight line. Thus, if we wish to check whether a given distribution is Poisson or not, we do not need to compute m. Taking semilogarithmic coordinates, we multiply the observed occurrence number E_n at each n-by-n factorial and plot this number on the log scale against n on the linear scale. (For the n equals zero time periods we let zero factorial equal 1.) Then if a plot of $E_n \times n!$ versus n is a straight line, or a reasonable approximation thereof, we suspect that we are dealing with a Poisson series. And we further suspect that the incidents or counts are the result of purely random or chance factors. Two examples will give this kind of statistical inference some objective reality.

Example 8-3. We are given the following data on cosmic-ray counts from coincident Geiger counters.

Counts in 1 min, n	0	1	2	3	4	5 or more
Numbers of minutes* having n counts, E_n	13	22	14	7	4	0

* Total = 60 intervals.

Cosmic-ray data in this basic form are expected to be completely random, and therefore to follow a Poisson series. Can we say that this is true with these data?

Solution. Let us first attempt our graphical test, as follows:

n	$n!$	No. of minutes, E_n	$E_n \times n!$
0	1	13	13
1	1	22	22
2	2	14	28
3	6	7	42
4	24	4	96
5	120	0	0

Now, a plot of the first column n on linear coordinates against the last column ($E_n \times n!$) on logarithmic coordinates constitutes our test and is shown in Fig. 8-3. The first four points form a very good straight line. The fifth point is high, but notice that a single count here will make a very large difference. Thus the low-n points are the most significant and indicate that a good Poisson distribution has resulted. A more rigorous test is the use of χ^2. The

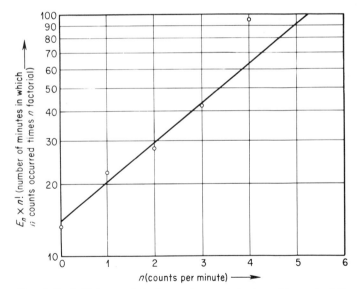

Fig. 8-3. A Poisson plot of cosmic-ray data from Example 8-3. The straight line indicates the predicted point distribution for a perfect Poisson series having the value of m of the sample.

average number of counts m is $\frac{87}{60}$ or 1.45. Using this, we can compute a predicted value for each cell in the table from Eq. (8-5), obtaining

n	E_n, observed	E_n, Poisson prediction
0	13	14
1	22	20
2	14	15
3	7	7
4	4	3
5	0	1
Total.....	60	60

where the predicted values have been rounded to the nearest whole number. Following the same technique used in Example 8-1, we get for our χ^2 value

$$\chi^2 = \frac{(13 - 14)^2}{14} + \frac{(22 - 20)^2}{20} + \frac{(14 - 15)^2}{15} + \frac{(11 - 11)^2}{11} = 0.215$$

with three degrees of freedom. From Fig. 8-1 we see that the probability of this χ^2 value or one higher occurring is almost 0.99. Thus our hypothesis that these two distributions are from the same parent population is almost a certainty, and our χ^2 statistic agrees with our rougher graphical test.[1]

Example 8-4. A total of 647 women employed in a factory are observed over a given period. The number of accidents that each suffers is tabulated and the following distribution noted:

No. of accidents n	Women suffering n accidents, E_n
0	447
1	132
2	42
3	21
4	3
5	2
6 or more	0
Total.......................	647

[1] Data from P. G. Guest and W. M. Simmons, An Experiment on Cosmic Rays, *Am. J. Phys.* **21**(5):362–367 (May, 1953). The writers also show how a similar analysis can be applied to the distribution of time intervals between successive particles.

We expect accidental or chance happenings to follow a Poisson distribution. Is this true here?

Solution. For our graphical test we tabulate as before:

n	$n!$	E_n	$E_n \times n!$
0	1	447	447
1	1	132	132
2	2	42	84
3	6	21	126
4	24	3	72
5	120	2	240
6 or more	720	0	0

Plotting again the first versus the last columns on the appropriate coordinates, we see little resemblance to a straight line, even though the tabulated data looked "Poisson-like" to the casual eye. A χ^2 test can be made as before, and, if this is done, it will be found that the probability that this distribution came by chance from a Poisson series is much less than 0.001. Thus we conclude that the accident rate of factory workers does not follow a Poisson distribution. The reason is interesting and may give some insight into one reason why certain kinds of distributions are not of the simple Poisson type. If each of the 647 women is exposed to about the same accident risk and, furthermore, if each has the same propensity for accidents, the chance that any given woman might have an accident is identical with that of any other woman. If having one accident does not affect the woman's later behavior very much, her chance of having a second, when she goes back to work, is about the same as any other person having a first, and so on. Thus some persons will be "unlucky" and have one, some will be even less lucky and have two, and so on. But our Fig. 8-4 shows that there are too many women with high numbers of accidents. We might not be surprised if these points fell below the Poisson line, for this would suggest that having one accident would lead to greater caution and mitigate against a second.

What we have found here, of course, is the phenomenon of the "accident prone" personality. Our 647 women do not fall into a homogeneous single group in accident propensity. There are probably several groups present having varying accident propensities. Thus the basic assumption that any woman is as likely to have an

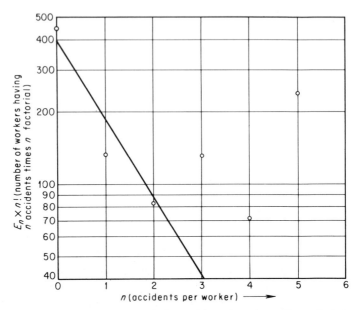

Fig. 8-4. A Poisson plot of the accident data from Example 8-4. The straight line indicates the predicted point distribution for a perfect Poisson series having the value of m of the sample.

accident as any other is demonstrably untrue. Many women having three, four, and five accidents quite obviously belong in a separate population[1] or populations.

8-6. Summary and Discussion

We have barely scratched the "statistical surface" in this chapter with our discussion of χ^2, t, and the Poisson distribution, nor has the author intended any more than this. Yet the reader can, if he chooses, move on from the basic ideas of significance testing here presented to further and more complex tests. Even if he never reads another line on statistical inference, he should at this point have some idea what this is, how it is analyzed, and the kind of

[1] Data from M. Greenwood and G. Yule, An Inquiry into the Nature of Frequency Distributions Representative of Multiple Happenings, *J. Roy. Stat. Soc.*, **83**:255–279 (1920). This is actually a *compound Poisson distribution* and a close fit can be achieved by assuming that the women fall into two separate groups as to accident propensity. This distribution is a matter for advanced statistics.

statement or conclusion that he can expect from the professional statistician.

These comments are not intended to deprecate the simple techniques here considered. Not only are they basic and quite rapid, but they are both valuable and practical for the average engineer in the mechanical, civil, and electrical fields. Virtually every inference test in undergraduate mechanical, chemical, and electrical engineering laboratories can be handled by either a χ^2 or a t approach. The Poisson distribution is probably the most common chance distribution, next to the ubiquitous normal law, and is central to all life-testing and industrial experimentation. Let us then briefly summarize these methods and suggest the more advanced subjects that can be found in many excellent books on statistics.

Whatever statistical test we choose, we recognize the possibility of two kinds of inference errors, a type 1 in which we ascribe to our data an effect that does not actually exist and a type 2 in which we throw out as insignificant an effect that is actually important. These two types of error are mutually exclusive. That is, if we set up a very rigid criterion for level of significance, we risk the type 2 error, but virtually eliminate the type 1. If, on the other hand, we relax our required probability figure for a rejection of our hypothesis, we admit the type 1 very greatly but almost exclude the type 2. There is no set rule as to which of these types is desirable, and this decision is dependent on many factors, including both moral and economic ones.

There are many cases in which our data are in the form of numbers of items, numbers of occurrences, and so on. When we can expect some distribution of these numbers, through either physical theory or simple probability reasoning, we then desire to test whether our observed data matched our anticipations or deviated from them. For such an analysis, it is customary to use the χ^2 test. Our basic hypothesis in this test is usually: the "observed numbers and the expected numbers are drawn from the same population or distribution." After computing the number of degrees of freedom and the value of χ^2, we enter our chart or a table and read the *probability that this or a higher value of χ^2 could occur by chance if the two sets of numbers did come from the same parent stock.* If the P value is 0.05, this means that there is one chance in twenty of our obtaining the observed numbers, if the hypothesis is true. P of 0.001 means that the observed χ^2 (or a larger one) could occur only once in one thousand times, if the hypothesis is true. For P values smaller than 0.02 or 0.01, we prefer to think that the hypothesis is not true and that the two sets of numbers do not come from the same family.

The χ^2 test is basic to all types of production testing, rating of materials, shifts, methods, and the general checking for distributions. Often, however, we will have a number of replicate readings, parts, or decisions made by a man, machine, instrument, and so on. We wish to compare this set of readings with a second set made by another man, machine, etc. For such a test, we use the Student's t test. Here, our hypothesis is simply: "The two sets of replicate readings come from the same population." When our probability value is found, the same ideas apply that were discussed in the χ^2 test. We have not considered here how the t test can be used when we wish to compare a set of replicate readings with a given value, but this can be done, and the method is explained in any basic statistics text.

These two tests will cover a wide variety of engineering problems. If we have several populations of replicate data, we can compare them with another by a series of t tests. If we have several number distributions, we can do the same thing with the χ^2 test. There are, however, a large number of other statistical tests that will apply to more complex engineering situations. Suppose, for example, we wish to know whether a change in independent variable X really has an effect on dependent variable Y. The usual engineering approach is to plot the two. But sometimes the data may be so badly scattered that it is difficult to know whether there is really any relation at all. The statistician investigates this problem with a *correlation coefficient* and with a *regression analysis*, and uses the *F distribution* and perhaps a number of other tools and "mathematical gadgetry." This is generally known as the *analysis of variance*. When continuing data are available, a control chart may be made, and this control chart not only keeps track of our experiment errorwise, but also will give a running check on the outliers (see Sec. 7-5), as well as suggesting whether scattered data are showing a real effect. The reader can obtain this material in a number of statistical books having varying degrees of difficulty.

The most common and familiar distribution is the normal one, and it is derived using the idea of a large number of tiny errors or deviations acting together and producing a net deviation or error. If we examine a similar situation, but one in which there is a definite zero limit to the results, we obtain a skewed distribution of the

Poisson type. We can test for Poisson distributions in the same
way we tested for the normal one, namely, by properly plotting
our data to achieve a straight line. A more exact indication of the
similarity (or lack of same) between our data and the Poisson series
can be had using the χ^2 test. The establishment of a Poisson distribution is of interest, since it tells us that our data are the result
of chance happenings. A non-Poisson distribution of cosmic-ray
counts would suggest that the chance of the counts had changed
during the test, or that the counter could overload and cut off for
high rates of counting. A non-Poisson distribution of reject parts
from a machine shop suggests that the chance of rejects is not the
same for each machine, each shift, or each man. A non-Poisson
distribution of matter in the observable universe might suggest pro-
found new ideas on cosmology. For distributions which we believe
to be chance-created, but which are far from zero, we would, of
course, return to the normal law and test for this.

Very many other distributions, some of them extremely subtle
and sophisticated, have been postulated by statisticians. Figure
8-5, for example, shows an *aging distribution*. That is, it shows the
number of failures versus time from fabrication. The resemblance

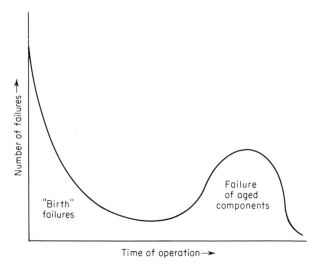

Fig. 8-5. A sketch of a possible failure distribution in which a
number of items fail when first used ("at birth") and the
remainder "mature" and mostly fail from aging causes.
Time would probably plot on a log scale for such a density
function.

of this to human mortality tables should be obvious. Such a distribution as this is obviously complicated and will require more complex functions than the simple equations that identify the normal and Poisson distributions.

PROBLEMS

8-1. Decide whether you would rather risk a type 1 or a type 2 error in the following tests of hypothesis, and give a one-sentence justification of your choice.

a. The hypothesis is: "There is no greater incidence of leukemia in children living in or out of the heavy fallout belt."

b. The hypothesis is: "Over a three-year period of test there is no difference in repair costs between an outboard motor with a bronze journal bearing and one with ball bearings."

c. The hypothesis is: "The addition of seat belts to automobiles makes no difference in survival in a crash."

d. The hypothesis is: "Flying saucer sightings are not more frequent during radar-to-Venus experiments."

8-2. Four methods, *A, B, C,* and *D,* are applied to the fabrication of a difficult machined part. The following rejection rates occurred:

	Method			
	A	*B*	*C*	*D*
Total parts made........	8	10	9	13
Number rejected........	5	8	9	10

Test the hypothesis that there is no difference in rejection rate among the methods.

8-3. During a semester's work in a fluid-mechanics lab, the Monday group blew the mercury out of nine manometers, the Tuesday group blew six manometers, and the Wednesday group blew two. Test the hypothesis that there is no difference in lab ability among the three groups.

8-4. Three shifts, *A, B,* and *C,* are producing identical units. In the first day, the following results occur:

Shift...................	*A*	*B*	*C*
Acceptable units........	6	6	9

Test the hypothesis that there is no difference among the three shifts. We suspect that shift *C* is the best one. Suppose the same results as above occurred in each succeeding shift. How many shifts need we wait before this hypothesis is disproved to a 5 per cent level? To a 1 per cent level?

8-5. Twenty specimens of the same kind are tested on a tension test machine to failure, ten at a fast rate and ten at a slow loading rate. Seven of the slow specimens show a complete cup-cone fracture, with the other three showing a partial cup. Four of the fast specimens show a complete cup cone, with six showing a partial one only. Test the appropriate hypothesis.

8-6. Two physicists count the number of delta rays per 100 microns on the same photographic plate as follows:

A counts...	10	23	9	46	7	11	10	15	7	8	12	36	28
B counts...	8	21	8	43	7	11	10	12	6	8	11	25	29
A − B.....	2	2	1	3	0	0	0	3	1	0	1	1	1

A similar series of counts is made on a second plate, and the absolute value of $A - B$ becomes (17 readings) 0, 0, 1, 2, 0, 1, 0, 0, 3, 1, 1, 0, 1, 6, 2, 0, 2. Using the t test, compare these two sets of deviations, and decide if they come from the same infinite population.[1]

8-7. In the years 1893 and 1894, Lord Rayleigh extracted nitrogen from air, using both iron and copper, and from nitrous oxide, again using iron. The resulting densities of nitrogen from the air were 2.30986, 2.31001, 2.31010, 2.31017, 2.31012, 2.31024, 2.31026, 2.31027, 2.31035 and from the experiment using nitric oxide, 2.29816, 2.29890, 2.31043, 2.30182, 2.29869, 2.29940, 2.29849, 2.29889.

From these data Lord Rayleigh concluded that the atmospheric nitrogen was actually heavier than the chemically produced nitrogen, and he was thus led to the discovery of the rare gases. Decide whether he was statistically correct in this decision, using the t test.

8-8. Repeat Prob. 8-7 but use the χ^2 test to test the hypothesis: "Taking the mean of all 17 determinations, there is no difference in the direction of deviation between the atmospheric and chemical methods." An alternative statement might be: "There is no difference in the two methods as to whether the given determination falls above or below the mean value."

8-9. The speed of a shaft is found by an absolute method (oscilloscope and signal generator calibrated against the line frequency) and a value of 1,010 rpm results. A strobotac and a hand tachometer give

    Strobe: 1,000, 980, 995, 1,020, 1,005
    Tach: 990, 1,020, 1,000, 1,010, 1,040

Test the following hypotheses in turn: "The two series of readings are from the same population of readings." "The deviations of these sets of readings from the true value are from the same population of such deviations." For this second hypothesis, you should obtain your averages of the deviations with regard to sign.

8-10. Metal- and glass-enclosed radio tubes of the same type are life-tested at extreme conditions. The results are

    Metal tube: 53, 40, 92, 67, 89 hr
    Glass tube: 45, 40, 47 hr

Use the t test to check the appropriate hypothesis.

[1] *Am. J. Phys.*, **24**(3):157–159 (March, 1956).

8-11. It has been proposed that the Martian canals are no more than eye-created constructions caused by surface dots and discolorations on the planet and by eye fatigue. If so, we would suspect that the apparent distribution might be a chance one. Test this hypothesis using Trumpler's data in Example 8-1. Treat the lack of data on the junction of two canals as though this particular item were simply missing from the table. Repeat for the crack and railroad network, plotting all on the same Poisson graph. What conclusions about these distributions can you draw? Check the one that seems to most closely resemble the Poisson with a χ^2 test.

8-12. Test the following distribution(s), using a Poisson plot and/or a χ^2 test:

a. Student's data on the number of yeast cells in given areas:

Cells/area, n	0	1	2	3	4	5	6	7	8	9	10	11	12
Areas with n cells	0	20	43	53	86	70	54	37	18	10	5	2	2

b. Number of defectives in 51 shifts:

Number/shift, n	0	1	2	3	4	5	6	7	8
Shifts with n defectives	3	7	9	12	9	6	3	2	0

c. Intervals between cosmic-ray counts using a cosmic-ray counting array and paper tape recording:

Paper marks per fixed interval, n	0	1	2	3	4	5	6	7	8
Intervals having n marks	2	33	182	333	318	194	70	17	4

8-13. The following data report an air-pollution survey over a period of 210 days at Crescent City, California. The average oxidant concentration during the day in parts per million is tabulated with the number of days that such a concentration occurred:

Oxidant concentration, ppm $\times 10^2$	0	1	2	3	4	5	6	7	8 or more
No. of days with concentration shown	1	5	28	19	11	7	1	1	0

Analyze these data for similarity to a Poisson distribution.

8-14. Out of a total of 100 six-month periods, 32 storms having force 7 or higher winds are recorded at a location on the Atlantic Ocean. Further, the distribution of such storms throughout the 100 periods is a Poisson one. The maximum waves generated by such storms are normally distributed in height with a mean value of 8 ft and a modulus of precision of 0.25 ft⁻¹. An offshore drilling-rig designer estimates that waves less than 13 ft high will not damage his equipment. He further estimates that the structure will not be totally lost unless it experiences wave damage at least twice in a 6-month period (longer times permit repairs). What is the chance of having two or more storms within a given 6-month period? What is the chance of a storm having damaging (13-ft) waves?   What is the probability of a given tower collapsing completely in a 10-year period?

8-15. Three different sets of relays, each having the same number (N), are to be tested for a million-cycle life test.   If all of groups A and B fail and three-fourths of group C fails, what must be the value of N to establish C as superior at the 5 per cent confidence level?

8-16. Two instruments, A and B, are used to give thermal conductivity of a given sample:

| A, Btu/(hr)(°F)(ft)....... | 9.56 | 9.49 | 9.62 | 9.51 | 9.58 | 9.63 | |
| B, Btu/(hr)(°F)(ft)....... | 9.33 | 9.21 | 9.47 | 9.01 | 9.56 | 9.0 | 9.47 |

What can we say about the *variability* of these two instruments?   Which is preferable from this standpoint, and would we be justified in using it exclusively?

8-17. A study of wrong numbers in a telephone system reveals the following data:

N	0	1	2	3	4	5	6	7	8	9	10	11	12	13	14	15	16
P	0	0	1	5	11	14	22	43	31	40	35	20	18	12	7	6	2

Decide whether a standard Poisson distribution fits the data when N is the number of wrong numbers and P the number of periods exhibiting the given N.

8-18. At a given station, the number of storms is counted in a year.   Over a period of several years and including data from a number of stations the following results:

Storms per station per year........	0	1	2	3	4	5	6 or more
No. of such occurrences...........	102	114	74	28	10	2	0

Decide whether this actual data [from E. L. Grant, *Trans. Am. Soc. Civil Engrs.*, **103**:384–388 (1938)] could be approximated by a Poisson distribution.

8-19. An engineer tests 32 "identical" metallurgical samples.   He notes that seven out of the first eight fail, then numbers 11 and 12, then none until numbers 17, 19, 27, 30, and 32.   He believes that the test equipment or test methods underwent a considerable alteration at some point during the test.   Decide whether it is more likely that this change occurred on specimen 9 or on number 13.

8-20. The following data were compiled in the state of Connecticut during the period 1931–1936 regarding the number of accidents any given driver in a random sample might have and the number of drivers during the period having this number:

Accidents per operator......................	0	1	2	3	4	5	6	7
No. of operators with this many accidents...	23,881	4,503	936	160	33	14	3	1

What do you conclude about this sample of drivers from these actual data (Johnson, *Proc. Highway Res. Board*, Washington, D.C., 1937, pp. 444–454)?

REFERENCES

Bennett, C. A., and N. L. Franklin: "Statistical Analysis in Chemistry and the Chemical Industry," John Wiley & Sons, Inc., New York, 1954.

Brownlee, K. A.: "Industrial Experimentation," Chemical Publishing Company, Inc., New York, 1953.

Fisher, R. A.: "Statistical Methods for Research Workers," Hafner Publishing Company, Inc., New York, 1954.

Greenshields, B. W., and F. M. Weida: "Statistics with Application to Highway Traffic Analysis," The Eno Foundation, Saugatuck, Conn., 1952.

Hald, A.: "Statistical Theory with Engineering Applications," John Wiley & Sons, Inc., New York, 1952.

Parratt, L. G.: "Probability and Experimental Errors in Science," John Wiley & Sons, Inc., New York, 1961.

Schenck, H.: An Accelerated Life Test Using a Graeco-Latin-square Test Plan, *Bull. Mech. Eng. Educ.*, **3**:241–245 (July–September, 1964).

Tippett, L. H.: "Technological Applications of Statistics," John Wiley & Sons, Inc., New York, 1950.

Volk, William: "Applied Statistics for Engineers," McGraw-Hill Book Company, New York, 1958.

Wilson, E. B.: "An Introduction to Scientific Research," chap. 8, McGraw-Hill Book Company, New York, 1952.

Young, H. D.: "Statistical Treatment of Experimental Data," McGraw-Hill Book Company, New York, 1962.

CHAPTER 9

Graphical Data Analysis

The end product of a purely statistical analysis, as described in the previous chapter, is usually a single numerical figure plus words of explanation. The number gives us the probability or level of significance while the words spell out the hypothesis that we have proved, disproved, or at least studied. Comparatively few engineers are completely at home with such statistical conceptions. Statistical inference appears to lack that certain precision and assurance desired by persons in exact technologies, and this is hardly surprising since statistics are most useful in tests which themselves have poor precision and inexact results. Facing a graph, we feel more confidence. Graphical plots present all the data with a minimum of manipulation. We are not nagged by the suspicion attendant on a formal mathematical process that engulfs dozens of data and regurgitates one figure or, at most, a few numbers. Unfortunately, this very familiarity often results in slipshod and inept utilization of the powerful graphical method of presenting and analyzing data. A graph can tell us many things about our test results, but very often the engineer fails to exploit the very method he most appreciates and uses. Graphical methods of analysis have fallen into some disfavor in modern engineering, mainly because of the wide availability of superfast numerical computing machines. Yet, as a means of presenting information to colleagues, as well as delivering the maximum amount of information in the minimum space, the graph is unexcelled and is perhaps the most important single method of data analysis available to the engineering experimenter.

9-1. The Classical Least-squares Method of Plotting

It will be assumed that the reader is already acquainted with the basic types of graph paper, scales, and precautions attendant on making an engineering plot. Such details as the proper labeling of scales, the choice of scale interval, and the caption of a graphical figure are usually taken up in the freshman year of engineering school and stressed, often with considerable variation of detail, in every laboratory course taken by the engineer in training. Of considerably greater importance than these superficialities are the *scientific* aspects of a graph, that is, such considerations as the relative precision of the plotted variables (considered in Chaps. 2 and 3), the retention of outliers (considered in Sec. 7-5), and the final act of choosing the best scales and then plotting the best line among the points. It is this latter problem that we will consider in this and in the following section.

The most accurate and the most rigorous way of drawing a best line or *correlation line* among a set of points on an XY coordinate plane is the already mentioned least-squares method. Suppose we vary an independent and controlled variable X over its range or envelope and read from instruments a dependent variable Y. Suppose further that both Y and X have precision error, which is large at their low range and decreases as Y and X are increased. If we were to set X at all its possible values, and repeatedly read Y until we had an infinite population of test points filling the (X,Y) envelope, we would have a two-dimensional normal distribution made up of an infinity of Y-reading populations. Plotting the number of readings at any interval versus the deviations in the usual manner, we might obtain the distribution sketched in Fig. 9-1.

In Sec. 2-5, we showed that when an instrument deviates in a normal manner, the sum of the squares of the deviations of the instrument from its best value must be a minimum. The same principles and proof will apply to the general case expressed in Fig. 9-1. Here, we have an infinite manifold of individual normal-type curves, to each of which the discussion of Sec. 2-5 will apply. Thus we can say the best line through a set of scattered points on an XY plane *must take that position that makes the sum of the squares of the point deviations from the line a minimum.* It is from this rule that the term "least squares" derives.

Let us consider the so-called "classical least-squares problem" in which we know (1) that the infinite population of points in the XY

plane delineates a straight line, (2) that all precision error is concentrated in the Y variable (Sec. 4-6 notes one way in which this criterion 2 can often be achieved in correlations involving dimensionless variables), and (3) that the precision error in the Y direction is the same for all Y values. With these three substantial restrictions, the general manifold shown in Fig. 9-1 becomes the much less general manifold shown in Fig. 9-2. The reader might wonder whether we have not so compromised our method as to make it almost useless. In Chaps. 2 and 3, we saw that it was quite typical for a dependent, measured variable to have a changing precision error within different portions of its envelope. Often we cannot say that we have chosen an X variable which is free of precision error, while the necessity of knowing that a straight-line function exists is hardly a commonplace of general experimental work. Yet to generalize this model of our XY function so adds to the computations and to the complexity of the interpretations that we are often tempted to apply our classical model to data seriously

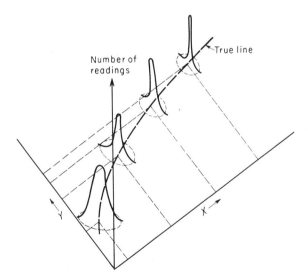

Fig. 9-1. If we were to replicate many times four XY readings that were expected to fall on the true line, as shown, and if both the X and Y readings had uncertainty or precision error that decreased with increasing X and Y, we would build up "mounds" of readings as shown here. Such mounds are two-dimensional normal curves.

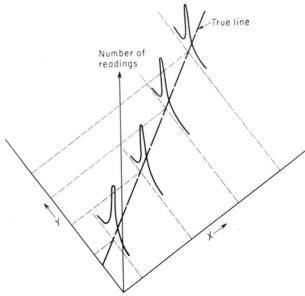

Fig. 9-2. If we were to replicate many times four XY readings that were expected to fall on a straight line, as shown, and if only the Y reading had precision error that was constant for all Y values, we would build up a uniform manifold of points sketched here.

deviating from the ideal. In many cases, however, it is possible through algebraic transformation to make our data tractable and reasonably approximate in form to this basic model.

Hoping that we can accept the model of Fig. 9-2, we now assume a general straight-line equation

$$Y_c = aX + b \qquad (9\text{-}1)$$

and we wish to obtain expressions for a and b such that the summed squares of the Y deviations from this line are minimized. Let Y_c be the true Y value at any X so that $(Y - Y_c)$ is the deviation at any X. We wish to minimize $\Sigma(Y - Y_c)^2$, which is the same as $\Sigma(Y - aX - b)^2$. Then

$$\frac{\partial \Sigma(Y - aX - b)^2}{\partial b} = 0 \qquad (9\text{-}2)$$

and

$$\frac{\partial \Sigma(Y - aX - b)^2}{\partial a} = 0 \qquad (9\text{-}3)$$

must hold true. If there are n readings, Eq. (9-2) becomes (since $\Sigma b = nb$)

$$nb + a\Sigma X = \Sigma Y \tag{9-4}$$

and Eq. (9-3) becomes

$$b\Sigma X + a\Sigma X^2 = \Sigma XY \tag{9-5}$$

We wish to find a and b so that a simultaneous solution must be made giving

$$b = \frac{\Sigma X^2 \Sigma Y - \Sigma X \Sigma XY}{n\Sigma X^2 - (\Sigma X)^2} \tag{9-6}$$

$$a = \frac{n\Sigma XY - \Sigma X \Sigma Y}{n\Sigma X^2 - (\Sigma X)^2} \tag{9-7}$$

If we had been fortunate enough to know that the XY function passed through zero-zero, such that b in Eq. (9-1) was exactly zero, we could have started over and obtained the simpler expression for a alone,

$$a = \frac{\Sigma XY}{\Sigma X^2} \tag{9-8}$$

The reader can review the section on extrapolation checking (Sec. 7-3) for examples of physical situations to which Eq. (9-8) might be applicable.

The application of Eqs. (9-6) and (9-7) using typical test data often results in large numbers plus tedious calculation. Some easing of the computations can be obtained by the following two short-cut methods. First select a middle X and Y value, X_m and Y_m, and fit the transformed variables X' and Y', which are found from $X' = X - X_m$ and $Y' = Y - Y_m$. This simply shifts the XY axis temporarily to the center of the point distribution and reduces the XY and X^2 values. The second simplification requires that a rough line be drawn by eye through the points and an approximate pair of constants A and B be estimated from this line. Then we have a known but approximate equation

$$U' = AX + B \tag{9-9}$$

We wish to use this to form an equation in terms of the difference $(Y' - U')$. From Eqs. (9-1) and (9-9)

$$U' - Y' = (A - a)X' + (B - b) \tag{9-10}$$

Now let $(U' - Y')$ be the Y's in Eqs. (9-6) and (9-7) with the X terms unchanged, and we will obtain, instead of a and b, $(A - a)$

and $(B - b)$, which will be small numbers amenable to quick operation on a desk calculator or slide rule. Let us watch this method work on an actual problem.

Example 9-1. A duct for a home-heating application is tested for loss in temperature versus different lengths of run. The following data result for a given type of duct and fixed surrounding conditions.

| Temperature, °F........ | 5 | 7 | 15 | 20 | 22 |
| Length, ft.............. | 4 | 8 | 12 | 16 | 20 |

What sort of least-squares plot do we get from this, and what can we say about the data in general?

Solution. Figure 9-3 shows a plot of the data on linear coordinates. We will assume that the function is a straight line, and we can plot a rough line by eye to establish our approximate constants A and B for Eq. (9-10). Obtaining over-all temperatures from a

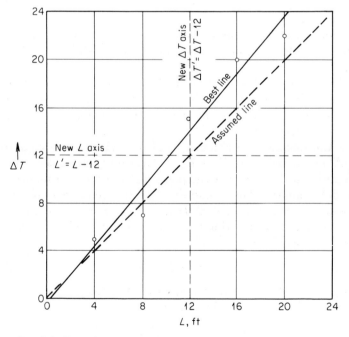

Fig. 9-3. Data from Example 9-1 plotted to show (1) the transformed axes, (2) the assumed line, and (3) the best or least-squares line found by computation.

duct is likely to lead to poor precision in ΔT because of the presence of gradients at any given cross section, while we suspect that L is correct with no error. We tend to force our assumed line through the zero-zero point since we know that the true line must pass through this point. We will not, however, use Eq. (9-8) since we are interested in the computed b value (which should be zero if all is well) as a partial measure of how reasonable our data really are. The estimated line shown in Fig. 9-3 has an obviously too small slope, but has been drawn with an eye to easy computation (slope of unity). Then the approximate equation (9-9) becomes for this case

$$U = 1 \cdot L + 0$$

with U in degrees Fahrenheit and L in feet. Equation (9-10) becomes

$$\Delta U - \Delta T = (1 - a)L + (0 - b)$$

since A is unity and B is zero for this assumed line. Let us make a further concession to computational ease by shifting the axis as shown in Fig. 9-3 such that $\Delta T' = \Delta T - 12$, $\Delta U' = \Delta U - 12$, and $L' = L - 12$. The entire computation is now tabulated as follows:

ΔT	L	$\Delta U = 1 \cdot L$	$\begin{array}{c}\Delta T - 12 \\ = \Delta T\end{array}$	$\begin{array}{c}\Delta U - 12 \\ = \Delta U'\end{array}$	$\begin{array}{c}L - 12 \\ = L' \\ (X)\end{array}$	$\begin{array}{c}(\Delta U' - \Delta T') \\ (Y)\end{array}$	$\begin{array}{c}L'^2 \\ (X^2)\end{array}$	$\begin{array}{c}L'(\Delta U' - \Delta T') \\ (XY)\end{array}$
5	4	4	−7	−8	−8	−1	64	8
7	8	8	−5	−4	−4	1	16	−4
15	12	12	3	0	0	−3	0	0
20	16	16	8	4	4	−4	16	−16
22	20	20	10	8	8	−2	64	−16

$n = 5$ $\Sigma X = 0$ $\Sigma Y = -9$ $\Sigma X^2 = 160$ $\Sigma XY = -28$

In this simple example, the axis transformation and the use of an approximate function are not really justified, but serve to demonstrate the methods in as complete a manner as possible. Now we apply Eqs. (9-6) and (9-7) as follows:

$$0 - b = \frac{160(-9) - 0(-28)}{5(160) - 0} = -\frac{9}{5} = -1.8$$
$$b = +1.8$$
$$1 - a = \frac{5(-28) - 0(-9)}{5(160) - 0} = -\frac{28}{160} = -0.18$$
$$a = 1.18$$

But we must remember that these values were found for the transformed axis. We now write $\Delta T - 12 = 1.18(L - 12) + 1.8$, or $\Delta T = 1.18L + 12 - 14.18 + 1.8$, or

$$\Delta T = 1.18L - 0.4$$

which is the least-squares equation for the data and is plotted on Fig. 9-3. Although we know that the b value should be zero rather than -0.4, we should not be too displeased with this small intercept. The data indicate that we cannot read the temperature loss to closer than about a degree, so that a $0.4°$ intercept is hardly enough to void the data.

At this point the engineer may be willing to stop and present his correlation line without further analysis, although additional interesting material can be obtained without too much more work. Since the model we assumed is no more than an infinite succession of identical normal-type curves extending from the best line in a plus-and-minus Y direction, we might logically ask what the precision indexes of this repeated normal distribution might be. In Chap. 2, we saw that the standard deviation s could be found from

$$s^2 = \frac{\Sigma x^2}{n - 1} \tag{9-11}$$

where x was the deviation of any given reading from the best value. Our best value is now a line, and we can easily compute or measure the deviation of any point from the least-squares line and thereby obtain the standard deviation of the Y measurement for the entire data set. The reader should not forget, however, that this procedure is only as good as our basic model (Fig. 9-2) is good. If the standard deviation is not constant along the line, or the line is not really straight, or precision error occurs also in X, our estimate will be poor or perhaps totally misleading. Of course, the classical least-squares line will be equally bad in such cases.

Example 9-2. What is the standard deviation of temperature-measuring precision error from Example 9-1?

Solution. Let us tabulate for each of the five points the true or least-squares value and also the measured value and obtain the standard deviation from Eq. (9-11):

L	$1.18L$	T (least squares) $= 1.18L - 0.4$	T (actual)	$(\Delta T_{ls} - \Delta T_a)^2$
4	4.75	4.35	5	0.42
8	9.5	9.1	7	4.42
12	14.2	13.8	15	1.45
16	19.0	18.6	20	1.97
20	23.7	23.3	22	1.7
Total.....	.....	.....	...	9.96

and
$$s = \sqrt{\frac{9.96}{5 - 1}} = 1.56°F$$

Because the standard deviation is about 1.5 times the probable error, we can say that our probable error in measuring here is about 1°F and that half of all our readings will be accurate to within 1°F, assuming, of course, that our temperature-reading errors are normally distributed.

It is impossible to deal with the many more advanced and extensive least-squares techniques still untouched. When we have an obviously curved line of points, and no simple algebraic transformation seems to straighten it out, we may have to fit, by least squares, a polynomial with several constants, and this type of work is now done on computing machines following standard programs. If the precision error cannot be isolated in Y, but appears in both X and Y, a more involved and tedious least-squares method is needed.[1] Should the precision error magnitude vary with X and/or Y, we must somehow weight points in some parts of the envelope differently from those in other parts, and to do this properly we should know quite closely how the precision actually changes.

End-of-chapter references will serve to introduce these more advanced topics to the beginner or serious, but nonstatistical, experimenter.

9-2. Straight-line Fitting, Short Cuts, and Approximations

The least-squares method, even with the numerical simplifications noted in the previous section, remains a tedious and lengthy computation if more than a few points are to be handled. In a series of

[1] See A. G. Worthing and J. Geffner, "Treatment of Experimental Data," chap. 11, John Wiley & Sons, Inc., New York, 1943.

interesting papers,[1] S. I. Askovitz has been developing a purely graphical least-squares method which seems, to this writer at least, to answer many practical objections to the general use of the method in laboratory work. In its present stage of development, the method is best applied to the special case of *equal X spacing*. Thus, if the Askovitz method is to be applied, the experimenter must plan before running his test to vary his no-error controlled variable X in equal increments, or to change it in such a manner that a straight-line plot will show equal intervals. This is best done following the techniques outlined in Sec. 6-1.

Once this has been accomplished, the establishment of the line is simplicity itself: Simply connect data points 1 and 2 by a straight line. Move along this line two-thirds of the horizontal distance S between adjacent points and mark. Connect this point with data point 3 and move the same distance horizontally toward 3 and mark on this new line. Repeat, until the final point has been marked. This last point marked lies on the best or least-squares line. Now, start at the other end, and repeat the process moving in the opposite direction. A second point will be found that lies on the line. The construction is completely shown for a five-point data set in Fig. 9-4. While appearing superficially complicated, the method is simple repetition, and two or three dozen points can be handled in a few minutes using a straightedge and compass set for the $\frac{2}{3}S$ distance. As a check, the construction can be repeated from either end using $\frac{1}{2}S$, and this third point will lie on the least-squares line as well. This latter construction is not shown in Fig. 9-4 but can be attempted by the reader.

The Askovitz method is *not* an approximation if the X variation is exactly equal in spacing, but it suffers from the same limitations as the classical, numerical approach, namely, Y only in error, line straight, and equal precision over the entire data envelope. This interesting construction has been ignored by most statistical text-books, apparently on the grounds that only a line is found, with no measure of precision in numerical form. Following the simple method outlined in the previous example, it is easy to continue and find the deviation of points from the line and compute the standard

---

[1] *J. Appl. Physiol.*, **8**:347–352 (1955); *J. Am. Stat. Assoc.*, **52**:13–17 (1957); *Am. J. Phys.*, **25**:254–256 (1957); *Am. J. Phys.*, **26**:610–612 (1958); *Am. J. Phys.*, **28**:164–168 (1958); all by S. I. Askovitz. See also H. Schenck, Jr., A Mechanical Analog of the Least-squares Problem, *Bull. Mech. Eng. Educ.*, **5**:183–185 (1966).

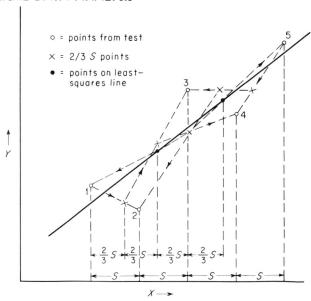

o = points from test

x = 2/3 S points

• = points on least-
    squares line

Fig. 9-4. An example of the Askovitz or graphical least-squares fitting method. The steps are explained in the text.

deviation. For engineers, this method would seem well worth the effort.

Example 9-3. Find the least-squares line from the data of Example 9-1, using this Askovitz graphical method.

Solution. The construction is possible here owing to equal L spacing and is shown in Fig. 9-5. The resulting line is exactly the same as one obtained by numerical means in Example 9-1 within the limits of graphical construction error.

A number of non-least-squares methods of plotting are now available,[1] and among the easiest is the so-called *method of grouping.* As we will treat it here, this method requires a knowledge of at least one point on the straight line (probably at the origin) since we will find only the slope of the line. On the other hand, the method is not restricted to precision error in Y only and is very quick.

---

[1] See Forman S. Acton, "Analysis of Straight-line Data," John Wiley & Sons, Inc., New York, 1959, for bibliography and discussions on several approaches.

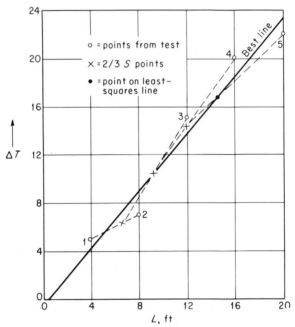

Fig. 9-5. Askovitz method applied to the data from Example 9-3; this is possible since these data are equally spaced along the X axis. Only one of the two points is found here for the sake of clarity.

Given a series of experimental points having coordinates X and Y, the slope of the straight line connecting these points will be found from

$$b = \frac{\Sigma Y - \Sigma Y'}{\Sigma X - \Sigma X'} \tag{9-12}$$

where Y and X are the coordinates of m points grouped at one end of the envelope and Y' and X' are the coordinates of m points taken from the other end of the envelope. We might wonder how many points we should take from the total numbers of data to make up our two sets of m points.

It can be proved from statistical analysis[1] that if the X intervals are spaced in a roughly even manner, we should divide the data set into three equal groups and use the upper third for our (X,Y) points and the lower third for our (X',Y') points, rejecting completely the

[1] See P. Guest, Fitting a Straight Line by the Method of Grouping, *Am. J. Phys.*, **18**(5):324–325 (May, 1950).

center third. This appears to violate a general common-sense rule of statistical analysis, namely: "The most powerful statistic uses all the data." Actually, we should say that if we know before the test that we are going to use grouping as the method, we should simply not bother taking data in the middle range of our X variable and concentrate on the first and last third of the test range. In a practical case, we would probably wish to take data over the entire range to ensure that a straight line is at least reasonable for correlation, and then, if grouping is desired, reject the center points. Since this is an inexact method, it is not wise to depend on it completely.

Example 9-3a. What is the slope of the best line through the data of Example 9-1, using the method of grouping?

Solution. We can apply Eq. (9-12) to the first two and to the last two points, leaving out the single center point only, since the number of points is not divisible by three. Then (Y is now ΔT and L is X)

$$b = \frac{(20 + 22) - (5 + 7)}{(20 + 16) - (4 + 8)}$$
$$b = 1.25$$

Figure 9-6 shows the least-squares line found in Example 9-1 or 9-2 compared with a line through the same L zero point, but with the slope found by grouping. With so few points, we are obviously better off drawing the line by eye than following this approximate procedure. With 20 or 30 data points, however, the method of grouping would show less deviation from the least-squares line, and, with so many points, its use becomes more a convenience for a hurried computation. One short but essential point might also be made here. No engineer should ever let a formal statistical method make him do something that is obviously wrong to the eye or to the urgings of common sense. Accepting the grouping line here would violate all promptings of engineering reasonableness.

9-3. Function Investigation by Graphical Analysis

We have seen in previous chapters how a large variety of XY functional relationships can be transformed to straight-line plots when this is convenient for spacing (Sec. 6-1), for extrapolation (Sec. 7-3), or for the use of least squares (Secs. 9-1 and 9-2). The reverse situation will often occur in test work. That is, we will be

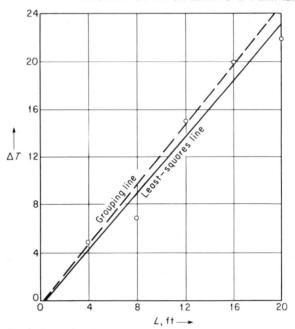

Fig. 9-6. A plot showing the temperature-loss data from Example 9-1 fitted to a line obtained by "grouping" as described in Example 9-4. With so few data available even a fit "by eye" would be preferable.

given data that investigation shows can be plotted as a straight line on one or another kind of coordinate system, and we want to find its functional relationship. Such an equation is known generally as an *empirical relationship*, meaning that it was found from data rather than from theoretical considerations. Empiricism is common in the determination of physical, chemical, and electrical properties, in heat transfer and fluid mechanics, and in many new fields still lacking a firm theoretical base.

Our basic strategy, whatever the test, is simply to search for a transformation or a set of axes that will yield the straightest possible line from the complete set of data. If the data do not form a straight line on linear graph paper, the engineer may next try log-log coordinates (or taking the log of both the X and Y values and plotting on linear paper). Log-log plotting will straighten out or rectify the simple yet important function

$$Y = kX^a \tag{9-13}$$

where the transformation is (with k and a as fitting constants)

$$\log Y = \log k + a \log X \qquad (9\text{-}14)$$

Next to the straight line, this is probably the most common form of experimental function and is often assumed in dimensional analysis (see Sec. 4-6).

A third common graph paper is the *semilogarithmic type* with one scale in log form and the other linear. This will give a straight line if the data are following a law of the type

$$Y = k(10)^{aX}$$

which is identical with

$$Y = ke^{2.3026aX}$$

The transformation of these functions is

$$\log Y = \log k + aX \qquad (9\text{-}15)$$

and to achieve a straight line the Y axis must be logarithmic with the X axis linear.

A number of special forms of paper (i.e., trilinear, hyperbolic) can sometimes be found, but are not really needed. For example, the hyperbolic curve

$$Y = \frac{X}{a + bX} \qquad (9\text{-}16)$$

can be rectified by plotting X/Y versus X or $1/Y$ versus $1/X$ on linear coordinates.

Some types of data will give peaks or hollows on linear coordinates. This immediately suggests a parabolic function, or more general *polynomial*

$$Y = a + bX + cX^2 \qquad (9\text{-}17)$$

which may have additional terms if there is more than one peak. For the three-term parabolic equation there are several means of rectification. Let (X_1, Y_1) be the coordinates of any point on a smooth curve through the data. Then

$$Y_1 = a + bX_1 + cX_1^2$$

which may be subtracted from Eq. (9-17) to give

$$Y - Y_1 = b(X - X_1) + c(X^2 - X_1^2)$$

We can divide both sides by $(X - X_1)$, obtaining

$$\frac{Y - Y_1}{X - X_1} = b + c(X + X_1)$$

$(b + cX_1)$ is constant, so that a plot of $(Y - Y_1)/(X - X_1)$ versus X will be a straight line if this is the equation governing the data.

Another approach is to differentiate Eq. (9-17),

$$\frac{dY}{dX} = b + 2cX$$

which suggests that a plot of $\Delta Y/\Delta X$ versus X will give a straight line if we take equal X intervals.

These and a number of other rectification rules are summarized in Table 9-1. The proofs of these rules are left as exercises.

It should be noted that one need not use only the actual data points in these tests. The best strategy is first to plot the data on linear coordinates and then to draw a smooth curve through it. Then, select the function most likely to fit and use any X and Y on the curve needed to obtain a suitable confirmation of (or negation of) the hypothesized function. Notice that any such algebraic test should be carried out over the entire data range. Some experiments will give straight lines over a portion of the data envelope and curved lines over the remainder. Even when this occurs, however, attempted rectification of the data is well worth the effort. A curve having even a portion of its range plotting in a linear manner is far more revealing than one which curves over its entirety.

An actual example of this type of analysis is shown in Figs. 9-7 and 9-8. A senior mechanical engineering experiment involved the

Table 9-1

To test for the function:	Obtain a straight line when:
a. $Y = aX + b$	X and Y are plotted on linear paper
b. $Y = kX^a$	X and Y are plotted on log-log paper
c. $Y = k(10)^{aX}$ or $Y = ke^{aX}$	$\begin{cases} X \text{ is plotted on the linear scale} \\ Y \text{ on the log scale of semilog paper} \end{cases}$
d. $Y = X/(a + bX)$ or $1/Y = a/X + b$	$(1/Y$ and $1/X)$ or $(X/Y$ and $X)$ are plotted on linear paper
e. $Y = a + bX + cX^2$	$(Y - Y_1)/(X - X_1)$ and X are plotted on linear paper
f. $Y = X/(a + bX) + c$	$(X - X_1)/(Y - Y_1)$ and X are plotted on linear paper
g. $Y = k(10)^{bX+cX^2}$ or $Y = ke^{bX+cX^2}$	$(\log Y - \log Y_1)$ and X are plotted on linear paper

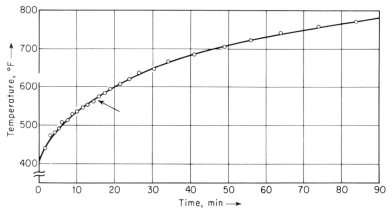

Fig. 9-7. A plot of student data taken during an experiment on a heated stack. A typical "French curve" line drawn by eye through the points is shown, with an arrow indicating the time at which the potentiometer range change occurred. The reader may judge for himself whether he would have noted a discontinuity here from such a plot.

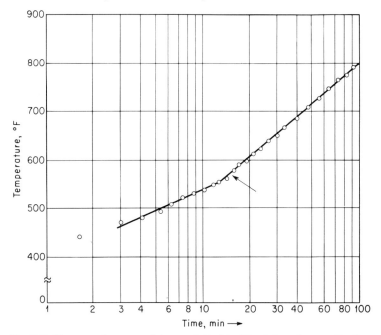

Fig. 9-8. Here are the same data as plotted in Fig. 9-7, only now the time axis is logarithmic. The range-change point is again indicated by an arrow, and the abrupt slope change at this point is unmistakable.

taking of continuous readings of temperature at various points in a stack being heated. Figure 9-7 shows a conventional time-temperature plot from the thermocouple in the center of the stack, and it can be noted that a slight dip or flat region seems to exist between 500 and 600°F. Transient heat-flow data are often rectified by plotting the log of time versus temperature, as shown in Fig. 9-8. This semilog plot shows clearly the sharp change in the temperature-versus-log (time) curve slope at 550°F. Armed with such concrete data, it was a simple matter to check the original data sheet and note that at this temperature the potentiometer indicating the reading of the several couples was changed from low to high range. Thus, we can say with some assurance that the instrument is in error on at least one range and should undergo calibration.

Curves of physical and chemical properties are often the result of two or more interacting effects and show such slope changes where one effect predominates over the other. Thus, the point where one curve follows the other is often of the utmost theoretical importance. An obvious example is the tensile curve of mild steel which is straight up to the yield point and curved thereafter. Worthing and Geffner[1] note a case in optical research where the detection of two different curves led to the discovery of the existence of two kinds of optical receptors, rods and cones, in the human eye.

Example 9-4. In Example 6-2 a Latin-square experiment was outlined in which a Dodge auto engine was operated over a range of loads, speeds, and engine temperatures. One of the resulting curves was a plot of specific fuel consumption versus engine-block temperature. Values from the smoothed curve are as follows:

Block temperature, °F	120	130	140	150	160	170	180	190
Specific fuel consumption	0.545	0.532	0.523	0.518	0.513	0.51	0.507	0.505

What is the equation of this curve?

Solution. Before attempting to fit these data we should first wonder whether we are dealing with the variables in their most significant engineering form. Experience with engines would lead us to expect somewhat better fuel consumption with increased temperature, for this is predicted in basic thermodynamic theory. But

[1] "Treatment of Experimental Data," pp. 50–54, John Wiley & Sons, Inc., New York, 1943.

is the Fahrenheit temperature the best variable or is not the temperature level above the surrounding datum of more fundamental significance? Again we realize that when thermodynamics predicts better fuel consumption from a hot engine, this means hot in relation to the datum. In this test, the lab temperature was recorded as approximately 80°F; therefore let us fit SFC versus $(T_{block} - 80)$ or ΔT.

The function has no peaks or hollows, only a continuously decreasing SFC with increasing ΔT, with, however, a decreasing slope. This suggests immediately an exponential curve, b in Table 9-1, with the exponent a negative fraction. The check is to plot log (SFC) and log $(T - 80)$ as shown in Fig. 9-9. This attempt fails to rectify the curve, and we must search for a more appropriate function. The hyperbolic curve d in Table 9-1 will also fit data of this sort. Let us test by obtaining 1/SFC and $1/\Delta T$:

1/SFC	1.83	1.88	1.91	1.93	1.95	1.96	1.97	1.98
ΔT	40	50	60	70	80	90	100	110
$1/\Delta T$	0.025	0.02	0.0167	0.0143	0.0125	0.0111	0.01	0.0091

which are shown in Fig. 9-10. This quite clearly rectifies the data, allowing for reading and slide-rule uncertainties.

The equation of this line is

$$\frac{1}{\text{SFC}} = \frac{k}{\Delta T} + b$$

where b is the intercept at $1/\Delta T$ of zero axis and equal by inspection to 2.07; k, the slope of the line, is found graphically as shown in

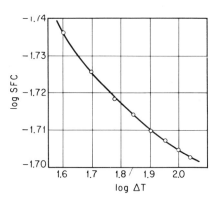

Fig. 9-9. A log-log plot of the data from Example 9-4, showing that such a transformation fails to rectify the data. For such small range of variables, log-log plots are best made as shown here rather than utilizing commercial paper.

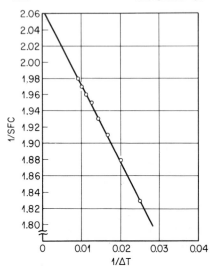

Fig. 9-10. Data from Example 9-4 plotted as reciprocals, a transformation that yields a straight line.

Fig. 9-10 and is equal to -9.5.   Then the equation is

$$\frac{1}{\text{SFC}} = 2.07 - \frac{9.5}{\Delta T}$$

or

$$\frac{\Delta T}{2.07\Delta T - 9.5} = \text{SFC}$$

the familiar hyperbolic form of the equation.   The data in the form of Fig. 9-10 and the equation derived from it are quite revealing. For example, we see that even if the engine were run at a very high temperature, the SFC would drop to only 0.485, only slightly below that already achieved in the test.   Extrapolating to the other end it appears that an SFC of infinity will result when ΔT drops to 4.7°F.   This probably means nothing more than that such an extrapolation is much too big to give any valid information.

The seasoned experimenter might, at this point, wonder whether we did not cheat a bit by assuming that $(T - 80)$ rather than T was the significant variable.   Should we not be able to find this fact in the data, rather than from theoretical considerations?   Let us see how this might be done.

From Fig. 9-10 we see that the equation involving the variables in their "raw" form is

$$\frac{1}{\text{SFC}} = b - \frac{k}{T - a}$$

This transforms to

$$T = \frac{k \, \text{SFC}}{b \, \text{SFC} - 1} + a$$

which is the form of Eq. (*f*) in Table 9-1 with T as Y and SFC
as X.   Let us tabulate the necessary quantities to perform the test
for this function as follows, with X_1 equal to an SFC of 0.505 and

SFC − 0.505	0.040	0.027	0.018	0.013	0.008	0.005	0.002
T − 190	−70	−60	−50	−40	−30	−20	−10
$\dfrac{\text{SFC} - 0.505}{T - 190} \times 10^4$	−5.72	−4.5	−3.6	−3.25	−2.68	−2.50	−2.0

Y_1 equal to the corresponding T of 190°F.   The plot of the third
row versus SFC is shown in Fig. 9-11.   As might be expected, the
line is straight, indicating that this formula will correlate the basic
data.   From the usual slope-intercept method we get from Fig. 9-11
the equation

$$\frac{\text{SFC} - 0.505}{T - 190} = 0.0046 - 0.0096 \, \text{SFC}$$

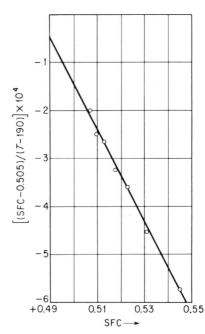

Fig. 9-11. In this curve an alternate
form from Table 9-1 is tested from the
data of Example 9-4.

which can be algebraically changed to the form (by solving for SFC)

$$\mathrm{SFC} = \frac{T - 80}{2.09T - 157}$$

which is identical with Eq. (f) in Table 9-1 when this equation is put in the form

$$Y = \frac{T + a}{bT + (ab + k)}$$

Comparing these last two equations, we see that a is -80, b is 2.09, and k must equal $(157 - ab)$ or -10. These constants in Eq. (f) in another form give finally

$$\frac{1}{\mathrm{SFC}} = 2.09 - \frac{10}{T - 80}$$

What exactly have we proved in this analysis? Simply this: The figure for surrounding temperature did not have to be assumed or known, nor was it necessary even to recognize that $(T - 80)$ was significant. This information exists and existed in the raw data themselves. At the risk of becoming repetitive, the author will reiterate a theme already stressed. A simple engine test is basic to most technical laboratory courses and seems to offer little in the way of challenge to either the student or instructor. Yet, even in these simple experiments lies rich and fruitful material submerged and waiting for discovery. The seasoned industrial experimenter who reads these lines might ponder this question: If basic and traditional tests can contain new material within a few pieces of raw data, what sort of discovery and inference is being missed in the vast outpouring of complex experimental data from the huge professional research establishments in this and other countries?

9-4. Uncertainty in Graphical Analysis

Throughout this book we have returned again and again to the idea of uncertainty and error. Graphs and curves, like instruments, are tools which have a fundamental uncertainty connected with their use. A calibration curve, for example, with its instrument might be used to set test points so that the uncertainty in reading the instrument is made up in part of the actual instrument variation and in part of the reading uncertainty of persons using the curve. When we use a graph for finding slopes, intercepts, or other constants, we expect such a process to add uncertainty to the already uncertain data points. The question we wish to consider in this section then is: How can we minimize the uncertainty of plotting, reading, and computing from a graph?

One general principle of plotting is that the least count or smallest division of the graph paper should about equal the probable error of the measurement. If, let us say, ten small divisions equal the probable error, we will have a curve so badly scattered that trends and laws may be obscured. On the other hand, if the probable error equals one-tenth of the smallest division, all scatter will disappear, and all indications of precision will be lacking. This is demonstrated in Fig. 9-12. Since most graphs are of a uniform size, this ideal is often not approached, but should be borne in mind.

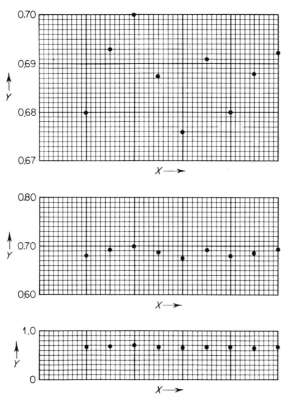

Fig. 9-12. Y-versus-X data plotted against three different Y-scale magnitudes with nothing else different. The probable error appears to be about 0.01 in the Y direction, and following the rule noted in the text, this amount should be our least graphical division. The center plot meets this criterion.

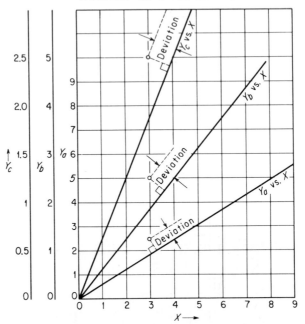

Fig. 9-13. A sketch showing the effect of increasing the size of the Y axis on the distance an outlier falls away from a given line. It is easily seen that the Y_c-versus-X plot gives the greatest deviation, suggesting that the Y scale should be made as large as practical.

A second principle of plotting is simply the rule that the analyst should usually attempt rectification of his data. Straight lines can be fitted most easily by eye or by analytic means. The straight-line equation requires that only two constants be taken from the graph, and deviations and scatter are most easily detected when straight lines are known to exist. The straight line also permits easy extrapolation for the checking of data consistency, and leads to easy computation of various statistical numbers such as the probable error or standard deviation.

It is sometimes proposed that a data set should be plotted on axes that cause it to form a line having a slope of roughly 1. The argument for such an axis choice is that precision errors are most clearly revealed when data points scatter around a 45° sloping line. It is easily shown that this is not the case. Taking a straight line as our best or correct function in Fig. 9-13, and a single point (X, Y)

lying off the line some distance (having precision error in X or Y or perhaps in both), we might say that the maximum indication of precision error occurs when the wild point lies at a maximum distance from the best line along a perpendicular to the best line. In Fig. 9-13, we select three Y-axis scale lengths, and it is apparent that this distance is not maximized when the slope is unity but becomes large as the Y axis is stretched out. Thus, if we are using an $8\frac{1}{2}$- by 11-in. piece of graph paper, we should not restrict our Y scale to maintain a square format, but should use all the graph paper. The best slope for data presentation therefore is not unity, but depends on the shape of the graph paper available.

9-5. Summary

In this chapter, we have touched on a few of the main graphical methods available to the experimenter. The classical least-squares method requires that only the Y or dependent variable be in error, that this precision error be of constant magnitude over the test envelope, and that the data form a straight line. Even though all these requirements may not be rigorously met, the experimenter may choose to use least squares simply because it gives a systematic plot rather than one having possibility of instinctive bias from the analyst. Most of these restrictive requirements can be relaxed or eliminated if more advanced least-squares treatment is used, but such methods are more difficult, more time-consuming, and usually not covered in any but advanced textbooks. If the X or independent variable can be equally spaced, the least-squares line can be fitted by a purely graphical procedure, which is both rapid and without approximation, but still retains the three basic requirements that restrict the use of the algebraic least-squares method. The lack of statistical figures regarding the variance of points from the line when the purely graphical method is used is easily remedied by reading off and tabulating the Y-axis deviations and then finding the standard deviation from these figures.

An approximate straight-line-fitting method consists in grouping the lower and upper thirds of the data, finding a mean X and Y for each, and drawing the line through these means. The method is quick, but may give an obviously poor line unless a relatively large number of data are available.

When we have a set of data that does not fall naturally along a straight line, we must examine it and attempt to see a transformation that will rectify or make it form a straight line. This can be done by plotting the basic data on special graph paper or by transforming the variables in accordance with suggestions in Table 9-1 until we obtain what we wish. When a straight line is obtained, we can easily get the equation by using the slope-intercept equation and then change it algebraically into what other forms we feel may be meaningful. A knowledge of the physical theory of the test will assist in selecting the rectification method best suited for the data, and we may hope the final equation will reveal unsuspected theoretical material, providing we have done a careful job. Although no example was done in the text, it should be obvious that the least-squares method is entirely usable for rectified (X,Y) variables and should be applied when the scatter is extensive and a straight line seems to best fit the data, or when we know from theory that data must plot straight following a certain transformation.

Three simple rules will give us plots that will minimize uncertainty and precision error due to reading. These are the use of a minimum graph division roughly equal to the probable error in the point, the rectification of all data when possible, and the selection of scale lengths such that as much of the chosen graph sheet as possible is utilized.

PROBLEMS

Using least squares, plot the following data. Decide whether the graphical (Askovitz) method can be used or not, and give the straight-line equation.

9-1

Machine speed $\times 10^2$ rpm, X	1	2	3	3	4	5
Number of accepted parts, Y	1	3	2	4	4	6

9-2

Pump flow, lb/sec, X	0.5	1.0	1.5	2.0	2.5	3.0
Pump efficiency, %, Y	1.8	3.2	4.5	5.0	6.4	7.5

9-3

Grid volts, 885 tube, X	0	-5	-10	-15	-20	-25	-30
Plate volts for starting discharge, Y	0	50	100	125	180	250	315

9-4. In Probs. 9-1, 9-2, and/or 9-3 use the line you find through least squares and the deviations from this line to obtain the standard deviation of the Y

measurement. (Note that in Prob. 9-1 there is no error in Y but rather a lack of control over the experiment that we assume is wholly concentrated in the Y variable.) Discuss the expected intercepts in Probs. 9-2 and 9-3 and the failure to exactly strike the zero-zero point in terms of the magnitude of the standard deviation.

9-5. The average failure time of heavily overloaded resistors was 38.5 min for 52.5-ohm units, 37 min for 53.5-ohm units, 44 min for 54.5-ohm units, and 45.5 min for 55.5-ohm units. Assume a straight-line function exists between failure time and resistance. Find the standard deviation of the failure times if all random variation is assumed in their values.

9-6. Use the least-squares method to plot the best line through 1/SFC-versus-1/ΔT data in the first part of Example 9-4, assuming all precision error to be concentrated in the 1/SFC measurement. The line shown in Fig. 9-10 was drawn by eye. Compare your result with this line and compare the formula you get from your line also. With this sort of data do you think the use of the least-squares method is worthwhile?

In the following problems, find the function that will rectify the data and the formula that fits the given points. Show a plot as proof that your choice is good.

9-7. A cooling experiment gives:

Temperature drop, ΔT....	19.9	18.9	16.9	14.9	12.9	10.9	8.9
Time from start, θ........	0	3.45	10.87	19.30	22.8	40.1	53.75

9-8. A nonlinear circuit device gives:

Volts........	67.7	65.0	63.0	61.0	58.25	56.25
Amperes.....	2.46	2.97	3.45	3.96	4.97	5.97

9-9. A pipe fitting gives the following pressure-drop data:

Velocity, ft/sec...........	1.3	1.45	1.6	1.7	1.95	2.5
Pressure drop, mm Hg....	0.200	0.25	0.290	0.32	0.43	0.70

9-10. A water pump gives the following data (rpm constant):

Flow, gal/min....	0	2	4	6	8	10	12
Head, ft..........	98	106	112	114	117	112	105

9-11. An alloy gives the following property data:

Per cent of A in mix............	0	0.2	0.4	0.6	0.8	1.0
Specific heat.................	0.2	0.27	0.35	0.47	0.69	1.0

(*Hint:* Try test for g in Table 9-1.)

9-12. In any or all of the above five problems study the function you have found for end points, and note any other items or values of theoretical interest.

9-13. Prove that any or all of the tests (a through g) in Table 9-1 will rectify the data equation noted.

9-14. Find the best equation for the following straight-line data relating the fraction of velocity head remaining downstream to the per cent flow area blocked off in a hydraulic fitting having adjustable blockage. In addition, decide whether the extrapolation(s) of these data is (are) reasonable.

Fraction remaining........	0.86	0.85	0.60	0.55	0.52	0.45
Per cent blockage.........	10	20	30	40	50	60

REFERENCES

Acton, F.: "Analysis of Straight-line Data," John Wiley & Sons, Inc., New York, 1959.

Bacon, R.: "Best" Straight Line among the Points, *Am. J. Phys.*, **21**(6):428–445 (September, 1953).

Bowker, A., and G. Lieberman: "Engineering Statistics," chap. 9, Prentice-Hall, Inc., Englewood Cliffs, N.J., 1959.

Hoelscher, R. P., J. N. Arnold, and S. H. Pierce: "Graphic Aids in Engineering Computation," chap. 2, McGraw-Hill Book Company, New York, 1952.

Mackey, C. O.: "Graphical Solutions," chaps. 5 and 6, John Wiley & Sons, Inc., New York, 1943.

Wilson, E. B.: "An Introduction to Scientific Research," chap. 8, McGraw-Hill Book Company, New York, 1952.

Worthing, A. G., and J. Geffner: "Treatment of Experimental Data," chaps. 1, 2, 3, and 11, John Wiley & Sons, Inc., New York, 1943.

CHAPTER 10

Mathematical Data Analysis

There is surely some question as to exactly what constitutes a purely statistical analysis, as opposed to a graphical analysis, which in turn is contrasted with a mathematical analysis. The least-squares method leads to the mathematical expression of a curve, obtained through purely numerical means and solidly based on statistical principle. About all we can say in defense of the rather arbitrary divisions used in these final four chapters is that some analytic methods are derived mainly from statistical principles, and these were considered in Chap. 8. Other methods derive from, or are associated with, graphs and pictorial conceptions and thus fell into Chap. 9. Topics that do not seem to fit in these two chapters are lumped here and are referred to as mathematical methods, although numerical might be a better word in some cases. Again, it must be stressed that the amount of material available in literature on the mathematical analysis of experimental data is staggering in extent, and we can again do little more than take up very briefly some of the more useful and elementary topics. Such vital ideas as harmonic analysis, numerical solution of differential equations, the construction of nomographic charts, and myriad other topics must be left to library-filling reference works. Actually, much of this specialized material is never assimilated by the general-test man, who can call upon a wide variety of specialists to render assistance. The methods outlined in this chapter are sufficiently quick and general to have use for many experimenters.

10-1. Significant Figures

We should probably have considered the problem of significant figures before this point, although it is in numerical and computational work that they assume the greatest importance. The significant figures are those numbers that convey information regarding the magnitude or value of the quantity being measured. Thus a capacitor measurement specified as 0.213 μf has three significant figures, and this fact is not changed if the measurement is given as 0.213 $\times$ 10^{-6} farad or 213,000 $\mu\mu$f. Some confusion may result if large numbers are written in the manner of this last one, since it may be implied that the capacitance is actually known to six figures, 213,000. To prevent such misunderstandings, it is good practice to write the value as 213 $\times$ 10^3 $\mu\mu$f.

As might be expected, the number of significant figures is (or should be) based firmly on the results of our uncertainty analysis in Chaps. 2 and 3. If the uncertainty of a measurement is, say, 10 per cent (referring perhaps to the standard deviation), we would report no more than two significant figures, and even two is optimistic. A reading of 98, for example, implies that we know the reading lies between 97 and 99, whereas with a 10 per cent uncertainty it could be 95 or 101 or even worse. For a 1 per cent uncertainty we report three figures, for a 0.1 per cent, four figures, and so on. The natural tendency is to err on the optimistic side, and there is nothing wrong with this if it is not overdone.

When we begin processing data, we begin to propagate errors as described in Chap. 3. We also may begin to "lose" significance if care is not taken. Suppose we are computing loss of weight in a corrosion test. Weight before was 1.54 lb, and weight afterward is 1.52 lb. The weight loss is then 0.02 lb, and we are reduced to only one significant figure. We wish to compare this weight loss with the loss from another test, which also comes out as 0.02 lb. Obviously we can draw no useful conclusions. Our significant figures have practically disappeared, and we should have begun by getting a weighing scale that would give us at least four and perhaps even five figures.

When extensive processing is to be done by the test man, his engineering aides, or digital machines, it is usually wise to retain at least one additional figure throughout. Suppose we wish to square a velocity of 107 ft/sec, obtaining exactly 11,449 ft^2/sec^2. Since we started with three significant figures, we now round off to

11,400. Suppose we wish to add 6,540 to this, obtaining exactly 17,989, but only 17,940 if we add to the rounded value. Thus, by rounding we have lost one unit in the third place. Had the 11,449 been rounded to four places, 11,450, then the result of the addition of 6,540 gives 17,990, which rounds finally and correctly to 18,000 (or better, 180×10^2). In digital computing machines, up to twelve places are available and such rounding errors can be made as unlikely as the investigator chooses. Once the computational chain is complete, however, the rounding to the anticipated number of figures must be done if suspicion and/or distrust on the reader's part are to be forestalled.

The standard 10-in. slide rule has a maximum uncertainty of about 0.3 to 0.5 per cent (these figures might include 95 per cent of all readings) on the standard multiplication and division scales. A 20-in. rule might have half this, and a spiral rule having a 60-in. scale could have one-sixth the uncertainty. With such a rule, general four-place accuracy with five places at the smaller numbers is perfectly feasible. Four-place log tables have, obviously, four-place accuracy plus almost an additional place if interpolation is done with care. Nomograms, charts, and graphical computation aids must be examined individually by the user to detect the number of places. If the charts and curves are drawn following the suggestions in Sec. 9-4, the engineer will read to about twice the smallest division. It should not have to be stressed at this point that just as various instruments having various precisions should not be mixed in a test, so, using 0.1 per cent accurate instruments that give data which will be processed on a pocket slide rule is equally senseless. Similarly, long and tiresome work on a desk computer having many significant figures is a waste of time if an error analysis shows a 5 per cent uncertainty in the readings or the result of their combination.

10-2. Fitting Polynomials to Data

In the previous chapter, we saw several ways in which data could be fitted by an empirical equation, using graphical techniques. All these methods depended on either starting with data that plotted on a straight line or transforming the variables algebraically such that straight lines could be formed. Many experimental curves will not be amenable to such transformations and must be fitted to more general functions than considered in Chap. 9. The most common type is the general polynomial having $(n + 1)$ terms,

$$Y = a + bX + cX^2 + dX^3 + \cdots + nX^n \qquad (10\text{-}1)$$

If only two terms are used, we have the usual slope-intercept straight line. Three terms give a parabola, for which tests are available as shown in Table 9-1. Beyond this, we can continue to add terms and thereby fit more and more complex or difficult curves.

The obvious way to fit a polynomial of the form of Eq. (10-1) is to find as many points on the XY curve as there are constants to be determined and then solve simultaneously the $(n + 1)$ equations. When n is 2 or more, such an approach becomes quite tedious, and the equation is often solved through the use of determinants.[1] Unfortunately, an n-of-2 equation leads to a fourth-order determinant, which is often more tedious to work with than the simple simultaneous solution of three equations. In fact, it can be said, in general, that determinants are useful mainly in hand computations if simplifications can be made.

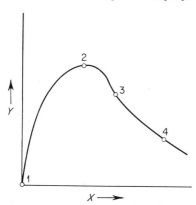

Fig. 10-1. Sketch of a possible peaking function, to be fitted using four points (one at origin). Since the portion to the right of the peak inflects, we place two of our chosen points here, and the other one to the left.

When fitting of curves by computing machine is to be undertaken, the use of determinants becomes essential since the method is automatic and adapts to standard programs.

Whether the fit is made using simultaneous solution or determinants, the analyst must select the two, three, or more points to be used so as to achieve the best possible fit. Suppose we wish to fit an n-of-3 equation to the curve in Fig. 10-1. We note that to the left of the peak we have a simple-appearing function with continuously decreasing slope, while to the right of the peak there is an inflection point. We might thus suspect that fitting the right-hand portion might be more difficult, and we would tend to take more of

[1] For a short résumé of determinants in curve fitting see appendix 1 of A. G. Worthing and J. Geffner, "Treatment of Experimental Data," John Wiley & Sons, Inc., New York, 1943.

our required points from this region as shown. After the n-of-3 equation has been found, we should naturally check other points to see that the fit is satisfactory over the entire range. If the fit is not good enough for our purposes, we may try another set of four points, or we may go to an n-of-4 equation. Notice that when the function goes through zero-zero, the constant a in Eq. (10-1) is zero, and we need one less equation in our simultaneous solution (or a determinant of one lower order).

We can always obtain this favorable result by temporarily moving the axis of the problem as shown in Fig. 10-2. Now every (X,Y) point becomes $(X - \Delta X)$ and $(Y - \Delta Y)$ in the (X',Y') coordinate system. The n-of-2 polynomial

$$Y = a + bX + cX^2 \quad (10\text{-}2)$$

becomes

$$Y - \Delta Y = a' + b'(X - \Delta X) + c'(X - \Delta X)^2 \quad (10\text{-}3)$$

and we see by inspection that a' is zero in the (X',Y') coordinate system. After b' and c' have been found we can transform Eq. (10-3) back to the original system,

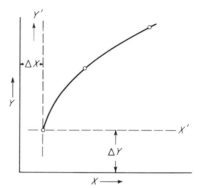

Fig. 10-2. Sketch showing how an axis transformation will place one of the fitting points at the fictive origin, thereby reducing the number of simultaneous equations by one.

$$Y = \Delta Y - b\,\Delta X + c\,\Delta X^2 + bX + c(X^2 - 2X\,\Delta X)$$
or $$Y = \Delta Y - b\,\Delta X + c\,\Delta X^2 + X(b - 2\,\Delta X) + cX^2$$

Such transformations are almost always worthwhile, since a polynomial having more than three constants is usually too complex to fit by hand.

Example 10-1. Figure 10-3 shows a smoothed curve of plate current versus plate voltage from a triode with grid voltage held constant at -5 volts. What is the polynomial expression for this curve?

Solution. With no peaks or obvious inflection points, an n-of-2 polynomial should easily correlate these data. Let us shift the axis so that $V' = V - 20$, and $I' = I$. Then the equation is (with

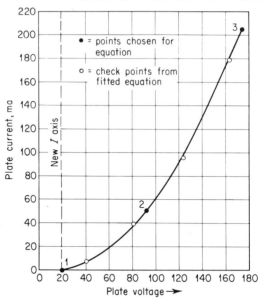

Fig. 10.3. Plot of plate current versus plate voltage for a triode used as a curve-fitting exercise in Example 10-1. The numbered points (1, 2, and 3) were used to make the fit, and the other points show how the fitted function graphs over the data range.

a' equal to zero due to the transformation)

$$I' = b'(V - 20) + c'(V - 20)^2$$

We can choose two points equally spaced along the V axis if we wish, but we note that the curvature is sharpest at the lower end, and there might be more difficulty fitting here. Let us then choose the points (V of 90, I of 50) and (V of 170, I of 200) to find b' and c'. Then, the two equations

$$50 = b'\,70 + c'\,70^2$$
and
$$200 = b'\,150 + c'\,150^2$$

are easily solved simultaneously, giving a c' value of 0.007 and a b' value of 0.171. Now,

$$I = 0.171(V - 20) - 0.0077(V^2 - 40V + 400)$$

which becomes

$$I = 0.0077V^2 - 0.137V - 0.33$$

as the polynomial that fits this curve. The fit is checked by solving for I with various chosen V values. This is easily done, and the results are plotted on Fig. 10-3 at V values of 40, 80, 120, and 160 volts. The I predicted is about 1 ma high at the lower end and as much as 2 ma low at the higher end. This is an error of about 2 per cent or less and can be improved by resolving for a polynomial with n of 3. If this were carefully done, the fitting error could be reduced to less than 0.5 per cent over the entire range.

10-3. Interpolation and Extrapolation

In Sec. 7-3, we saw how a set of points could be extrapolated graphically as a means of checking for data consistency. Graphs can also be used for interpolating values with great assurance if the points form a smooth curve on (X,Y) coordinates. Interpolation may also be accomplished by a variety of numerical means, one of which will be discussed here. The simpler numerical interpolation methods, such as basic linear interpolation, are known to all engineers. Similarly, we need not consider any further the establishment of an equation as described in previous sections or in Chap. 9, and then using this equation to find intermediate values. What we would like is some method that does not require an extensive computation leading to an equation or curve fit, yet a means that uses more than the two surrounding points and a straight line between them. Interpolation is particularly necessary when we are operating a factorial test (Secs. 6-3 to 6-5) and, for one reason or another, have failed to obtain a test point inside the square plan.

The method to be described here involves the *Lagrange interpolation formula*, which derives from a study of determinants,[1] and will be used here without proof. Suppose we have a test that gives us data points (X_1, Y_1), (X_2, Y_2), . . . , (X_n, Y_n), and we wish to find the value Y for a value X that was not set on the test apparatus. Then the Lagrangian form becomes

$$
\begin{aligned}
Y = Y_1 &\frac{X - X_2}{X_1 - X_2} \times \frac{X - X_3}{X_1 - X_3} \times \cdots \times \frac{X - X_n}{X_1 - X_n} \\
&+ Y_2 \frac{X - X_1}{X_2 - X_1} + \frac{X - X_3}{X_2 - X_3} \times \cdots \times \frac{X - X_n}{X_2 - X_n} \\
&+ Y_n \frac{X - X_1}{X_n - X_1} \times \frac{X - X_2}{X_n - X_2} \times \cdots \times \frac{X - X_{n-1}}{X_n - X_{n-1}} \quad (10\text{-}4)
\end{aligned}
$$

Quite apparently this will be an extensive computation for n of 10

[1] Worthing and Geffner, *op. cit.*, pp. 20–21.

or more.   It does, however, adapt well to machine computation.
If an analyst wishes to use a set of data in a digital program, he
need only insert the Lagrangian formula in his program and then
introduce as many data points as he wishes in the memory.   Then,
when an XY value is required that has not been found in test, the
Lagrangian values can be computed using all the data.

Example 10-2.   In Example 6-2, the internal-combustion engine
test, the following data were obtained after an averaging procedure:

Load on engine, lb...............	22	44	66	87.5
Fuel consumption, lb/hr..........	8.2	11.9	17.5	25.5

Let us imagine that, for some reason, the 44-lb readings were not
obtained or were incorrectly obtained.   What value for fuel consumption would the Lagrange formula predict?
Solution.   Let us allow load and fuel consumption to take the
following positions in our Eq. (10-4):

Load.................	22 (X_3)	66 (X_2)	87.5 (X_1)
Consumption........	8.2 (Y_3)	17.5 (Y_2)	25.5 (Y_1)

Then our Lagrangian form becomes

$$Y = 25.5 \frac{44 - 66}{87.5 - 66} \times \frac{44 - 22}{87.5 - 22} + 17.5 \frac{44 - 87.5}{66 - 87.5} \times \frac{44 - 22}{66 - 22}$$
$$+ 8.2 \frac{44 - 87.5}{22 - 87.5} \times \frac{44 - 66}{22 - 66}$$

$Y = -8.75 + 17.6 + 2.72 = 11.57$, compared with the experimental value of 11.9.   If the reader graphs these three points and
plots a smooth curve through them, he will probably obtain a value
of 11.4 to 11.5 depending on the French curve used.   The advantage
of the mathematical approach is that it is automatic and can be
duplicated later by anyone else to obtain the exact interpolated
value that we obtain.

We have not said anything yet about extrapolation to points
outside the range covered in our test.   We might, for example, have
omitted the 87.5-lb reading above and then solved for it using Eq.
(10-4).   Such a procedure conflicts with various mathematical
arguments that prohibit extrapolation by such formulas beyond the

data range. On the other hand, the Lagrange formula will give reasonable extrapolation values if the method is not "stretched" too far, and is probably to be preferred over a graphical extrapolation by eye. A certain class of academic mind finds such "desperate" measures disturbing, doubtless because such persons are seldom, if ever, confronted with an irrevocably lost piece of test data. For the practicing engineer, extrapolation, when used with caution and common sense, is one more tool to move the job ahead.

10-4. Differentiation and Integration

The main advantage of a formula, as opposed to a graph, table, or statistical figure, lies in the many powerful and ingenious mathematical manipulations that can be applied to general formulas. It is possible to graphically integrate or differentiate a curve,[1] but it is often better first to obtain the equation and then to attack the function mathematically. The reason for this is that each graphic computation is likely to be long and tedious, and we may have to try several different approaches before finding what we wish. A single fit will give us a general equation, which we can then integrate or differentiate at will and in any manner that is mathematically possible.

When to differentiate or integrate cannot be generally spelled out in any detail. Each engineering test is unique and may require new or imaginative mathematical treatment. Two possible undergraduate tests will serve as examples of these ideas.

A large bank of war-surplus capacitors has an effective capacitance of 1,000 μf and is to be charged through a 10,000-ohm resistance to 1,000 volts d-c. The 10,000-ohm resistor is enclosed in a water calorimeter so that its energy dissipation can be measured. With an RC time constant of 10 sec, a number of readings of voltage across the capacitor and across the resistor are made (versus time) and the results plotted. By a proper transformation (on semilog paper in this case) the functions

$$e_r = Ee^{-t/RC}$$
and
$$e_c = E(1 - e^{-t/RC})$$

are established for the instantaneous voltage across the resistor e_r and capacitor e_c as a function of time-from-switch closure t with E

[1] R. P. Hoelscher, J. N. Arnold, and S. H. Pierce, "Graphic Aids in Engineering Computation," chap. 4, McGraw-Hill Book Company, New York, 1952.

the impressed voltage (1,000), R the resistance (10,000 volts), and C the capacitance ($1,000 \times 10^{-6}$ farad).

The rate at which energy is being generated in the resistor must be e_r^2/R, and the total energy dissipated in "infinite" time must be found by integration,

$$\text{Total energy} = \int_0^\infty \frac{E^2}{R^{-2t/RC}}\, dT$$

This integrates to

$$\text{Total energy} = \frac{E^2RC}{2R}\, e^{-2t/RC}$$

or finally

$$\text{Total energy} = \frac{CE^2}{2}$$

With the values given, this quantity equals (a farad equals 1 coulomb squared per joule)

$$\text{Total energy} = \tfrac{1}{2} \times 1{,}000 \times 10^{-6} \times 1{,}000^2 = 500 \text{ joules}$$

or 0.494 Btu. The 10,000-ohm resistor in this test need only handle a maximum of 1,000 volts/10,000 ohms or 0.1 amp and thus can be small in size. If the calorimeter in which it is immersed has perhaps 0.1 lb of water, the temperature rise will be 5°F and the energy summation can be checked. A similar analysis will show that the energy actually stored in the capacitor is exactly equal to the energy dispersed in the resistance during the charging period. This conclusion can be verified by discharging the capacitor through the resistor and again measuring the calorimeter temperature rise.

Even if a d-c capacitor test does not permit measurement of the energy stored and dissipated, the use of integration to find energy from the established charge and/or discharge function is usually worthwhile. A given capacitor and voltage source can be charged through several resistances, and a curve of e_r^2/R plotted against time for each case. The integration of each curve using a planimeter or Simpson's rule of area summation[1] should give identical values

---

[1] Divide the x axis under the curve into n equal increments, h units wide, making sure that n is even. Then, the area $\int Y\, dx$ is found from

$$\text{Area} = \tfrac{1}{3}h[(Y_0 + Y_n) + 4(Y_1 + Y_3 + Y_5 + \cdots + Y_{n-1})$$
$$+ 2(Y_2 + Y_4 + Y_6 + \cdots + Y_{n-2})]$$

where the first segment is bounded by Y_0 and Y_1, the next by Y_1 and Y_2, and so on.

so that significant differences in area under the curves serve as error indications.

A series of slender columns of various length-to-radius-of-gyration ratios L/R are compressed, and the maximum load each can support is recorded. The data (maximum stress versus L/R) are correlated by a function of the form

$$S = \frac{a}{b + c(L/R)^2}$$

where S is the stress in pounds per square inch, and a, b, and c are experimentally determined constants that are presumably functions of the kind of material and the end condition of the column during test. Let us see if we can learn any more about this test through differentiation of the experimental function.

The first differentiation gives

$$dS = -2ac \frac{L}{R} \left[b + c \left(\frac{L}{R}\right)^2 \right]^{-2} d\frac{L}{R}$$

Setting $dS/d(L/R)$ equal to zero, we soon see that there is no maximum or minimum point other than L/R of zero. We could, if we wished, study various portions of the curve as to slope. Instead, let us find the second derivative and test for inflection points. This is

$$\frac{d^2S}{d(L/R)^2} = -2ac \left[b + c \left(\frac{L}{R}\right)^2 \right]^{-2} + 8ac^2 \left(\frac{L}{R}\right)^2 \left[b + c \left(\frac{L}{R}\right)^2 \right]^{-3}$$

Setting this second derivative equal to zero and making the appropriate cancellations and algebraic operations, we obtain

$$\frac{L}{R} = \pm \sqrt{\frac{b}{3c}}$$

where only the positive root is of interest. Thus, we see that a single inflection point exists. With values of 1.1 for b and 4.0×10^{-5} for c, our inflection L/R is 165. Those familiar with strength-of-materials work will realize that this L/R is close to the slenderness ratio at which this particular series of columns deviated from the simple Euler curve and theory.[1]

Probably the main lesson to be gained from these two examples is that mathematical analysis of test data is most fruitful when the

[1] See R. Liddicoat and P. Potts, "Laboratory Manual of Materials Testing," The Macmillan Company, New York, 1952.

investigator has some idea of what to expect and in what direction to move. Failure to see that $(e_r{}^2/R)\,dt$ is the instantaneous energy dissipated in the capacitor will forestall any important use of an integral, while time spent differentiating the et curve is not likely to tell us much unless there is something vitally wrong with the test. Although we may find the inflection point in the column formula, we derive little use from this figure unless we realize that this point represents a region where one theoretical mechanism changes to another. Undoubtedly, curves exist in literature right now which could reveal secrets to anyone who wished to integrate or differentiate them in one manner or another. The man who finally harvests such dividends will be the engineer most intimately acquainted with the theory of the test itself, rather than the "hardware expert" whose horizon ends at the test apparatus.

10-5. Summary

In this chapter we have considered a few of the common analytic approaches to test-data analysis. Basic to all tests giving quantitative data is the correct handling of significant figures during data processing and analysis. Too few significant figures and we may lose important accuracy or significance during processing, while too many significant figures lead to more difficult calculating problems and perhaps the necessity of longhand or machine work. Also, excess numbers of significant figures in reported results may lead the reader astray and are dishonest in the sense that they suggest an experimental accuracy that did not actually exist. If there is any doubt on this score, it is best to play safe and use extra figures, since too few can cause accumulated "rounding errors."

When a curve cannot be fitted using least squares or other graphical means, we usually resort to fitting a general polynomial of the form of Eq. (10-1). The formal method of doing this utilizes determinants and is readily adapted to digital computing-machine use. When hand fitting is to be undertaken, a series of simultaneous solutions is often quicker, providing we transform the axis of the XY function so that one of the constants in the polynomial is zero. The selection of points used in this simultaneous solution is important, since selection from the wrong region of the curve will often give a poor fit in the difficult region. The rule of thumb is to take points from the extremes of the data envelope, and then take the other selected points from the region in which the slope is changing most radically, in which the curve is peaking, or in which inflection points exist. The fitted equation should always be checked at selected intervals for adequacy of fit. Failure to get a fit, whatever points we choose, means simply that we need a higher-order polynomial.

There may be situations in which we do not wish to bother fitting a set of data to a formula, but where we may need some intermediate value not actually run on the test apparatus. This value can be found by plotting the data and using the curve for interpolation, but this method may show variation depending on who plots the curve and how uncertain its location may be. The usual linear interpolation is obviously defective in that it uses only two adjacent points rather than all the data. The best and most standard method, then, is the use of the Lagrange formula, which can handle as many data points as the computist wishes to include, can be used for extrapolation if desired, and will give the same interpolated value regardless of who makes the analysis.

If a mathematical function, obtained from graphical analysis or a polynomial fit, is available, the basic mathematical tools that can reveal new information are differentiation and/or integration. Differentiation gives exact values of maxima and minima and points of inflection or slope change, either of which may have great theoretical interest. Integration yields the area under curves. The use of these tools does require considerable familiarity with the theoretical aspects of the test, and they are most fruitfully applied by an analytically oriented engineer.

As noted, this chapter hardly begins to discuss this topic, and, if the reader begins to apply these basic or "kindergarten" methods to his own test situations, more elegant and imaginative analytic tools may become evident.

PROBLEMS

10-1. The hook gauge in Prob. 2-1 reads depths of (a) 0.123, (b) 1.234, and (c) 12.34567 ft. Round these numbers in a reasonable manner.

10-2. In Example 2-3 we considered a Brinell hardness machine. If our average indented hole diameter in this example is 4.0475 mm, how should we round this average for (a) presentation in a report and (b) use in computations where further mathematical manipulations are to be made?

10-3. Suppose that we are sure of reading a dimension to three significant figures with good confidence, plus an additional figure which is questionable. We wish to present a result with only two figures. The dimension is 1.899 in. How many places should we keep in the following computational situation? The reading is to be cubed, and then the number 1.1 is to be raised to this power.

10-4. The following data are to be fitted to a polynomial:

X	40	60	80	100	120
Y	800	1,090	1,290	1,450	1,600

Try the form $y = A + Bx + Cx^2$, and check your fit.

10-5. In Fig. 6-8 are four points forming a specific fuel-consumption-versus-temperature curve. These data are analyzed graphically in Example 9-4. Assuming that you did not see that the data could be fitted to a straight-line equation as shown in this example, fit it to an n-of-2 polynomial and compare the "goodness of fit" (by eye) with Figs. 9-10 and 9-11.

10-6. In Appendix A is a discussion of a viscosity measuring test. Use the values of time and mass for masses 30, 40, and 50 grams (ignore the other two pieces of data) in the Lagrange formula and extrapolate to the time for 60 grams. Compare with that predicted on the plot (Fig. A-2).

10-7. Four points give the following values:

X	1	3	4	6
Y	3	3	2	2

Use the Lagrange formula to estimate Y values for the X of 2, X of 0, and X of 5 points. Use only the four given points for each determination, and sketch the result.

10-8. In the following experimental functions, decide whether inflection points and/or maxima or minima occur and, if so, how knowledge of such points could assist in the experimental operation or in the data analysis.

 a. The Francis formula for a contracted weir is $Q = 3.33(B - 0.2H)H^{3/2}$, where Q is the flow in cubic feet per second, H is the head on the weir in feet, and B is the width of the spillway. We wish to run a test on a specific weir to verify (or modify) the constant 3.33 in the equation.

 b. A correlation relating the heat-transfer J factor to Reynolds number and the ratio of tube length L to tube diameter D is

$$J = 0.023 \left(\frac{VDP}{\mu}\right)^{-0.2} \left[1 + \left(\frac{D}{L}\right)^{0.7}\right]$$

We wish to verify this equation for a special kind of entrance condition by holding everything constant but the tube diameter and finding the effect of D on J. Around what values of L/D should we operate our test?

 c. Richardson's equation for the electron emission current i from a surface heated to an absolute temperature T is $i = AT^2e^{-b_0/T}$, where A and b_0 are constants. Given a plot of i versus T, how could we estimate a value of b_0? (*Hint:* Investigate the slope changes using the second derivative.)

10-9. A long thermal "fin" is heated at one end and loses heat from its surface. We are given an equation of surface temperature versus length, and we know that, at any point on the surface, the rate of heat loss from the fin will equal $h \, \Delta A \, (T - T_c)$, where h is the known heat-transfer coefficient, ΔA the small increment of area at which the temperature is T, and T_c the fixed surrounding temperature. If $T = (T_h - T_c)e^{-mx} + T_c$, where m is a system constant, T_h is the known root temperature, and A is $2\pi R^2\, dx$, show how we can use integration to find the total heat flow lost from a rod L ft long, thereby checking the known energy input. (This is a rather sophisticated form of the energy balance discussed in Chap. 7.)

REFERENCES

Hoelscher, R., J. N. Arnold, and S. H. Pierce: "Graphic Aids in Engineering Computation," chap. 4, McGraw-Hill Book Company, New York, 1952.

Oldenburger, R.: "Mathematical Engineering Analysis," The Macmillan Company, New York, 1950.

Smith, E., M. Salkover, and H. Justice: "United Calculus," John Wiley & Sons, Inc., New York, 1947.

Wilson, E. B.: "An Introduction to Scientific Research," chaps. 11 and 12, McGraw-Hill Book Company, New York, 1952.

Worthing, A. G., and J. Geffner: "Treatment of Experimental Data," chaps. 3, 4, and 10, John Wiley & Sons, Inc., New York, 1943.

CHAPTER 11

FORTRAN Methods in Experimentation

Many of the experiment-planning and data-analysis methods presented throughout this book require considerable amounts of computation. Certainly one deterrent to the extended use of statistics in engineering laboratories is the lack of time available to students required to carry out the lengthy, tedious, yet simple arithmetic needed in a t test or a computation of error propagation. In such a situation, the ready availability of digital computing machines can only have, and is having, a revolutionary effect.

Modern digital computers are set in motion by a *program* or set of instructions transmitted to the machine on punched cards, by magnetic tape, or by a typewriter. This set of instructions is then "translated" by a *compiler*, which is simply a second and standardized set of instructions designed to form an information bridge between the easily written program and the not-so-easily understood inner logic of the machine circuits. The details of compiler design need not be understood by experimental engineers nor, indeed, by anyone who will not write compilers themselves. Compilers, called *soft ware* in the computing trade, are nevertheless exceedingly important. It is they, more than almost any other aspect of the digital system, that make the practical writing of programs hard or easy. Some engineers feel that even the writing of programs should be done by specialists. This is an entirely incorrect view, and student engineers who adopt such a position are liable to suffer serious checks in their professional careers as well as miss out on what can be a rather interesting and challenging exercise in logical development.

Programs, at least in the United States, are largely written in the FORTRAN (FORmula TRANslator) language, a creation of the applied-programming groups at the International Business Machines Corp. FORTRAN has a vocabulary of only a dozen or so words and uses simple English where possible. It is found in many *dialects* such as FORGO, FORTRAN II, FORTRAN IV, and AFIT FORTRAN. These differ only in detail from each other. In some cases, they allow greater freedom of input and/or output statements. In other cases, they may permit the analyst to set up three-dimensional matrices or to construct logical syllogisms easily. For the experimentalist, the more advanced dialects are seldom required, and only the most basic FORTRAN methods will be discussed in this chapter. Just as this book has followed the typical experimental pattern from beginning to end, so in this chapter we will follow the construction of a typical program from input to readout, stressing in each section those aspects of the language most useful in a basic experimental context.

11-1. Input Statements

Two basic input statements are commonly applicable in compilers intended for small computers: READ (from cards) and ACCEPT (from the typewriter). In addition, two other statements are often required at the beginning of a program: FORMAT and DIMENSION statements.

Formating is probably the most bothersome and complicated aspect of program writing for the beginner, and those readers requiring FORMAT statements should refer to the more extended references at the end of the chapter. In general, formating simply tells the machine how many significant figures a given input number will have, where the decimal will appear, and how the input data will appear on a punched card. Some of the simpler FORTRAN dialects do not require FORMAT, in which case one simply inserts a number in the form 3.445, 0.00178, or 16700. If a number is too big or too small to comfortably fit into the eight-figure limit set by some compilers, power-of-ten notation is used. For example, 0.000000699 becomes $0.688E - 6$, which represents 0.688×10^{-6}. The reader should, however, carefully study his own compiler instructions and learn the FORMAT system for his own case.

The DIMENSION statement is often the first one in a program but refers specifically to situations where *subscripted variables* are used and will be discussed under that topic.

Suppose we wish to write a program to compute the average of a set of five numbers from Eq. (2-15). We must first tell the machine what we intend to label these numbers, and we can choose any names we wish providing our variable names do not exceed five characters in length. In addition, we should note that names beginning with the letters I, J, K, L, M, and N can be used only for *fixed-point numbers.* Fixed-point numbers lie between plus and minus 9999 and have no decimal point. They are intended specifically for subscripting work.

Suitable labels might be RPM1, RPM2, RPM3, etc., or FLOW1, FLOW2, and so on, providing they begin with letters from A through H or O through Z. COEFIC1 is too long. MORPO requires that the variable be in fixed point. If the machine is to average, say, five values of velocity in a duct and the input is on cards, the input statement might be (with no formating)

READ, VEL1,VEL2,VEL3,VEL4,VEL5

This instruction simply "tells" the machine to accept from one or more punched cards five numbers and to store them, in sequence, under the identifying labels VEL1, VEL2, and so on.

11-2. Subscripted Arrays, the DO Loop

In many data-processing applications, the amount of input data will vary from test to test. We might not always have exactly five velocities as in the previous example, but wish to be able to average N velocity figures up to, of course, some maximum number. To write such a more general and useful program, we need some way to vary the amount of data to be labeled at input. This is accomplished in FORTRAN by the important DO *loop* plus subscripting. First we must tell the computer how big an N value we have in any given case, so that N must now be part of the input data, written in fixed point with no decimal. The first input statement now becomes

111   READ, N

where N might vary from 2 to 25 or 50, and 111 is the *statement number* which identifies this particular statement in case we wish to return to it. Note that *not* every statement needs a statement number.

Next we use a DO statement which takes the general form

DO X M = I,J,K

X is the number of the statement that completes the DO loop, as we will demonstrate in a moment. M is a fixed-point variable which is set equal to the fixed-point constant I on the first pass through the loop. At each pass or cycle through the loop, M is incremented by the amount of the fixed-point constant K until M = J, the middle fixed-point constant on the right-hand side of the statement. When this occurs, the machine exits from the loop and continues beyond it.

We will use the DO loop to insert and label the velocities with the general label VEL(M), where M is a *subscript*. Thus

```
111    READ, N
       DO 4 M = 1,N,1
  4    READ, VEL(M)
```

The machine will now read the number of data to average, N, from a card and label it N. It will then set M equal to 1 and read the first velocity figure and label it VEL(1). If N is greater than 1, it will cycle back to the beginning of the DO loop and index M by 1, making it 2. The next velocity data are labeled VEL(2) and so on until M = N. At this point, the machine continues on beyond statement 4. By using FORMAT methods we can put several velocity data on a single card. Also, the DO statement can be written

```
       DO 4 M = 1,N
```

with the final 1 omitted. This third fixed-point number is understood to equal 1 if it does not appear. Note that we chose the number 4 to number the second READ statement. We could have chosen 44, 444, 5678, or any one- to four-digit number we wished.

The machine, however, will not compile even this much unless we place a DIMENSION statement first. Such a statement tells the machine how many spaces in memory to reserve for the subscripted variables. If we never plan to have more than, say, 50 input velocities, we write

```
       DIMENSION VEL(50)
```

Throughout the writing of these statements, the reader should note that although spacing is not too important when they are typed on cards, the punctuation must be exactly followed in almost every case.

11-3. Computational Statements

Having placed our data in the machine under a variety of labels, we now wish to operate on it arithmetically. FORTRAN allows a

variety of arithmetic operations including addition (+), subtraction
(−), multiplication (*), division (/), raising to a power P (**P),
and taking the absolute value of P [ABS(P)].   Finding of trigonometric
functions, logarithms, and more elaborate functions is possible when
the compiler has appropriate *subroutines* included.

    If we wish now to average our velocity figures, we must first
accumulate them using another DO loop.   We will do this accumula-
tion using a *sum bucket* with symbol SUM, first setting SUM to zero:

$$\text{SUM} = 0.$$
$$\text{DO 6 J} = 1,\text{N}$$
$$6 \quad \text{SUM} = \text{SUM} + \text{VEL(J)}$$

The machine enters the DO loop with SUM equal to zero and, on the
first pass through the loop, adds VEL(1) to zero so that SUM = VEL(1).
On the second pass, VEL(2) is added to VEL(1) and so on until J = N.

    Now we might be tempted to form the average by writing

$$\text{AVE} = \text{SUM/N}$$

but the machine would *not* accept this statement since it is a *mixed-
mode expression;* that is, it has a floating-point number (SUM) and
a fixed-point number (N) on the same side of an equals sign.
FORTRAN compilers will accept fixed- and floating-point variables in
the same statement if they are separated by an equals sign.   Thus

$$\text{DATA} = \text{N}$$

will transform the fixed-point N (say 19) to the floating-point DATA
(say 19.0).   Now we write

$$\text{AVE} = \text{SUM/DATA}$$

to obtain the average.   Let us continue to find the standard deviation from Eq. (2-16).   We use a second sum bucket (SUM2) to
accumulate the squared deviations of the individual velocity values
from AVE.   Thus

$$\text{SUM2} = 0.$$
$$\text{DO 9 K} = 1,\text{N}$$
$$\text{DEVI(K)} = \text{AVE} - \text{VEL(K)}$$
$$\text{SQDE(K)} = \text{DEVI(K)**2.}$$
$$9 \quad \text{SUM2} = \text{SUM2} + \text{SQDE(K)}$$

    Some of these statements could be combined, of course, and the
addition of new subscripted variables [DEVI(K), SQDE(K)] requires

that they be added to the DIMENSION statement. The variance is SUM2 divided by (N − 1) which must become (DATA − 1.).

$$\text{VAR} = \text{SUM2}/(\text{DATA} - 1.)$$

Use of the parentheses is quite simple and can be grasped from the examples herein discussed. In general, too many parentheses are better than too few. However, there must be exactly the same number of right- and left-hand parentheses in any statement.

If we want the standard deviation (STDE), we write

$$\text{STDE} = \text{SQRT}(\text{VAR})$$

where SQRT is a FORTRAN arithmetic symbol meaning "take the square root of."

11-4. Transfer Statements

Transfers within a program can be either *conditional* or *unconditional*. The unconditional transfer in FORTRAN is called for simply by the statement GO TO X, where X is any statement number in the program.

Two conditional transfer statements are possible. The IF *statement* takes the general form

$$\text{IF } (\text{A} - \text{B}) \text{ X,Y,Z}$$

where A and B are any two floating-point numbers. If their difference is *negative*, transfer is to statement X. If their difference is exactly *zero*, transfer is to statement Y, and if their difference is *positive*, transfer is to statement Z.

The *computed* GO TO *statement* takes the form

$$\text{GO TO } (\text{P,Q,R,S, . . . ,Z),J}$$

where P, Q, R, and so on are statement numbers. If fixed-point J is equal to 1, transfer is to P. When J = 2, transfer is to Q. J = 3 transfers to R, and so on. The number of different transfers possible using a computed GO TO statement is limited only by the number of characters that can be typed on one line of an input card.

An additional transfer statement possible with the IBM 1620 machine is

$$\text{IF (SENSE SWITCH N) Y,Z}$$

where N can take the value 1, 2, 3, or 4 to correspond to the four numbered switches on the machine console. If the appropriate switch is *on*, transfer is to statement Y, and if the switch is *off*, transfer is to statement z.

Now let us consider how we might take our velocity data and combine them with a second set to compute Student's t and the F ratio. However, we might also wish to use the program in its present form to obtain the standard deviation of a single family of velocity data. We first rewrite the initial input statement

    111   READ, N,NN

where NN is the number of data in the second set. Now returning to the previous statement that found the standard deviation of the first sample, we wish to have a conditional transfer to one of two places: either to a routine that finds the standard deviation of sample two or to an output routine that prints the average and standard deviation of sample one. First we write

    DATA2 = NN

and then an IF statement

    IF(1.0 − DATA2) 12,100,100

Now if we have, at the first data insertion, put in a value greater than 1 for NN, the IF statement will be negative and transfer will be to statement 12, which follows immediately. With NN inserted as 0 or 1 (a so-called *dummy-variable* insertion), transfer is to statement 100, which will be described later. The statements involved in processing sample number two follow:

```
12   DO 16 MM = 1,NN
16   READ, VEL2(MM)
     SUM3 = 0.
     DO 18 JJ = 1,NN
18   SUM3 = SUM3 + VEL2(JJ)
     AVE2 = SUM3/DATA2
     SUM4 = 0.
     DO 20 KK = 1,NN
     DEVI2(KK) = AVE2 − VEL2(KK)
     SQDE2(KK) = DEVI2(KK)**2.
20   SUM4 = SUM4 + SQDE2(KK)
     VAR2 = SUM4/(DATA2 − 1.)
     STDE2 = SQRT(VAR2)
```

If this program is to go into a small computer, we may already be in *memory-overflow* trouble. So far we have used six different arrays of subscripted variables, only two of which [VEL(K) and VEL2(K)] we really need. If each data sample is to have 50 items, the initial DIMENSION statement will set aside memory space for 300 numbers, and to this requirement we add a variety of statements, variable names, and so on. After this program is completed, we will show a revised version with greatly reduced memory requirements.

Let us continue to find the total standard deviation (STOT) from Eq. (8-4):

DEGF = (DATA + DATA2 − 2.)
VARTO = (SUM2 + SUM4)/DEGF
STOT = SQRT(VARTO)

and *t* from Eq. (8-3):

CONST = (1./DATA) + (1./DATA2)
STUDT = (AVE − AVE2)/(STOT*(SQRT(CONST)))

This might come out to be negative in some cases so we write

STUDT = ABS(STUDT)

which takes the absolute value of our Student's *t* from Eq. (8-3).

Even though we might not want it in every case, the *F* ratio (FRATO) is easily obtained, after first deciding with an IF statement which variance is the larger.

```
      IF (VAR2 − VAR) 22, 23, 24
  22  FRATO = VAR/VAR2
      GO TO 101
  23  FRATO = 1.0
      GO TO 101
  24  FRATO = VAR2/VAR
```

We have now obtained all the statistical material of interest from the two data samples and are ready to read this material out of memory.

11-5. Output Statements

Two output statements are commonly used with FORTRAN on the smaller machines: TYPE or PRINT (on the typewriter) and PUNCH (on cards). Again, most compilers require output FORMAT statements for each TYPE or PUNCH command. Output FORMAT specifies where on cards or typewriter the output is to appear and in what decimal form. Again, leaving out FORMAT, we obtain

    101   PUNCH, STOT, DEGF, STUDT

which are the total combined standard deviation, the number of degrees of freedom, and Student's t. Also,

       PUNCH, FRATO
       PUNCH, AVE2,VAR2,STDE2

will read out the F ratio and the average, variance, and standard deviation of the second data set. Finally,

    100   PUNCH, AVE,VAR,STDE

gives the three important statistical quantities for the first or original set of data. Note that this final PUNCH statement is all that we get as output if we placed 0 or 1 in for NN back at the beginning of the program.

We now wish to *initialize* the program using a GO TO transfer, in case there may be additional sets of data to be analyzed,

    GO TO 111

and, finally, all FORTRAN programs must end with

    END

to tell the machine where to stop.

Three additional FORTRAN commands exist, but only one is of much importance. CONTINUE is used as the last statement in a DO loop when the DO loop would ordinarily end with an IF or GO TO transfer statement. FORTRAN compilers will permit transfer out of an "unsatisfied" DO loop providing the CONTINUE statement is used. An example will be given later.

The PAUSE statement is used to stop the machine at the place in the program where PAUSE appears. STOP also halts operation and, in addition, produces a typed "STOP." These two commands are used mainly in checking out long and complex programs. When the computation is restarted, the machine continues to the next statement following PAUSE or STOP.

Having completed our statistical program, let us "trim the fat" by cutting down on the number of subscripted arrays and named variables that do not have to be held in memory. We will establish only two subscripted variable sets, SUB(N) and SUB2(NN), which will serve to store the various subscripted variables as we come to them. Actually, a single array would suffice in the program since we complete the work on one set of data before starting on the other, but we will use two for clarity. We will not condense the statements, again in the interests of intelligibility. FORMAT statements are still left out.

```
          DIMENSION SUB(50), SUB2(50)
111       READ, N,NN
          DO 4, M = 1,N
4         READ, SUB(M)
          SUM = 0.
          DO 6 M = 1,N
6         SUM = SUM + SUB(M)
          DATA = N
          AVE = SUM/DATA
          SUM2 = 0.
          DO 9 M = 1,N
          SUB(M) = AVE - SUB(M)
          SUB(M) = SUB(M)**2.
9         SUM2 = SUM2 + SUB(M)
          VAR = SUM2/(DATA - 1.)
          STDE = SQRT(VAR)
          DATA2 = NN
          IF (1. - DATA2) 12,100,100
12        DO 16, M = 1,NN
16        READ, SUB2(M)
          SUM = 0.
          DO 18 M = 1,NN
18        SUM = SUM + SUB2(M)
          AVE2 = SUM/DATA2
          SUM4 = 0.
          DO 20 M = 1,NN
          SUB2(M) = AVE2 - SUB2(M)
          SUB2(M) = SUB2(M)**2.
```

```
20   SUM4 = SUM4 + SUB2(M)
     VAR2 = SUM4/(DATA2 − 1.)
     STDE2 = SQRT(VAR2)
     DEGF = (DATA + DATA2 − 2.)
     VARTO = (SUM2 + SUM4)/DEGF
     STOT = SQRT(VARTO)
     CONST = (1./DATA) + (1./DATA2)
     STUDT = (AVE − AVE2)/(STOT*(SQRT(CONST)))
     STUDT = ABS(STUDT)
     IF (VAR2 − VAR) 22,23,24
22   FRATO = VAR/VAR2
     GO TO 101
23   FRATO = 1.0
     GO TO 101
24   FRATO = VAR2/VAR
101  PUNCH,STOT,DEGF,STUDT
     PUNCH,FRATO
     PUNCH,AVE2,VAR2,STDE2
100  PUNCH,AVE,VAR,STDE
     GO TO 111
     END
```

This may look reasonably complicated to the beginner but is really nothing but elementary arithmetic tied together with a few logical statements. It would be handy if we could now insert the t and F ratio tables in the computer and have the final probability figures print out as well. Such a trick is possible with large machines, but programming such a "table look-up," especially with the F ratio which has three entries, is simply not worth the work. A single-variable "table look-up" will be described in the next section.

11-6. Special Topics

The foregoing material covers a considerable number of the skills needed to write programs for the processing of test data. Special situations that arrive frequently in experimentation deserve some comment here.

a. Computed GO TO *in error analysis.* The differentiation of functions required for error propagation studies in Chap. 3 is not easily done on a digital computer, although special programs for such requirements do exist. A reasonably general program could be written including a number of the commoner results of the sort tabulated in Table 3-1.   Access to these would be through a computed GO TO with each formula coded by an appropriate number used in the GO TO statement's indexing parameter.   For example,

```
      GO TO (1,6,8,9),K
1     ERROR = SQRT(PX**2. + PY**2.)
      GO TO 100
6     ERROR = SQRT(((PX/X)**2.) + ((PY/Y)**2.))
      ERROR = R*ERROR
      GO TO 100
8     ERROR = (B*R*PX)/X
      GO TO 100
9     ERROR = R*PX
      GO TO 100
```

where we have included the first four equations from Table 3-1 and can gain access to any of them by inserting either 1, 2, 3, or 4 for K at the start of the program.   Unfortunately, a program using this scheme will require a number of dummy inputs since all variables named in the equations must appear in a READ input statement. That is, we will have to insert a dummy number for B in statement 8, even though we do not use this statement in a given situation.

   b. *Double subscripting.* The Latin-square designs of Chap. 6 invite the use of *double subscripting.*   Taking a four-by-four square, we might define the rows, reading from top to bottom, by the symbols I(1), I(2), I(3), and I(4).   Similarly, the columns reading from left to right might be labeled J(1), J(2), J(3), and J(4).   Now we can use a *double DO loop* or *nested DO loop* to read the 16 values of, say, fuel consumption in Example 6-2 into our square:

```
      DO 5 I = 1,4
      DO 5 J = 1,4
5     READ, FUCON(I,J)
```

On entering the DO loop, I is set equal to 1, and then J is set equal to 1, so that the first entry (of 21.2 in Example 6-2) is labeled FUCON(1,1).   The rule governing such nested DO loops is that the lowest DO statement must be satisfied first.   Thus the J variable is indexed to 2, I stays at 1, and we have moved to the second column of the top row (value 24.5) with label FUCON(1,2).   We proceed across the top row until the lower of the two DO statements is satisfied (J = 4), and then I is indexed to 2, and the second row is covered in the same manner. The traverse pattern of the square is thus

	J(1)	J(2)	J(3)	J(4)
I(1)	1	2	3	4
I(2)	5	6	7	8
I(3)	9	10	11	12
I(4)	13	14	15	16

where the numbers 1 through 16 show the sequence of insertion.

Changing the result square to a log-of-result square is very simple:

```
    DO 7 I = 1,4
    DO 7 J = 1,4
7   FUCON(I,J) = LOG(FUCON(I,J))
```

In this type of experimental analysis, we often want to average the results in the square by row, column, and by other combinations. Row and column averages are easy. For example, the four columns can be averaged by the following:

```
    DO 9 J = 1,4
    AVER(J) = FUCON(1,J)+FUCON(2,J)+FUCON(3,J)
    +FUCON(4,J)
9   AVER(J) = AVER(J)/4.
```

Other averages within the square are most easily handled by a "brute force" approach rather than in a DO loop. The average of the diagonal including square numbers 1, 6, 11, and 16 would be

```
    DIAV1 = (FUCON(1,1)+FUCON(2,2)+FUCON(3,3)
    +FUCON(4,4))/4.
```

and so on.

c. *Readout from an XY function.* "Looking up" values in large tables such as those relating t and probability or pressure, volume, and enthalpy in the steam tables is usually not worth the effort and memory space. In many experimental data-processing situations, however, it is handy to be able to include a simple X-versus-Y function such as Table 2-1 or property relationships between viscosity or thermal conductivity of a test fluid and its temperature. We can easily read a table of values into memory with the DO loop

```
     DO 12 J = 1,N
     READ, X(J)
12   READ, Y(J)
```

but getting any Y out again, given a specific X, is a bit more complicated. One approach is to use the Lagrange interpolation formula, Eq. (10-4), which will take all the tabulated values to locate a Y for a specific and nontabulated X.   If we had a dozen or twenty X and Y values, the Lagrangian equation would become lengthy and unwieldy, even with a digital computer. Using four surrounding points should give an extrapolated Y sufficiently accurate for most purposes, but now we have the problem of locating the four surrounding X and Y table values when we are given any X value that lies within the extent of the tabulation, that is, between $x(1)$ and $x(N)$.

One way to accomplish this is to start at one end of the list of X values and make comparisons using an IF statement. Letting XNEW be our given X value for which we desire a YNEW, we write

$$NN = N - 2$$
$$DO\ 16\ J = 3, NN$$
$$IF\ (x(J) - XNEW)\ 16, 17, 18$$

17 $XNEW = x(J)$
  GO TO 25

18 $K = J$
  GO TO 26

16 CONTINUE

Since we need two values on each side of XNEW, we work in the range $J = 3$ and $J = N - 2$.   Entering the DO loop with J at 3, we compare XNEW and $x(3)$. If XNEW is large (the difference is negative), we transfer to statement 16 which permits the DO loop to "continue"; that is, J is indexed to 4, and we repeat the test. If XNEW lies below $x(3)$ and we have been careful to have it above $x(2)$, we store the J value with counter K and go to statement 26 at once:

26 $x1 = x(K-2)$
  $x2 = x(K-1)$
  $x3 = x(K+1)$
  $x4 = x(K+2)$
  $y1 = y(K-2)$
  and so on for Y2, Y3, and Y4.

These are the four surrounding X and Y values from the table needed to enter the Lagrange formula, two on either side of our XNEW and YNEW.   The rewriting of Eq. (10-4) to find YNEW using these values will be left as an exercise.

If it happens that XNEW is exactly equal to a table entry, we skip all intermediate steps and formulas and go to statement 25 directly, which is

$$25 \quad \text{YNEW} = \text{Y}(\text{K})$$

11-7. Computer Simulation

The modern digital computer is becoming a kind of experimental device itself. Complex engineering systems, which are beyond even the most rarefied forms of higher mathematical analysis, can often be easily *simulated* using a series of simple interlocking equations that describe their complete behavior pattern. These sets of equations are then solved with a variety of input parameters to investigate the ranges of the dependent output values and to study the relationship between input and output.

As a single example, a geological theory suggested that the form of streams and river basins was the result of a great many small chance occurrences happening over geological periods of time, each occurrence being essentially random. The multiple combination of these random occurrences led to river basins having various stream lengths and numbers of streams of various sizes that were common for basins studied throughout the world. To test such a theory by experiment would be impossible, but it can be simulated, using so-called *random-walk methods*, on a digital computer. The results of a variety of such simulated growth experiments were in striking confirmation of the theory. Stream and river basins were created numerically having length, size, and frequency distributions almost identical to those observed in nature.[1]

The variety of possible simulations in geology and biology, in traffic, heat transfer, mechanics, and social-science fields, is, as yet, hardly imagined. Simulation work requires an entirely different (and much simpler) sort of mathematics from that now thought essential to engineering work. Already it is possible to teach clever high school students how to solve, on a computer, engineering problems that a postdoctoral fellow using formal mathematics cannot solve. As always, there is considerable resistance to computer simulation by those who have a vested interest in their own special and hard-won skill.

For the experimentalist, simulation offers the chance of "running" experiments entirely on the computer. Although instrument accu-

[1] See H. Schenck, Jr., Simulation of the Evolution of Drainage-basin Networks with a Digital Computer, *J. Geophys. Res.*, **68**:5739–5745 (Oct. 15, 1963).

racy is not a problem there, error will appear as uncertainties in physical properties and in constants used in the simulation program. Simulations and parametric studies can draw help from dimensional analysis and from the factorial test plans of Chap. 6, which may allow a considerable reduction in the number of cases to be run on a computer.

Perhaps the most direct and immediate application of simulation for the experimenter lies in the estimation of total experimental error in test programs too involved and complicated for the methods of Chap. 3. If we can simulate the performance of the complete instrument system on a computer, we can introduce a variety of errors and, by judiciously trying a number of combinations, create a total "error envelope," which will give an estimate of the worst to be expected under all test conditions. Much work on this sort of analysis remains to be done.

Computer simulation is a fitting note on which to end this book. Closer in some ways to experimentation than to analysis, it suggests the future importance of clever and imaginative test operations of the most complex sort.

PROBLEMS

11-1. Write a FORTRAN program designed to read in the data of Table 2-1 and read out any interpolated value, using the Lagrange equation.

11-2. Write a FORTRAN program to accept N pieces of x and y data and to obtain the least-squares line of x on y (y in error), using the methods of Chap. 9.

11-3. Write a FORTRAN program that will carry out Example 10-1 for the case of a second-degree polynomial.

11-4. Write a FORTRAN program that will test a set of N data points, having x and y coordinates to see whether the best straight line will result from linear, semilog, or log-log plotting. Decide on a criterion of "straightness" that can be numerically handled by the computer.

11-5. Write a program that will (a) take N pieces of data and compute the predicted Poisson distribution as described in Chap. 8 and (b) make a chi-squared check for goodness of fit (without reading in the chi-squared values and probabilities) on the data to see if the Poisson distribution predicts it. Be careful to include logic such that no cell has less than five items.

11-6. Write a program to run a Latin-square analysis on a three-by-three square similar to that done in Example 6-2.

REFERENCES

Hamming, R. W.: "Numerical Methods for Scientists and Engineers," McGraw-Hill Book Company, 1962.

McCracken, D. D.: "A Guide to FORTRAN Programming," John Wiley & Sons, Inc., New York, 1961.

Ralston, A., and W. Wilf: "Mathematical Methods for Digital Computers," John Wiley & Sons, Inc., New York, 1960.

Schenck, H., Jr.: "FORTRAN Methods in Heat Flow," The Ronald Press Company, New York, 1963.

Sherman, P. M.: "Programming and Coding Digital Computers," John Wiley & Sons, Inc., New York, 1963.

Weiss, E.: "Programming the IBM 1620," McGraw-Hill Book Company, New York, 1965.

APPENDIX A

Three Simple Experiments

Although it is impossible to even begin a discussion of the vast number of undergraduate, graduate, and industrial types of experiments, there may be some purpose in extensively examining three simple tests from the standpoint of experimental planning, technique, and analysis. The purpose here is not to establish a particular sequence or a form for report writing, but rather to apply the various topics of the book to well-known experiments common to most college-trained engineers.

Example A-1. *Viscosity Measurement Using a Stormer-type Rotating Viscosimeter.* The Stormer-type viscosimeter is shown in schematic form in Fig. A-1. Following the nomenclature of this figure, the viscosity is found from the equation,[1] where l is the height of the fluid and e is the additional fictive height due to friction on the bottom of the rotating cylinder.

$$\mu = \frac{\Delta\theta}{1/\Delta m} \frac{(b^2 - a^2)k^2 g}{4\pi a^2 b^2 S(l + e)} \tag{A-1}$$

The quantities a, b, k, s, and l are measured with calipers or scales and, owing to difficulties, we estimate a maximum possible uncertainty of $\frac{1}{32}$ of an inch or, roughly, 0.03 in. in all these measurements; e is given as 2.4 in. (no uncertainty is assumed, although

---

[1] J. K. Vennard, "Elementary Fluid Mechanics," pp. 227–229, John Wiley & Sons, Inc., 1949.

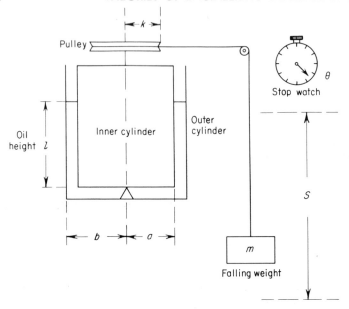

Fig. A-1. Diagram of the Stormer-type viscosimeter, showing the nomenclature of Eq. (A-1).

some is probably present); and $\Delta\theta/(1/\Delta m)$ we will find later by actual test. Writing Eq. (A-1) in the form

$$\mu = \frac{C\,\Delta\theta}{1/\Delta m} \tag{A-2}$$

let us find the propagated error in C and decide whether some or all of the dimensional readings should be replicated to reduce excessive uncertainties. Let us tabulate the values that make up our C:

	Quantity						
	a	b	k	s	l	e	$l+e$
Magnitude, in....	1.97	2.38	0.61	22.5	3.0	2.4	5.4
Uncertainty, in...	±0.03	±0.03	±0.03	±0.03	±0.03	0	±0.03

and we assume that g is 386 in./sec² and without uncertainty.

To simplify the Chap. 3 propagation analysis, let us write an equation for C in the form

$$C = D\left(\frac{1}{a^2} - \frac{1}{b^2}\right) \qquad (A\text{-}3)$$

where D is simply $k^2g/4\pi S(l + e)$ and, with the above values inserted, equals 0.0935. Now we apply Eq. (3-15) to each of the uncertain portions of Eq. (A-3). We see that

$$\frac{\partial C}{\partial a} = -\frac{2D}{a^3} = 2 \times \frac{0.0935}{1.97^3} = -0.0247$$

Then, $(\partial C/\partial a)^2 w_a^2 = (-0.0247)^2(0.03)^2 = 0.55 \times 10^{-6}$. This is the contribution that the uncertainty in a makes to the square of the over-all uncertainty in C. Similarly,

$$\frac{\partial C}{\partial b} = +\frac{2D}{b^3} = \frac{2.0935}{2.38^3} = 0.0149$$

and $(\partial C/\partial b)^2 w_b^2 = 0.0149^2 \times 0.03^2 = 0.187 \times 10^{-6}$.

Let us next investigate the uncertainty contributed by k. From Eq. (A-1)

$$\frac{\partial C}{\partial k} = \frac{b^2 - a^2}{a^2b^2}\left[\frac{g}{4\pi S(l + e)}\right]2k$$

The term $(b^2 - a^2)/a^2b^2$ equals 0.081. With the values for g, s, $(l + e)$, and k inserted, we obtain $\partial C/\partial k = 0.025$ and

$$\left(\frac{\partial C}{\partial k}\right)^2 w_k^2 = (0.025)^2(0.03)^2 = 0.565 \times 10^{-6}$$

Thus, we see at once that the uncertainty in k will contribute about as much to the final uncertainty in C^2 as will the a measurement uncertainty.

Next we find the S uncertainty effect from

$$\frac{\partial C}{\partial S} = -\frac{b^2 - a^2}{a^2b^2} \times \frac{h^2g}{4\pi(l + e)} \times \frac{1}{S^2}$$

Putting in the proper numbers, we find that

$$\left(\frac{\partial C}{\partial S}\right)w_s^2 = 0.000135 \times 10^{-6}$$

which is a negligible contribution, and it can be shown that the same applies to the $(l + e)$ uncertainty. Thus, we write Eq. (3-15) in the form

$$w_c = \left[\left(\frac{\partial C}{\partial a} \right)^2 w_a{}^2 + \left(\frac{\partial C}{\partial b} \right)^2 w_b{}^2 + \left(\frac{\partial C}{\partial k} \right)^2 w_k{}^2 \right]^{\frac{1}{2}}$$

and w_c will equal $(0.55 \times 10^{-6} + 0.187 \times 10^{-6} + 0.565 \times 10^{-6})^{\frac{1}{2}}$ or 0.00114. The value of C is 0.0076, so that the percentage uncertainty owing to measurement is $0.00114/0.0076$ or 15 per cent. To reduce this rather high uncertainty we can do one of two things. We can use more accurate measuring tools and methods and thereby decrease the uncertainty of 0.03 in., or we can replicate the a, b, and k readings to improve the over-all precision of measurement. We would expect a ninefold replication of these three critical quantities to reduce the uncertainty to 5 per cent, providing, of course, that the uncertainty is wholly due to random measuring error and not to bias or accuracy error.

We now must find $\Delta\theta/(1/\Delta m)$, which is the slope of a time-of-fall-versus-$(\text{mass})^{-1}$ curve, with all else (including s and l) held constant. Theory predicts that this will be a straight line, which, in turn, should suggest a least-squares analysis. Unfortunately, sufficient fractional masses were not available so that m^{-1} could be varied uniformly, and the Askovitz graphical plotting method utilized (Sec. 9-2). Viscosity is a strong function of temperature. Thus it would be quite foolish to change our masses in ascending or descending order, for the temperature of the oil may be rising or dropping slightly as well. The run sequence is easily randomized using a gaming method (Sec. 6-2).

A typical set of data (not in the sequence taken) is

Mass m, grams	10	20	30	40	50
Time to fall 22.5 in., sec	2.8	1.7	1.2	1.00	0.70
Mass^{-1}, 1/gram	0.100	0.05	0.033	0.025	0.020

Although perfectly equal spacing of mass^{-1} was not possible, this choice of mass intervals could surely be improved upon, providing the precision of time measurement is the same over the entire curve (which we must assume to use our least-squares equations). If it should happen that the uncertainty in interval measurement is worse at the short times, then the above choice looks better, for it puts more points at the short-interval end of the time-versus-$(\text{mass})^{-1}$ plot.

Let us fit a straight line to these data:

m^{-1}, X	θ, Y	$m^{-1}\theta$, XY	$(m^{-1})^2$, X^{2*}
0.1	2.8	0.28	0.01
0.05	1.7	0.085	0.0025
0.033	1.2	0.0395	0.00109
0.025	1.0	0.025	0.000625
0.020	0.7	0.014	0.000400
$0.228 = \Sigma m^{-1}$	$7.4 = \Sigma\theta$	$0.4435 = \Sigma m^{-1}\theta$	$0.014615 = \Sigma(m^{-1})^2$

* Nomenclature in Eqs. (9-6) and (9-7).

Equations (9-6) and (9-7) will now yield the intercept b' and the slope a':

$$b' = \frac{0.0146 \times 7.4 - 0.228 \times 0.4435}{5 \times 0.0146 - 0.228^2} = 0.333$$

$$a' = \frac{5 \times 0.4435 - 0.228 \times 7.4}{5 \times 0.0146 - 0.228} = 24.5$$

The data and the fitted line are shown in Fig. A-2.

We might now wonder about outliers. The obvious doubtful point is the one at minimum time, and therefore should not be rejected unless more data points at shorter times can be obtained. In such a simple test, it is quicker to rerun a trial several times than go through a statistical point rejection anyway. We note that the curve intercepts the time axis at a value of 0.333 sec, suggesting that some form of extrapolation check may be possible. The question is, of course, what should this intercept be, and how can we predict it? A study of Fig. A-1 should convince the reader that as m^{-1} approaches zero (m increases without limit), the retarding frictional effect of the fluid and viscosimeter walls will become negligible, and the weight will fall in a time predicted by the

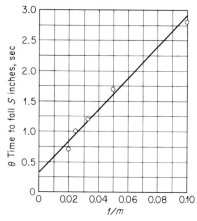

Fig. A-2. Data taken with the viscosimeter and used to find the slope of the time-versus-(mass)$^{-1}$ line. The solid line is drawn by a "least-squares" analysis.

usual equation for gravitationally accelerated motion,

$$S = \frac{g\theta^2}{2} + V_0\theta \qquad \text{(A-4)}$$

where S = 22.5 in., as noted

g = 386 in./sec²

V_0 = initial velocity of mass as it enters timing portion of its fall

The distance from start to the timed portion is selected so that the weight achieves steady or terminal velocity before entering the timed area, for the range of weights chosen. Suppose that the infinite weight fell 22.5 in. and then was timed for the next 22.5 in. (actually, the starting portion was around half of 22.5 in.). In the first 22.5 in., the weight requires $(2S/g)^{1/2}$ or 0.342 sec. To fall the total distance of 45 in. requires 0.482 sec. Thus, the second 22.5 in. takes $0.482 - 0.342$ or 0.14 sec. Since the weight did not get a full 22.5-in. start, we expect that the true time of fall in the timed 22.5-in. interval will lie somewhere between 0.342 sec (the time to fall from a dead start) and 0.14 sec (the time of fall with a 22.5-in. start). The extrapolation to 0.333 sec is therefore encouraging, though perhaps a bit high.

We would now like to estimate the uncertainty or error in line slope, since we must use this slope to find viscosity in Eq. (A-1). The slope is a function of $\Delta\theta$ and $1/\Delta m$, but m has no uncertainty, being read directly from unchanging standard masses. $\Delta\theta$ over all is 2.8 sec, and the absolute maximum time error at the $1/m$-of-zero origin is $(0.333 - 0.14)$ or 0.193 sec. (It is probably about half this.) This suggests that the maximum possible error will be on the order of 0.193/2.8 or about 7 per cent with perhaps 3.5 per cent a more likely estimate.

We can finally find the viscosity from Eq. (A-1):

$$\mu = 24.5 \times 0.0076 = 0.186 \text{ gram/(in.)(sec)}$$

or in English units, 0.00494 lb/(ft)(sec). Considering the already noted uncertainties, 0.0049 (that is, two significant figures) is the best we should report. Actually, with a maximum error of 15 per cent in the C factor and up to 7 per cent in the slope, 0.005 might be most honest, except that our maximum error may be unduly pessimistic.

To summarize this analysis: Our viscosity value is uncertain by as much as 15 to 20 per cent. We can improve this high uncertainty by (1) reducing the dimensional measuring uncertainties from 0.03 to 0.01 in. or less and (2) taking more points on our mass-versus-time test.   There is, however, no sense in doing (2) until (1) is undertaken.   Our mass-time curve can be checked by extrapolation, and a least-squares analysis applied.   By providing fractional weights, this line fitting could be greatly hastened.   Point sequence should always be randomized to offset any effect of regular temperature variations during the various drop-timing runs.

The manual dexterity and special theory associated with this rather archaic device are trivial and of slight importance.   Conversely, the ability to estimate errors, plan the runs, and completely analyze the results is crucial to the engineer, and such ability is immediately applicable in all modern technological investigation.

Example A-2.   *Stability of Simple Columns.*   Figure A-3 shows the arrangement used in a basic investigation of column stability. The columns are simply $\frac{3}{8}$-in.-diameter aluminum-alloy rods supported in ball-ended holders which are designed to prevent any end restraint.   The rods are aligned as nearly vertical as possible

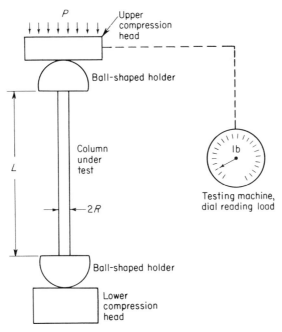

Fig. A-3. Schematic diagram of the column experiment.

between the heads of a standard testing machine and a compression load is slowly applied. The maximum load, P lb, and the length of each column, L in., are recorded. A primary purpose here is to investigate the applicability and range of utility of the so-called Euler formula

$$\frac{P}{A} = \frac{K\pi^2 E}{(L/R)^2} \tag{A-5}$$

where A = column cross-sectional area

E = modulus of elasticity (10×10^6 psi for material used)

R = radius of gyration of column

K = constant that depends on column end conditions and should be unity for this situation[1]

The machine in use reads P on a scale having a minimum division of 20 lb. Since A is always $(\pi/4)(\frac{3}{8})^2$ or 0.111 in.^{2}, and we assume this value is without uncertainty, we anticipate a maximum error in P/A of (taking half the least-scale division for P) 10/0.111 or 90 psia. It is doubtful whether this figure of uncertainty or any others estimated for E or L/R have much significance here. The reason is that imperfect control over the perpendicularity of the column in its mount and lack of control over its true straightness are likely to produce significant variations in P, whatever the precision of the instrumentation and measurement may be. Thus if we wish an estimate of the random character of the test, we should subject a series of identical columns to loading and use these data to predict the degree of precision error. This was not done, but it was possible to get a crude estimate of random variations from the actual test data, as we will see.

Selection of test-point spacing is possible through choice of cut lengths for the aluminum rod. Unfortunately, we do not know, before taking data, over what range the Euler formula is applicable, nor do we know what form the curve will take outside the "Euler region." The values chosen are not too bad, although they could certainly be improved on in a future test of this sort. The resulting data, then, are:

L/R.......	42.5	53	85	117	149	182	213
P/A, psi...	36,400	32,500	21,700	10,300	6,400	4,000	2,800

[1] See R. Liddicoat and P. Potts, "Laboratory Manual of Materials Testing," pp. 95–97, The Macmillan Company, New York, 1952.

Our first reaction is probably to plot P/A versus L/R on linear paper, since such curves are shown in most strength-of-materials books.   Figure A-4 shows such a plot, and we note little more from such a curve than was evident in the tabular material.   Those points forming the Euler region will lie on an exponential curve, but few experimenters can see an exponential line in such a plot. Does the L/R of 85 lie on the same exponential line as the outer four or not?   We must obviously replot the data.

Figure A-5 shows a log-log representation of the same data. We now see that our curve breaks into two different curves, one a straight line extending to an L/R of about 80 to 85 (the lower L/R limit of the Euler region for this column family), the second a curve of relatively undefined shape, having a lesser slope and appearing to go asymptotic to some log P/A value.   If we were to take further trials at this point, it is obvious that they should lie at L/R values of less than 80.   A scale will show that the slope of the straight-line portion is almost exactly -2, as predicted by the Euler equation. Furthermore, we see that the maximum deviation of a point from the line (drawn using least squares, computations omitted here) is P/A of 6,400 to P/A of 6,100, which is a deviation due to measuring error.   We can hardly say from only four points that this is the maximum possible error, but we know the uncertainty is *at least* this much.

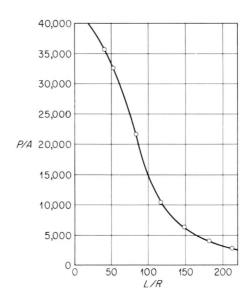

Fig. A-4. Standard plot of the column test data with a "French curve" line drawn through the points.

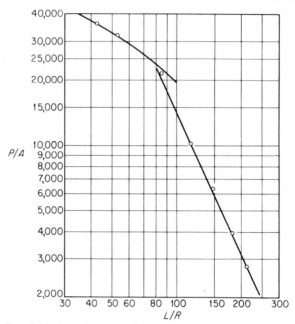

Fig. A-5. A log-log plot of the column data. Notice how much more information is given by this coordinate choice. The "Euler region" is clearly revealed by the straight-line portion.

This about exhausts the material that can be inferred from Fig. A-5 but still more can be found from further graphic analysis. Let us plot P/A versus $(L/R)^{-2}$ as shown in Fig. A-6. The slope of this line (only Euler region points shown) must be $K\pi^2E$. Using the given E value and a slope of 160×10^6, we obtain a K value of 1.63, instead of the 1.0 expected. This could mean that the ball-shaped holders do give some stability to the columns, or it could indicate a general bias in the measurements. Some error is certain y present since the extrapolation of the line to infinite L/R [or zero $(L/R)^{-2}$] should pass through the origin instead of below, as shown. This intercept is about 800 psi low, suggesting that the 300 psi uncertainty estimated from scatter is optimistic. Experience indicates that the long columns give the most questionable results. Thus the line of Fig. A-6 may have too great a slope as suggested by the high value of K and the failure to strike the origin. Further speculation is more questionable, and some more very long

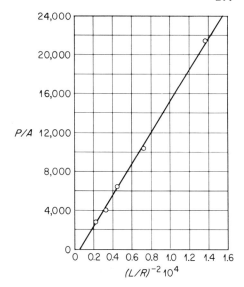

Fig. A-6. A plot of failure stress against $(L/R)^{-2}$ for the column data. This type of plot allows us to check the "infinite end" of the curve and also to find the slope and obtain K in Eq. (A-5).

columns should probably be tested. Indeed, we could say that the proper plan for a future test would be to bunch the column lengths in the short and the long regions: the short because we do not get a simple straight line and thus need more points to delineate the function, the long because the data are most doubtful here, and the random errors are greatest.

Example A-3. *Tests of Speed-measuring Instruments.* Figure A-7 shows, diagrammatically, a simple experiment designed to evaluate four different kinds of rotational speed-measuring devices: a hand tachometer, a small visual sighting device known as a "Visutac," a standard strobotac (light flasher), and a mechanical revolution counter used in conjunction with a stop watch. As a standard, the rotating shaft contains a small magnet and a nearby pickup coil sends an alternating signal induced by the magnet to the vertical plates of an oscilloscope. The horizontal oscilloscope sweep is triggered by a high-quality signal generator that is calibrated against the 60-cycle line frequency. Lissajous patterns of one, two, or three nodes on the scope indicate what multiple of the signal-generator input frequency is represented by the pickup coil signal. Since a slight variation in shaft speed will upset the scope pattern, this standard sensing device not only is as accurate as the line frequency is accurate, but permits detection of shaft speed variability during a test run.

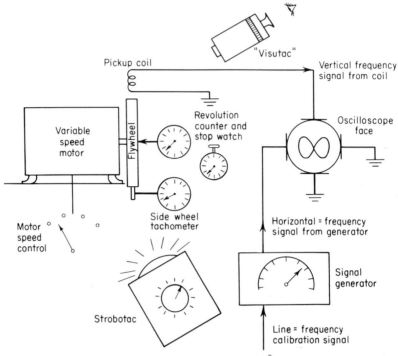

Fig. A-7. Diagram of speed-measuring tests designed to check various rotational speed-measuring devices against a signal-generator standard.

The test proceeded as follows: A shaft speed was set, and the oscilloscope–signal-generator combination was set to give a stationary pattern. When this was achieved, the four measuring instruments were read as rapidly as possible to obtain rpm values. If the oscilloscope pattern had drifted slightly, the signal generator was reset, and a second run was made with each of the four instruments. This was repeated five times at each set speed, and the speed sequence, as suggested in Chap. 6, was chosen by a gaming method. A better plan would have been to take a single complete reading at a speed, change to another speed, and then return to the first speed at a later time, following a completely randomized plan. This was not done owing to the difficulty of returning to exactly the same speed, using the motor and gearbox available.

The following data resulted for four settings of shaft rotation speed (all in rpm):

Group I

Tachometer	Visutac	Strobotac	Counter	Oscillo-scope	
1,080	1,094	1,070	1,094	1,092	
1,073	1,080	1,069	1,088	1,089	
1,079	1,078	1,070	1,083	1,092	
1,079	1,075	1,070	1,088	1,086	
1,078	1,075	1,070	1,082	1,086	
1,078	1,080	1,070	1,087	1,089	Gr. I averages
11	9	19	2		Osc. minus other
7	19	1	14	6	Max. variation of each

Group II

909	910	905	916	902	
909	900	902	910	914	
909	908	901	914	914	
910	898	902	916	916	
909	902	901	908	916	
909	904	902	913	912	Gr. II averages
3	8	10	−1		Osc. minus other
1	12	4	8	14	Max. variation of each

Group III

848	810	840	856	855	
847	920	840	848	855	
848	820	840	849	855	
852	820	840	844	855	
844	817	841	850	855	
849	817	840	850	855	Gr. III averages
6	38	15	5		Osc. minus other
4	10	1	12	0	Max. variation of each

Group IV

729	735	728	736	734	
728	735	727	730	734	
728	725	725	728	734	
729	720	725	728	734	
729	724	724	726	734	
729	728	726	730	734	Gr. IV averages
5	6	8	4		Osc. minus other
1	15	4	8	0	Max. variation of each

A number of aspects are visible in this compilation without further analysis. The strobe shows almost no variation in a given group, even though the "standard" (oscilloscope) reading shows a failure to control the speed exactly for five consecutive replications of measurement. This suggests that whatever varied the motor speed may also have affected the strobe reading in the same direction, and was probably line-voltage surge. The strobe is obviously biased (has accuracy error), but this error shows no obvious pattern over the four speeds considered. The Visutac has the greatest precision error in all but one of the groups. Next in precision error magnitude is the counter. Groups III and IV were made when control was good, as evidenced by the constant oscilloscope reading. From these groups, we can see that the strobe has almost no random error, even though it is biased (reads low for all four sets of data).

· Let us now make a more detailed statistical analysis of these data to test for agreement among the four instrument reading samples and the standard oscilloscope sample. For group I:

Tachometer		Visutac		Strobotac		Counter		Oscilloscope	
$\bar{X} - X$	$(\bar{X} - X)^2$	$\bar{X} - X$	$(\bar{X} - X)^2$	$\bar{X} - X$	$(\bar{X} - X)^2$	$\bar{X} - X$	$(\bar{X} - X)^2$	$\bar{X} - X$	$(\bar{X} - X)^2$
2	4	14	196	0	0	7	49	3	9
7	49	0	0	1	1	1	1	0	0
1	1	2	4	0	0	4	16	3	9
1	1	5	25	0	0	1	1	3	9
0	0	5	25	0	0	5	25	3	9
	$\Sigma(\bar{X} - X)^2$ $= 55$		$\Sigma(\bar{X} - X)^2$ $= 250$		$\Sigma(\bar{X} - X)^2$ $= 1$		$\Sigma(\bar{X} - X)^2$ $= 92$		$\Sigma(\bar{X} - X)^2$ $= 36$

Let us now use these values to make a series of t-test comparisons in turn between the oscilloscope sample of readings and the other samples. Taking the tachometer first, we test the hypothesis: "The tachometer and oscilloscope samples have the same mean." From Eq. (8-4), we first obtain the standard deviation of the two samples taken together:

$$S = \left(\frac{\Sigma x_a^2 + \Sigma x_b^2}{n_a + n_b - 2}\right)^{1/2} = \left(\frac{55 + 36}{8}\right)^{1/2} = 3.4$$

Now from Eq. (8-3) the t value is

$$t = \frac{1,078 - 1,084}{3.4 \sqrt{1/5 + 1/5}} = \frac{11}{3.4 \sqrt{0.4}} = 5.1$$

With eight degrees of freedom, we enter Fig. 8-2, and we see that

the chance of this or a larger t value occurring with the hypothesis
being true is about 0.001. We thus are wise to reject the hypothesis and state that the tach and oscilloscope, though they are only
11 rpm apart in mean value, are not giving the same mean. In
other words, if we were to read each one a hundred times or a
thousand times, we would expect the means to be different. The
same calculation can be made for each of the other instruments and
for the other three groups of figures. This has been done, and the
resulting probabilities are given in the following table. Each P
value is related to the test of the hypothesis that the given instrument at a given speed gives data that have the same mean as the
standard (oscilloscope).

Group	Tach. osc.	Visutac osc.	Strob. osc.	Counter osc.
I	0.001	0.03	<0.001	≫0.1
II	>0.1	0.009	0.005	≫0.1
III	<0.001	≪0.001	≪0.001	0.015
IV	≪0.001	0.19	≪0.001	0.08

From this tabulation, it is apparent that, lacking further calibration
or repair, the revolution counter and stopwatch (which might be
guessed to have the highest random error since each measurement
requires two readings) are the best choice. In three out of the four
groups, this device satisfies our "hypothesis of agreement" above
the 5 per cent level of significance. On the other hand, the strobe
shows the lowest random error throughout and is in poor agreement
with the standard owing to a pronounced accuracy error. If this
can be either repaired or "calibrated out," we might prefer a strobe
for use in speed-measuring problems.

These three simple experiments can only suggest the fruitful
application of planning and statistical ideas in engineering testing.
Notice that the methods are not equally useful in a given test. In
Example A-1, we made most use of the material in Chaps. 2 and
3 in investigating the possible errors and their propagation, and
this study suggested proper ways of making the viscosity measurements. In the column experiment, the graphical methods of Chap.
9 were extensively applied in examining the column data and in
estimating error and validity of the data. In both these experiments, extrapolation checking (Chap. 7) also played a part. In the
final example, we used mainly the methods of Chap. 8 to make meaningful statistical comparisons among the speed-measuring devices.

APPENDIX B

Dimensional Formulas

M = mass, L = length, θ = time, T = temperature, H = heat, K = dielectric constant, μ = magnetic field constant.

Mechanics

Quantity	Dimensional formula
Length L	L
Volume V	L^3
Curvature	L^{-1}
Velocity V	$L\theta^{-1}$
Acceleration A or g	$L\theta^{-2}$
Angular velocity ω	θ^{-1}
Density ρ	ML^{-3}
Momentum	$ML\theta^{-1}$
Angular momentum	$ML^2\theta^{-1}$
Force F	$ML\theta^{-2}$
Work and energy	$ML^2\theta^{-2}$
Power	$ML^2\theta^{-3}$
Viscosity μ	$ML^{-1}\theta^{-1}$
Kinematic viscosity	$L^2\theta^{-1}$
Surface tension	$M\theta^{-2}$
Pressure P	$ML^{-1}\theta^{-2}$

Thermal Quantities

	Thermal formula	Dynamical formula
Quantity of heat H	H	$ML^2\theta^{-2}$
Specific heat C_p	$HM^{-1}T^{-1}$	$L^2\theta^{-2}T^{-1}$
Thermal conductivity k	$HL^{-1}\theta^{-1}T^{-1}$	$LM\theta^{-3}T^{-1}$
Heat-transfer coefficient h	$HL^{-2}\theta^{-1}T^{-1}$	$M\theta^{-3}T^{-1}$
Entropy s	HT^{-1}	$ML^2\theta^{-2}T^{-1}$
Coefficient of thermal expansion β	T^{-1}	T^{-1}

Magnetic and Electrical Quantities

	Electromagnetic	Electrostatic
Magnetic field strength	$M^{1/2}L^{-1/2}\theta^{-1}\mu^{-1/2}$	$M^{1/2}L^{1/2}\theta^{-2}K^{1/2}$
Magnetic pole strength	$M^{1/2}L^{3/2}\theta^{-1}\mu^{1/2}$	$M^{1/2}L^{1/2}K^{-1/2}$
I Electric current	$M^{1/2}L^{1/2}\theta^{-1}\mu^{-1/2}$	$M^{1/2}L^{3/2}\theta^{-2}K^{1/2}$
m Quantity of electricity	$M^{1/2}L^{1/2}\mu^{-1/2}$	$M^{1/2}L^{3/2}\theta^{-1}K^{1/2}$
V Potential difference	$M^{1/2}L^{3/2}\theta^{-2}\mu^{1/2}$	$L^{1/2}M^{1/2}\theta^{-1}K^{-1/2}$
R Resistance	$L\theta^{-1}\mu$	$L^{-1}\theta K^{-1}$
C Capacitance	$L^{-1}\theta^{+2}\mu^{-1}$	LK
L Inductance	$L\mu$	$L^{-1}\theta^2 K^{-1}$
μ Permeability	μ	$L^{-2}\theta^2 K^{-1}$
ε Permittivity	$L^{-2}\theta^2\mu^{-1}$	K

APPENDIX C

Graeco-Latin Squares

The following designs may be used in the planning of randomized experiments as explained in Chap. 6. Notice that each plan is actually two different Latin squares.

3 × 3

A1	B3	C2
B2	C1	A3
C3	A2	B1

4 × 4

A1	B3	C4	D2
D4	C2	B1	A3
B2	A4	D3	C1
C3	D1	A2	B4

5 × 5

A5	B3	C2	D1	E4
B1	C4	D5	E3	A2
C3	D2	E1	A4	B5
D4	E5	A3	B2	C1
E2	A1	B4	C5	D3

6 × 6 (only the Latin square possible)

A	B	C	D	E	F
B	F	D	C	A	E
C	D	E	F	B	A
D	A	F	E	C	B
E	C	A	B	F	D
F	E	B	A	D	C

Index